KV-059-910

igloobooks

Published in 2019
by Igloo Books Ltd
Cottage Farm
Sywell
NN6 0BJ
www.igloobooks.com

LEO002 0419
2 4 6 8 10 9 7 5 3 1
ISBN 978-1-78905-495-8

Cover designed by Nicholas Gage
Edited by Bobby Newlyn-Jones

Puzzle compilation, typesetting and design by:
Clarity Media Ltd, http://www.clarity-media.co.uk

Printed and manufactured in China

Contents

Puzzle 1

Across

1 ___ emptor: warning to buyers (6)
5 Band who sang Shining Light (3)
7 Chopped finely (5)
8 Ban on trade with a country (7)
9 Wanderer (5)
10 Manner of giving a speech (8)
12 Bodyguard (6)
14 Relative social standing (6)
17 Grace (8)
18 Ice hockey buildings (5)
20 Edible mollusc (7)
21 Private room on a ship (5)
22 Newt (3)
23 Wanders off; drifts (6)

Down

2 Having no purpose at all (7)
3 Large burrowing African mammal (8)
4 Examine quickly (4)
5 Inflexible and unyielding (7)
6 Deals with (7)
7 Workers (5)
11 Having no current (of a body of water) (8)
12 Clasp (7)
13 Link together (7)
15 Mysterious (7)
16 Free from dirt (5)
19 Cries (4)

Crossword

Puzzle 2

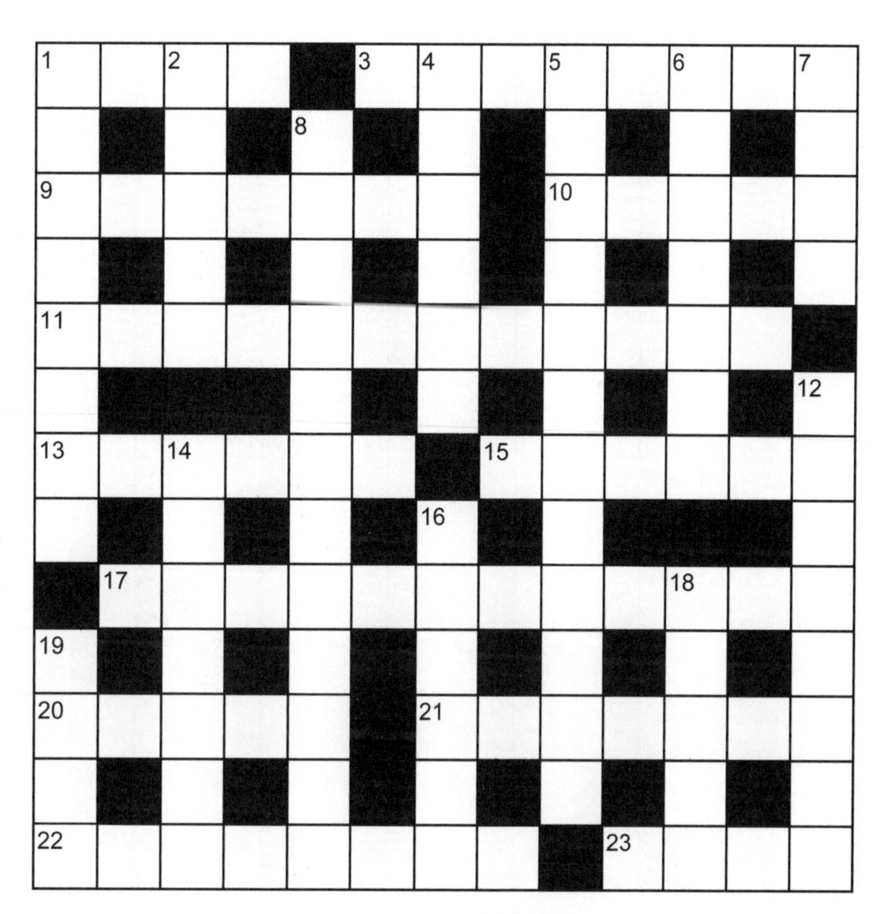

Across

1 Take a breath owing to astonishment (4)
3 Italian cheese (8)
9 Non-professional (7)
10 Powerful forward movement (5)
11 Enhancements (12)
13 Oppose (6)
15 Legendary king of Britain (6)
17 Radishes grin (anag) (12)
20 Personal attendant (5)
21 Sleeveless garment (7)
22 In these times (8)
23 Paradise garden (4)

Down

1 Huge ice masses (8)
2 Rascal (5)
4 Accepted (6)
5 Give a false account of (12)
6 Extend an arm or leg (7)
7 Christmas (4)
8 Showed (12)
12 Make more light (8)
14 Swift-flying songbird (7)
16 Of inferior quality (6)
18 Lazed (5)
19 Not odd (of a number) (4)

Puzzle 3

Across

1 Make thirsty (5)
4 Hits with a lash (5)
10 Reveal (7)
11 Ray (5)
12 Stirling ___ : racing driver (4)
13 Gloaming (8)
16 Biters (anag) (6)
17 Enter into combat with (6)
20 Capital of Jamaica (8)
21 Use land for growing crops (4)
23 ___ Sarandon: US actress (5)
25 Small piece of fried bread (7)
26 Increase in size (5)
27 Religious doctrine (5)

Down

2 Attainment of a position (9)
3 Bay (4)
5 One's native country (8)
6 Tack (3)
7 Peak (6)
8 Trousers (5)
9 Drift in the air (4)
14 Promise with certainty (9)
15 Depending on the time of year (8)
18 Expensive white fur (6)
19 Come into contact with (5)
20 Lock lips (4)
22 Jest (4)
24 Fasten with stitches (3)

Crossword

Puzzle 4

Across

1 Obtains (4)
3 Roman building (8)
9 Ate a midday meal (7)
10 A gold coin (5)
11 Do really well at (5)
12 High spirits (7)
13 Wild dog (6)
15 Willow twigs (6)
17 Tar-like hydrocarbon (7)
18 Civilian dress (5)
20 Lindsay ___ : actress (5)
21 Doing as one is told (7)
22 Improves in flavour (8)
23 Catch sight of (4)

Down

1 50th anniversary of a major event (6,7)
2 Uniform jacket (5)
4 Mixes up or confuses (6)
5 Unseasonably warm period (6,6)
6 Slope (7)
7 Amazingly (13)
8 Devoted to music (12)
14 The ___ in the Rye: novel (7)
16 Money received (6)
19 Does not succeed (5)

Puzzle 5

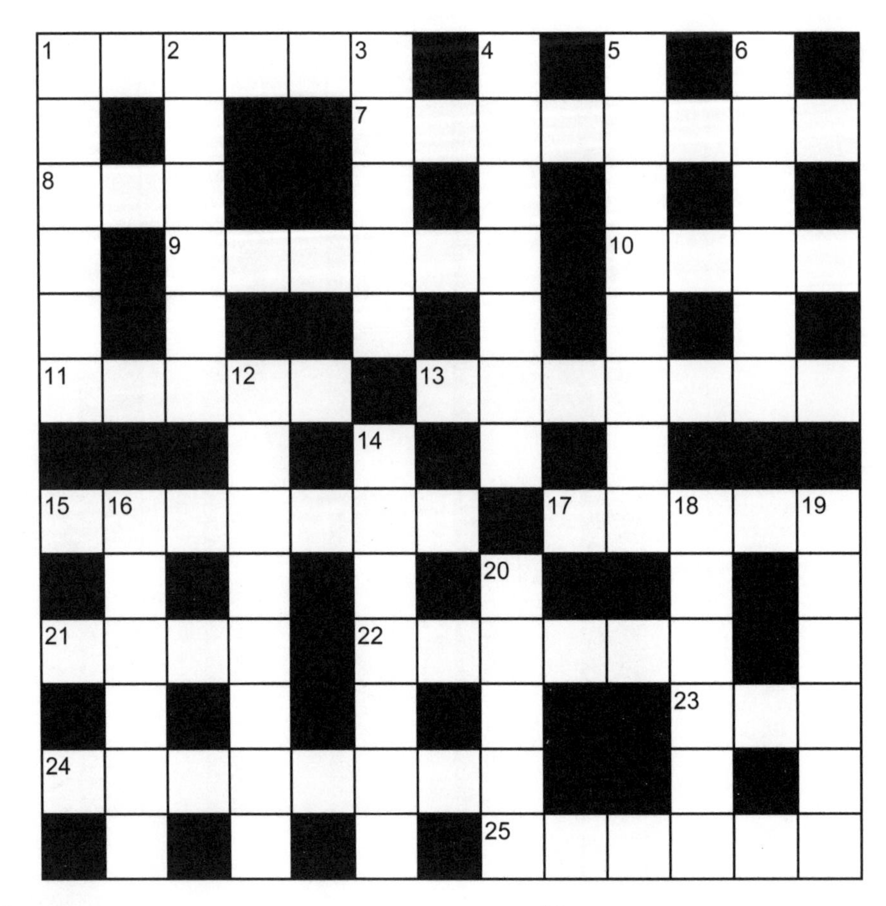

Across

1 Choose (6)
7 In spite of the fact (8)
8 Rubbish holder (3)
9 Table linen (6)
10 Piece of office furniture (4)
11 ___ John: pop star (5)
13 The small details of something (7)
15 Country in Africa (7)
17 Practice of lending money at high interest rates (5)
21 Proofreader's mark (4)
22 Good luck charm (6)
23 Trouble in body or mind (3)
24 Where photographs are developed (8)
25 Throes (anag) (6)

Down

1 Quash; tame (6)
2 Small finch (6)
3 Military vehicles (5)
4 Domestic implement (7)
5 Low spirits (8)
6 Andre ___ : former US tennis player (6)
12 Go past another car (8)
14 Self-contradictory statement (7)
16 Background actors (6)
18 Action of making use of something (6)
19 Surrenders (6)
20 Cathedral (5)

Crossword

Puzzle 6

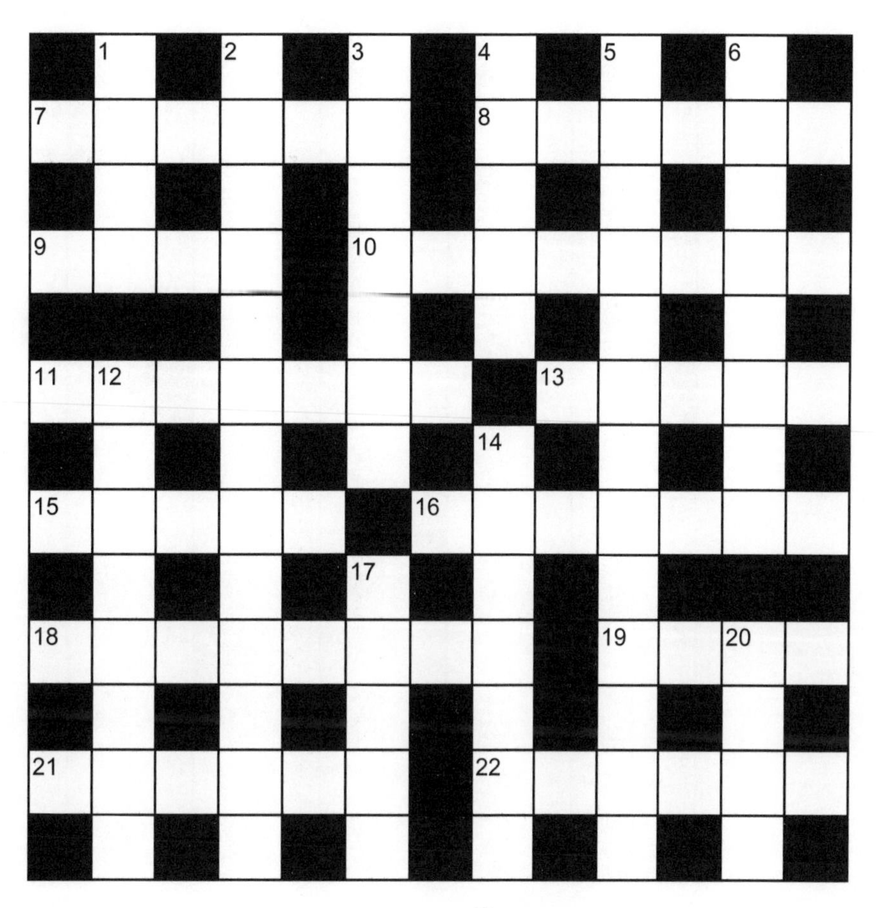

Across

7 Electric generator (6)
8 Written in verse (6)
9 Soon; shortly (4)
10 Be heavier than (8)
11 Release from captivity (3,4)
13 ___ Adkins: English singer (5)
15 Soft juicy fruit (5)
16 Thieves (7)
18 Household implements (8)
19 Crazy (informal) (4)
21 Drooped (6)
22 Series of eight notes (6)

Down

1 Blue-green colour (4)
2 Splendidly (13)
3 Army rank (7)
4 Desire to hurt someone (5)
5 Reliability (13)
6 Remarkable (8)
12 Act of hard work (8)
14 Random criticism (7)
17 Breezy (5)
20 Spanish sparkling wine (4)

Puzzle 7

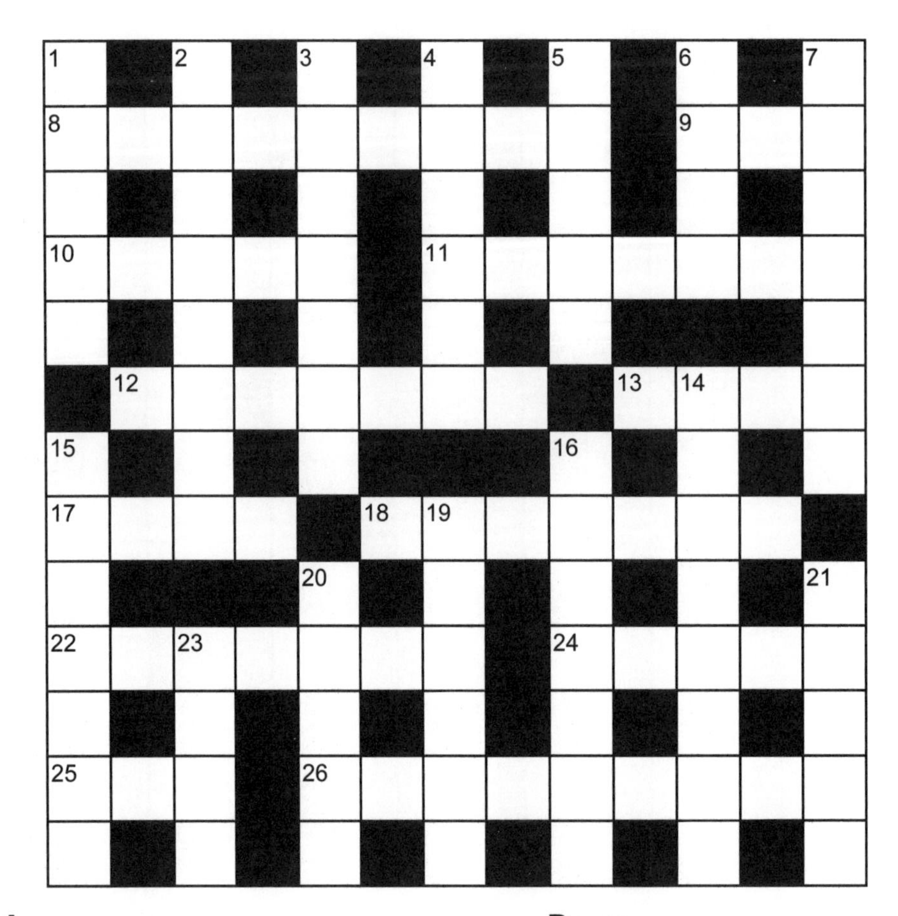

Across

8 Theatrical form of entertainment (9)
9 Recede (3)
10 Shafts dug to obtain water (5)
11 Diacritical marks (7)
12 Ben ___ : US comedian and actor (7)
13 Prima donna (4)
17 Showing vigour or spirit (4)
18 Keep for future use (7)
22 Gun holder (7)
24 Underground worker (5)
25 Herb (3)
26 Places (9)

Down

1 Produce eggs (5)
2 Cyan tail (anag) (8)
3 Confer with others (7)
4 Sixty seconds (6)
5 Stomach (5)
6 Domesticated ox (4)
7 Extremely bad (7)
14 One who creates new products (8)
15 The ___ : radio soap opera (7)
16 Recluses (7)
19 Make better (6)
20 Stable compartment (5)
21 Brittle; snack food (5)
23 Told an untruth (4)

Crossword

Puzzle 8

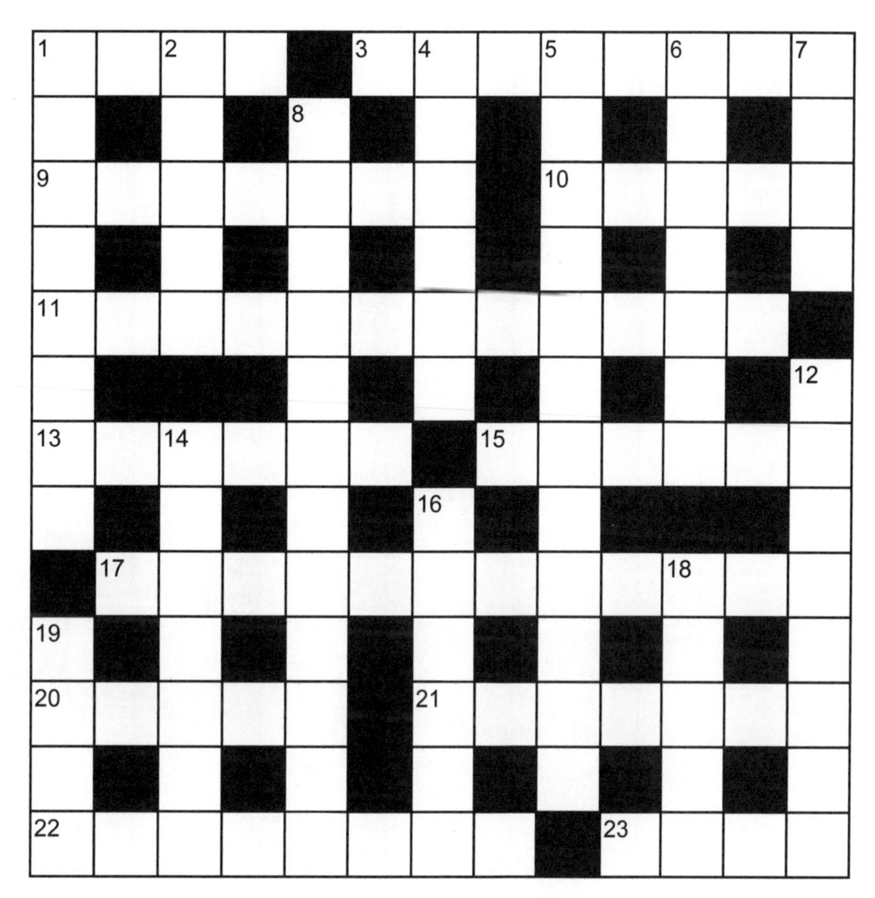

Across

1 Soft drink (US) (4)
3 Apprehended (8)
9 Observes (7)
10 Establish as the truth (5)
11 Showing total commitment (12)
13 Trigonometric function (6)
15 Cloud of gas in space (6)
17 Terrified or extremely shocked (6-6)
20 Small farm (5)
21 Endurance (7)
22 Clear of trees (8)
23 Coloured (4)

Down

1 Popular lunch food (8)
2 Mark of repetition (5)
4 Shares (anag) (6)
5 Derived from past events (12)
6 Henry David ___ : US author and poet (7)
7 Hold as an opinion (4)
8 Creator of film scripts (12)
12 Not forward (8)
14 Exhibitionist (4-3)
16 Deletes (6)
18 Oneness (5)
19 Move fast in a straight line (4)

Puzzle 9

Across

1 Cowers (anag) (6)
5 Shuffle playing cards (6)
8 Foolish (4)
9 Float in the air (8)
10 Item of cutlery (5)
11 Remaining (7)
14 Survey (13)
16 Tropical cyclone (7)
18 Sanctimonious (5)
20 Hard shell of a crustacean (8)
22 Work hard (4)
23 Moral guardian (6)
24 Storage space for a car (6)

Down

2 Tax on buying property (5,4)
3 Allocations (7)
4 Crafty (4)
5 Engrossing (8)
6 Oily; greasy (5)
7 Auction item (3)
12 Rearing; caring for (9)
13 Enormous extinct creature (8)
15 Pilot (7)
17 Makes well (5)
19 Alban ___ : Austrian composer (4)
21 Affirmative vote (3)

Crossword

Puzzle 10

Across

1 Form of identification (5)
4 Work hard (5)
10 Passionate (7)
11 Showing a willingness to achieve results (3-2)
12 Bursts (4)
13 Buffed (8)
16 Cricket statistician (6)
17 Bloodsucking insect (6)
20 Overcame (8)
21 Make a hole in; drill (4)
23 Equipped (5)
25 Breathed in (7)
26 Engages in an argument (5)
27 Rotates (5)

Down

2 Lacking definite form (9)
3 Hold tightly (4)
5 Gets given (8)
6 Cooling tool (3)
7 Entices to do something (6)
8 Confuse or obscure (5)
9 Empty space (4)
14 Mischievous supernatural creature (9)
15 Protector; guardian (8)
18 Avaricious (6)
19 Stinky (5)
20 Ditch filled with water (4)
22 Vessel (4)
24 Amp (anag) (3)

Crossword

Puzzle 11

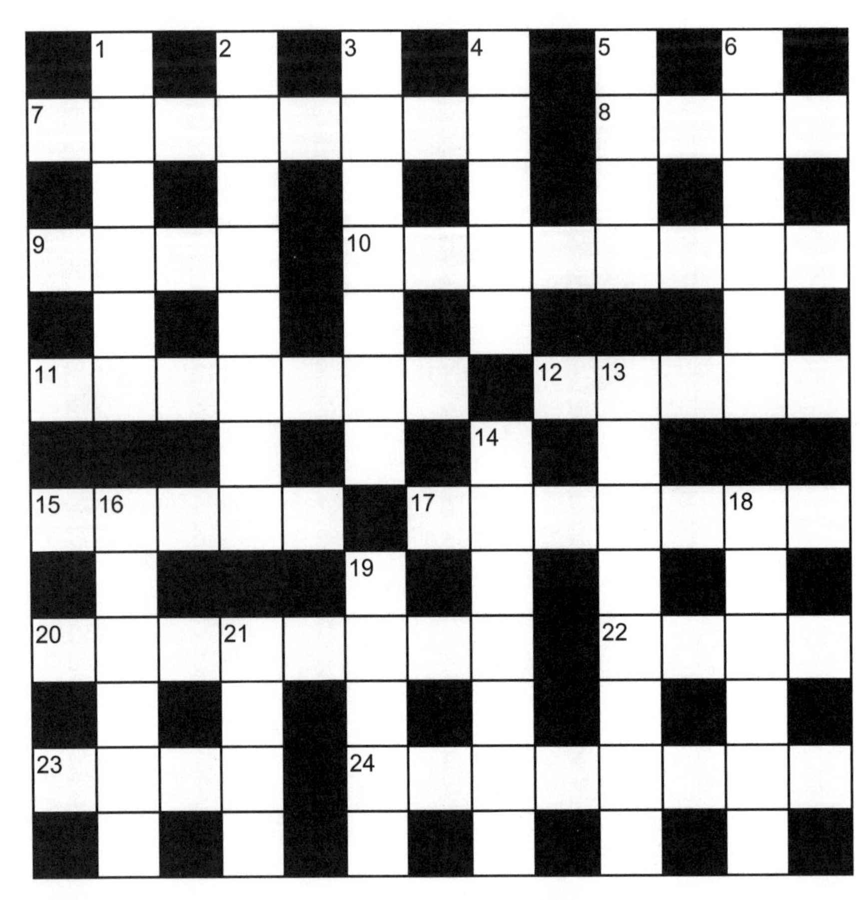

Across

7 Hairstyle (8)
8 Inspired by reverence (4)
9 Head coverings (4)
10 Diligence (8)
11 Seed with a fibrous husk and edible white flesh (7)
12 Covers with gold (5)
15 Insurgent (5)
17 Substitute (7)
20 Roadside board showing directions (8)
22 Garment of ancient Rome (4)
23 Part of a door fastening (4)
24 Unknown person (8)

Down

1 Trinidad and ___ : country (6)
2 Away from land (8)
3 Obedient (7)
4 Unwanted plants (5)
5 Film about a shark (4)
6 Was scared of (6)
13 Setting fire to (8)
14 Degree of eminence (7)
16 ___ Wood: US actor (6)
18 Brass instruments (6)
19 Electronic device one clicks (5)
21 Back of the neck (4)

Crossword

Puzzle 12

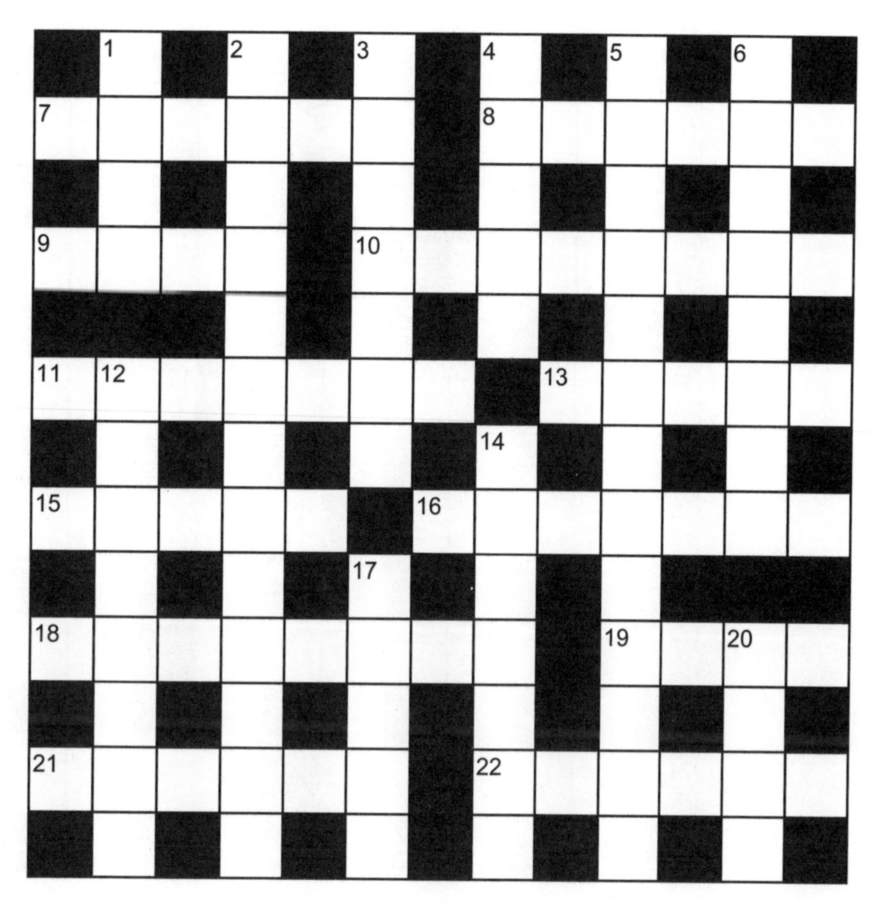

Across

- **7** Lively Spanish dance (6)
- **8** Not moving (6)
- **9** Hint (4)
- **10** Wood preserver (8)
- **11** Went around and around (7)
- **13** Barely sufficient (5)
- **15** Ghost (5)
- **16** Egg white (7)
- **18** User; purchaser (8)
- **19** Trees of the genus Ulmus (4)
- **21** ___ Kay: TV presenter (6)
- **22** Make illegal (6)

Down

- **1** Sequence of concentric circles (4)
- **2** Railway and road intersection (5,8)
- **3** Came into contact with (7)
- **4** Awry (5)
- **5** US state (13)
- **6** Space between two objects (8)
- **12** Not appropriate (8)
- **14** War trumpet (7)
- **17** Change (5)
- **20** Average value (4)

Puzzle 13

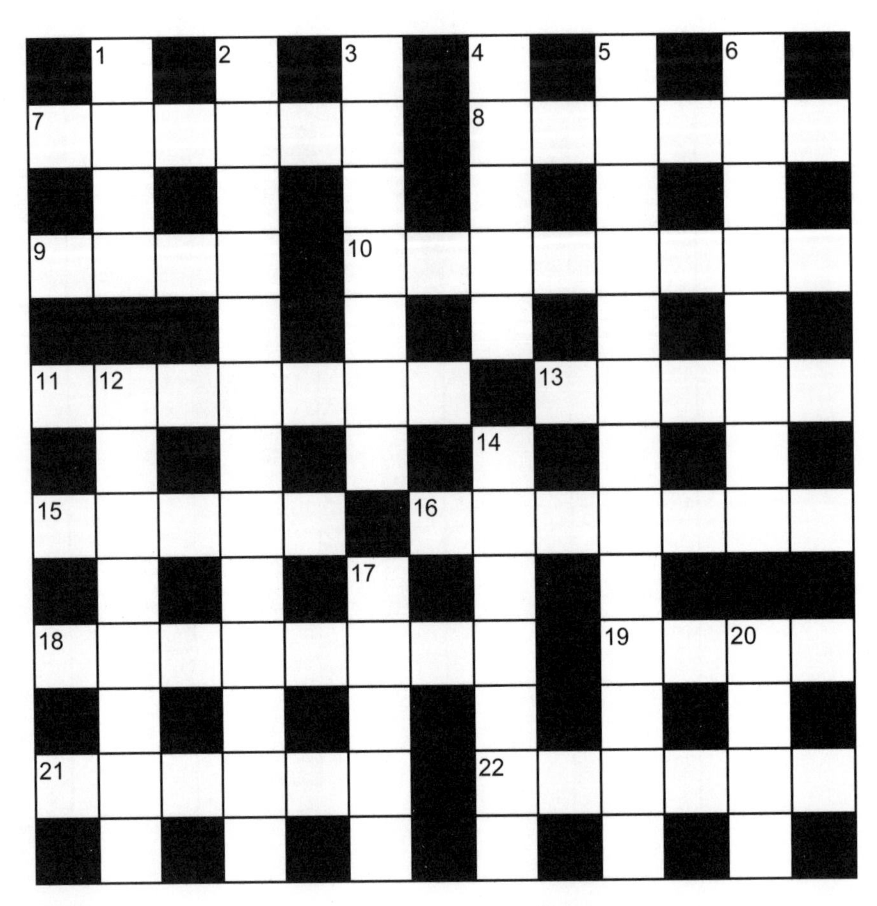

Across

7 ___ Holden: English actress (6)
8 Where bees are kept (6)
9 Parched (4)
10 Highly seasoned smoked beef (8)
11 Educational establishment (7)
13 John ___ : English poet (5)
15 Danielle ___ : US romantic novelist (5)
16 Take out (7)
18 Light afternoon meal (5,3)
19 Droops (4)
21 Get by with what is available (4,2)
22 Set of steps (6)

Down

1 Mire (anag) (4)
2 Pure (13)
3 Period of violent behaviour by a group of people (7)
4 Not true (5)
5 Irish James Bond actor (6,7)
6 Theatrical (8)
12 Sudden eruption (8)
14 Wear out completely (7)
17 Bend forwards and downwards (5)
20 Female child (4)

Crossword

Puzzle 14

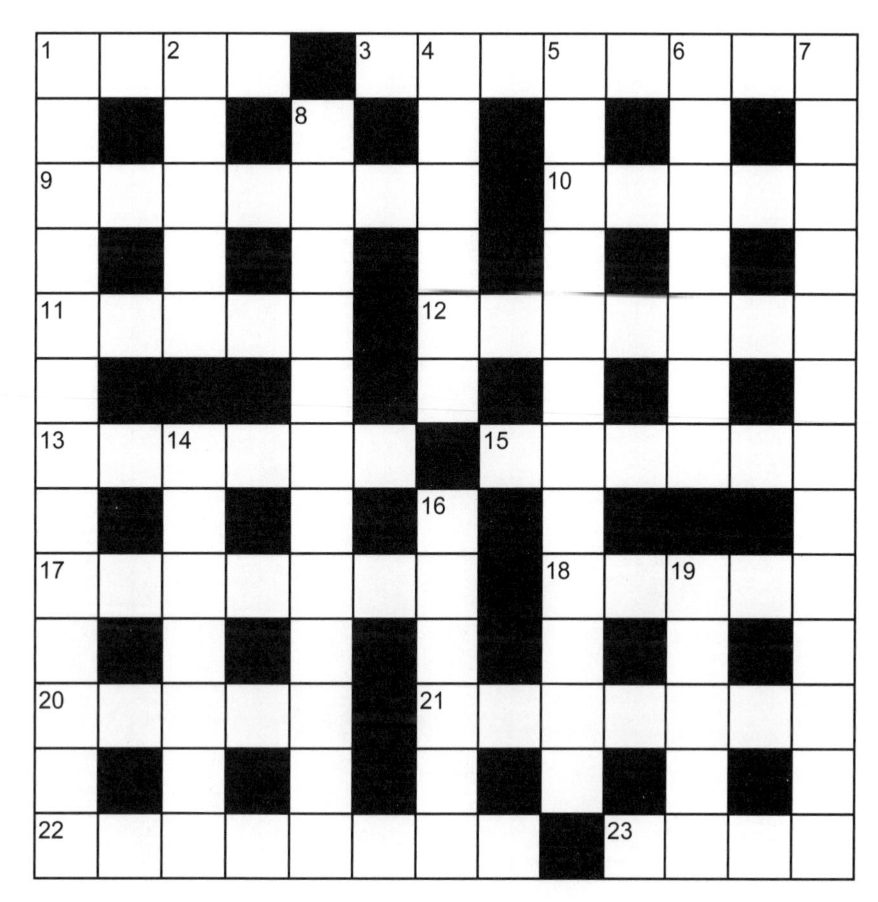

Across

1 Gangs (4)
3 Commotion (8)
9 Female siblings (7)
10 Love affair (5)
11 Dismiss from office (5)
12 Prescribe (7)
13 Old measure of distance (6)
15 Assurance; composure (6)
17 Tell a story (7)
18 Fruit (5)
20 Unit of weight (5)
21 Slanting (7)
22 Fortified wines (8)
23 Areas of ground for growing plants (4)

Down

1 Of mixed character (13)
2 Moisten meat (5)
4 Live in (6)
5 Intolerable (12)
6 Pear-shaped fruit (7)
7 Pleasantness (13)
8 Eating place proprietor (12)
14 Place in order (7)
16 Set of chromosomes (6)
19 Wound the pride of (5)

Puzzle 15

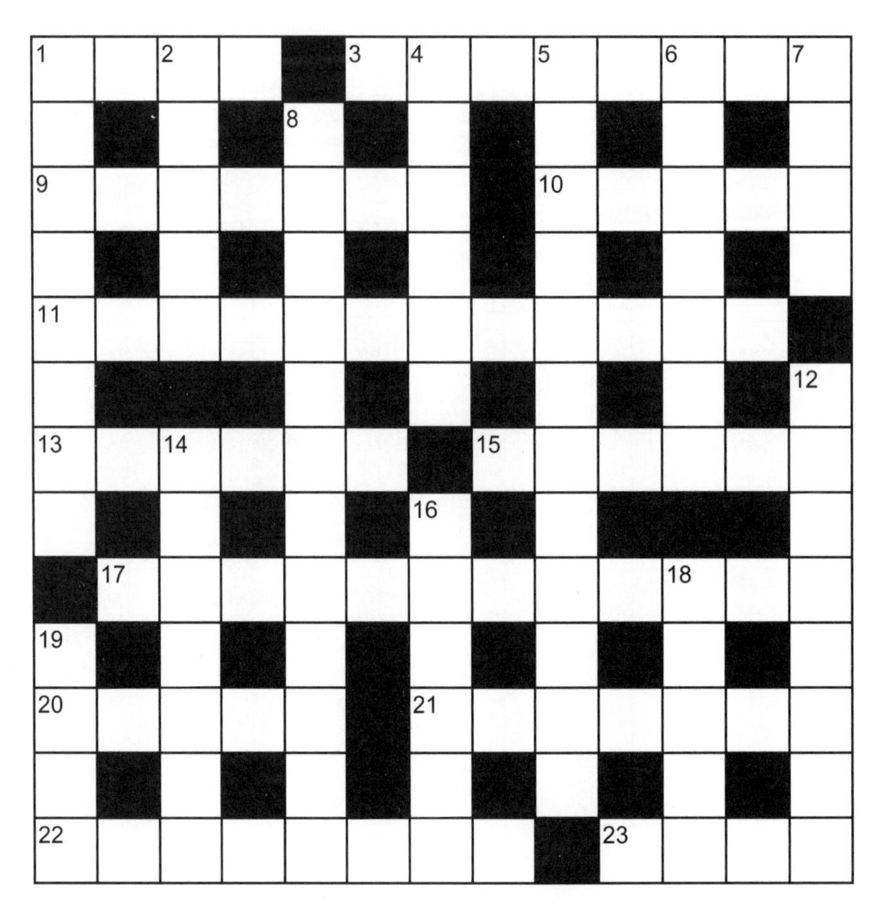

Across

1 Male deer (4)
3 Exposes (8)
9 Electric mixing machine (7)
10 Willow twig (5)
11 Thick-skinned herbivorous animal (12)
13 Tasty morsel (6)
15 Sincere; serious (6)
17 First language (6,6)
20 At that place; not here (5)
21 Paired (7)
22 Place (8)
23 Long-running dispute (4)

Down

1 New World quail (8)
2 Faint bird cry (5)
4 Limited in scope (6)
5 Use of words that mimic sounds (12)
6 Connoisseur; gourmet (7)
7 Feudal labourer (4)
8 Firm rebuke (12)
12 Not necessary (8)
14 Gardening tools (7)
16 Small cave (6)
18 Variety or kind (5)
19 Halt (4)

Crossword

Puzzle 16

Across

1 Pond-dwelling amphibians (5)
4 Large group of people (5)
10 Aerial (7)
11 Spiritual nourishment (5)
12 Emit light (4)
13 Blue toys (anag) (8)
16 Someone who buys and sells (6)
17 Unintelligent (6)
20 Excessive amount of something (8)
21 Pile (4)
23 Strength (5)
25 Husbands or wives (7)
26 Large woody plants (5)
27 Intoxicating (5)

Down

2 Explanation (9)
3 Award (informal) (4)
5 Gets back on a horse (8)
6 Finish first (3)
7 Victim (6)
8 Wounding remarks (5)
9 Doing little (4)
14 Conveyed an opinion (9)
15 Reload (8)
18 Remove from office (6)
19 Corn ground to make flour (5)
20 Apple seeds (4)
22 Garden watering device (4)
24 State of armed conflict (3)

Puzzle 17

Across

1 Another option (11)
9 Dairy product (5)
10 Bed for a baby (3)
11 Lively Bohemian dance (5)
12 Find the solution (5)
13 Heard (8)
16 Extravagant fuss (8)
18 Stroll (5)
21 Legendary stories (5)
22 Boy (3)
23 Media (anag) (5)
24 Instantly (11)

Down

2 Uncovered (7)
3 Fugitive (7)
4 Sewing instrument (6)
5 Domesticates (5)
6 Pertaining to the voice (5)
7 Unappetising (11)
8 Energetically or vigorously (11)
14 Mild (of weather) (7)
15 Personal possession (7)
17 Birthplace of St Francis (6)
19 Darken (5)
20 Wipe (5)

Crossword

Puzzle 18

Across

1 Wafer-thin potato slices (6)
5 Put a question to (3)
7 Spends time doing nothing (5)
8 Enthusiastic reception (7)
9 Aqualung (5)
10 Rubbish (8)
12 Piece of text that names the writer of an article (6)
14 Protect from danger (6)
17 Day after Friday (8)
18 Pipes (5)
20 Human-like robot (7)
21 Waggish (5)
22 Large salt water body (3)
23 Grime; rock music style (6)

Down

2 Lively festivities (7)
3 Opting in (anag) (8)
4 Large deer (pl) (4)
5 Make less intense (7)
6 Worked dough (7)
7 Printed insert supplied with a CD (5)
11 Take responsibility for (8)
12 Fights (7)
13 Brazilian dance (7)
15 Directing (7)
16 Proceeding from the pope (5)
19 Protective foot covering (4)

Puzzle 19

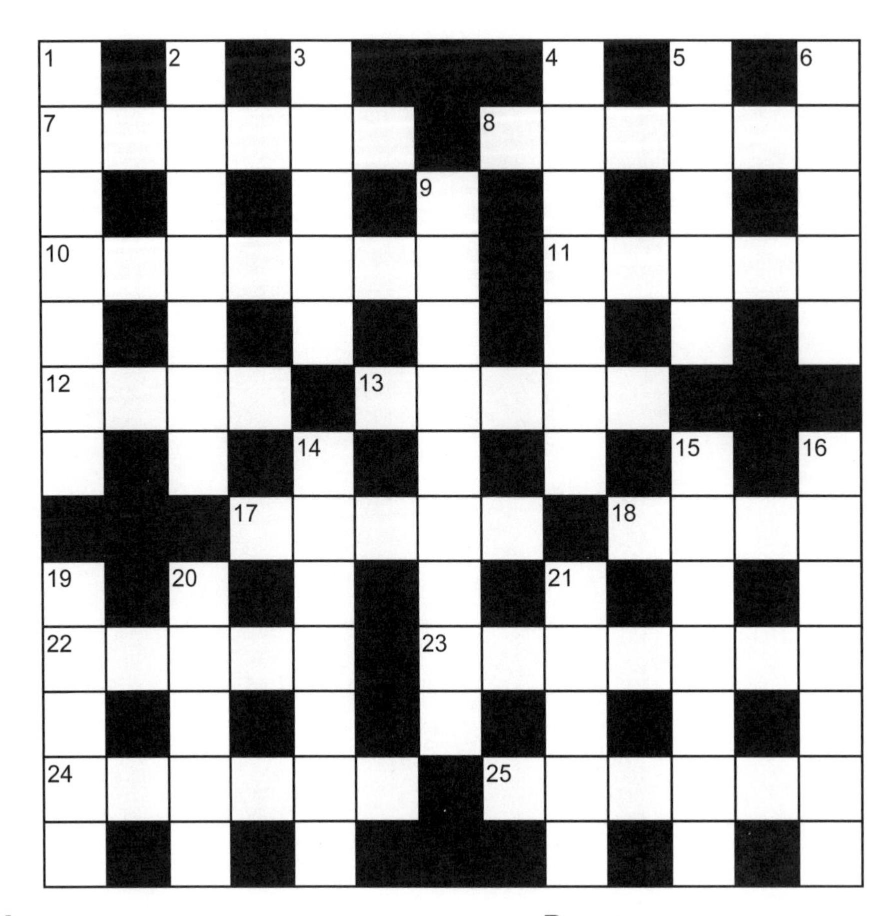

Across

7 Breathe in (6)
8 Cause to feel upset (6)
10 Clique (7)
11 Auditory ossicle (5)
12 Repents (4)
13 Removes the skin from (5)
17 Badgers' homes (5)
18 Run quickly (4)
22 Customary practice (5)
23 Dissimilar (7)
24 Hurrah (6)
25 Capital of Austria (6)

Down

1 Strife (7)
2 If (7)
3 Extreme (5)
4 Friendly (7)
5 Pass a rope through (5)
6 Mature person (5)
9 Dishonest (9)
14 Not limited to one class (7)
15 Angular units (7)
16 Fastest animal on land (7)
19 Growing thickly (5)
20 Capital of Vietnam (5)
21 Staple (5)

Puzzle 20

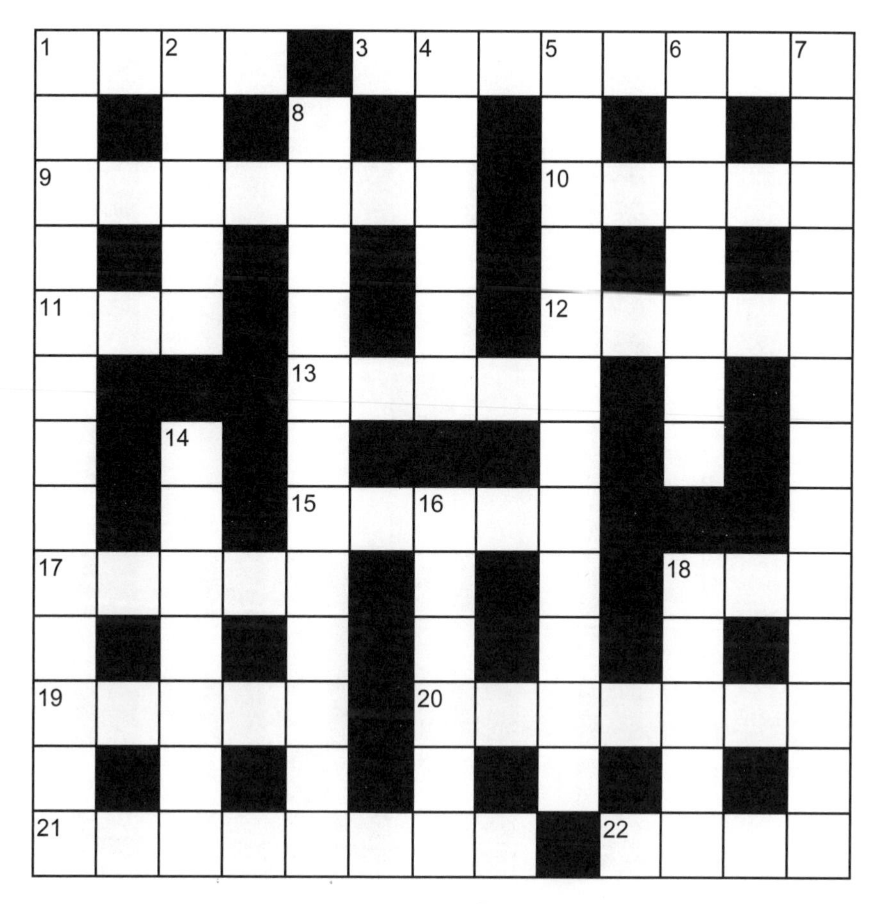

Across

1 Consumes food (4)
3 Boxing (8)
9 Self-important (7)
10 Long tubes (5)
11 Signal assent with the head (3)
12 Freshwater fish (5)
13 Wide-awake (5)
15 Backless sofa (5)
17 A score of two under par on a hole (golf) (5)
18 Cry of disapproval (3)
19 Military opponent (5)
20 Opposite of failure (7)
21 Stops temporarily (8)
22 Tax (4)

Down

1 Ebullience (13)
2 Domesticated (5)
4 Uncertain (6)
5 Impudence (12)
6 Call the validity of a practice into question (7)
7 Naughtily (13)
8 Pungent gas used as a preservative (12)
14 Return to a former state (7)
16 Served (anag) (6)
18 Musical note (5)

Puzzle 21

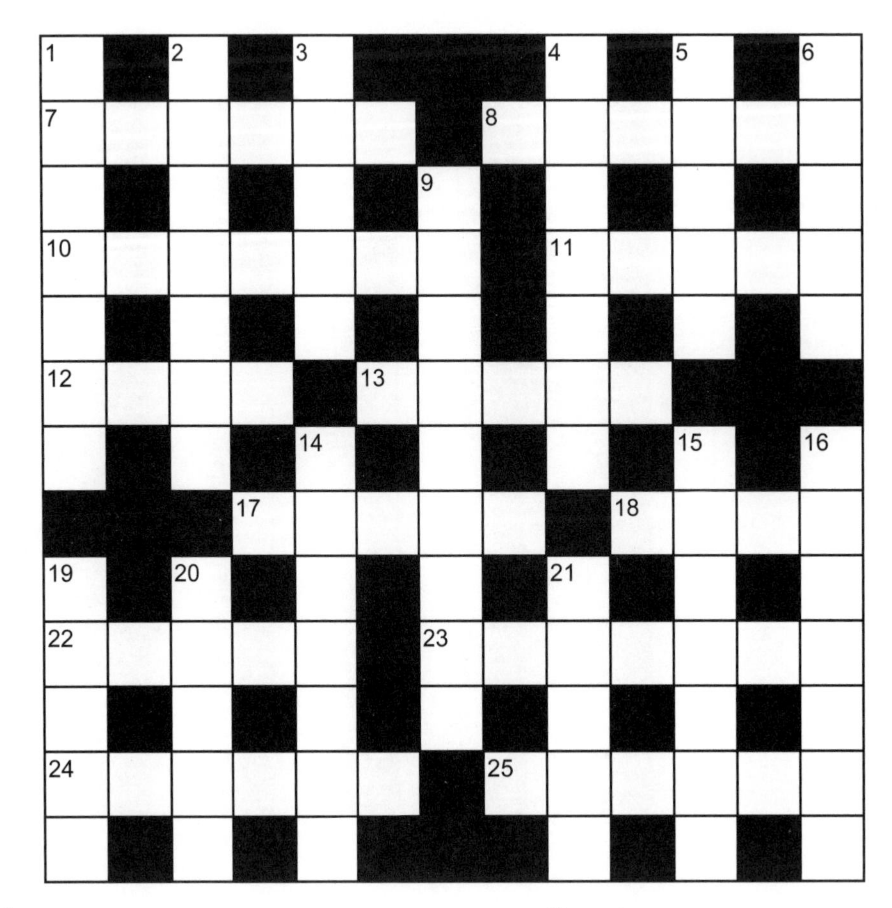

Across

7 Changes (6)
8 Sarcastic or cutting (6)
10 Clever but false argument (7)
11 Ability (5)
12 Tardy (4)
13 Historic nobleman (5)
17 Insect larvae (5)
18 ___ Forever: Spice Girls hit (4)
22 Governed (5)
23 Feeling embarrassed (7)
24 Comfort in times of misfortune (6)
25 Lumberjack (6)

Down

1 Incorrectly (7)
2 Floor coverings (7)
3 Of sedate character (5)
4 Lost (7)
5 Flightless birds (5)
6 Nimble (5)
9 Eg a frog (9)
14 Decorative style of the 1920s and 1930s (3,4)
15 Gently (7)
16 People who attack at speed (7)
19 Frozen dew (5)
20 Craftily (5)
21 Decaf (anag) (5)

Crossword

Puzzle 22

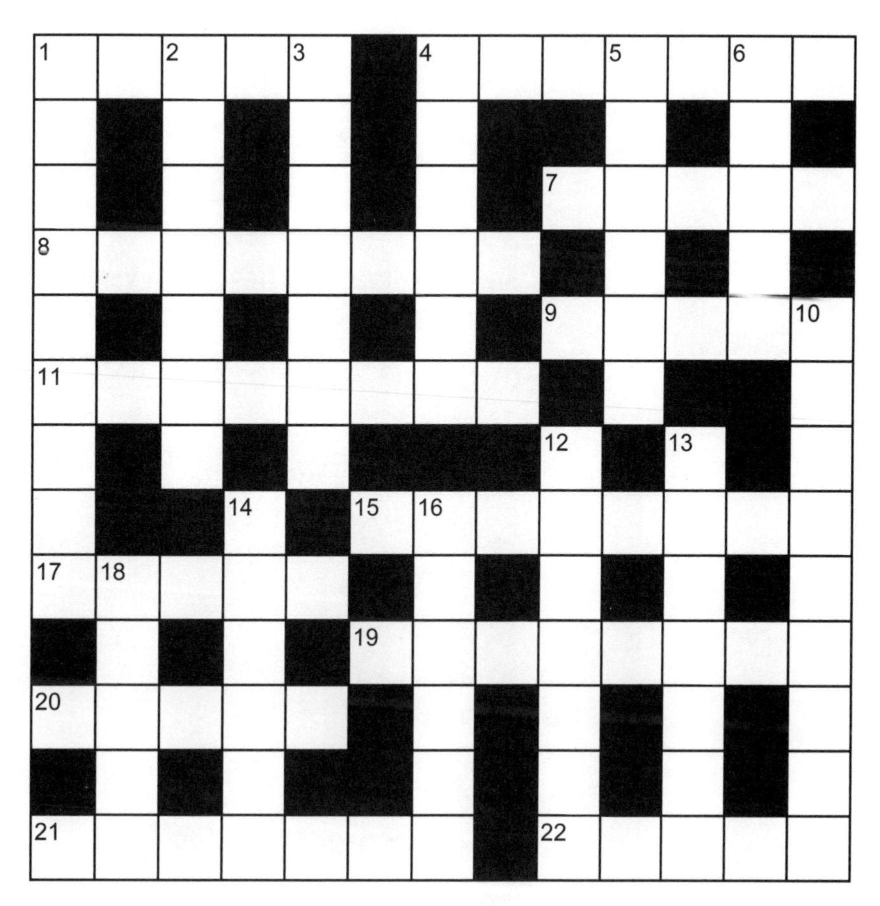

Across

1 Style of Greek architecture (5)
4 Foreboding (7)
7 ___ Davro: comedian (5)
8 Inaccurately (8)
9 Puff up; swell (5)
11 Christmas scene (8)
15 Long-tailed parrot (8)
17 Brusque (5)
19 Material used as a colourant (8)
20 Dramatic musical work (5)
21 Use again (7)
22 Retains (5)

Down

1 Unbearably loud (9)
2 Return a favour (7)
3 Prisoner (7)
4 Wildcat (6)
5 Pasta strip (6)
6 Shadow (5)
10 Gives evidence in court (9)
12 Item of clerical clothing (7)
13 Exile; fugitive (7)
14 Disturbance (6)
16 A person in general (6)
18 Indian monetary unit (5)

Puzzle 23

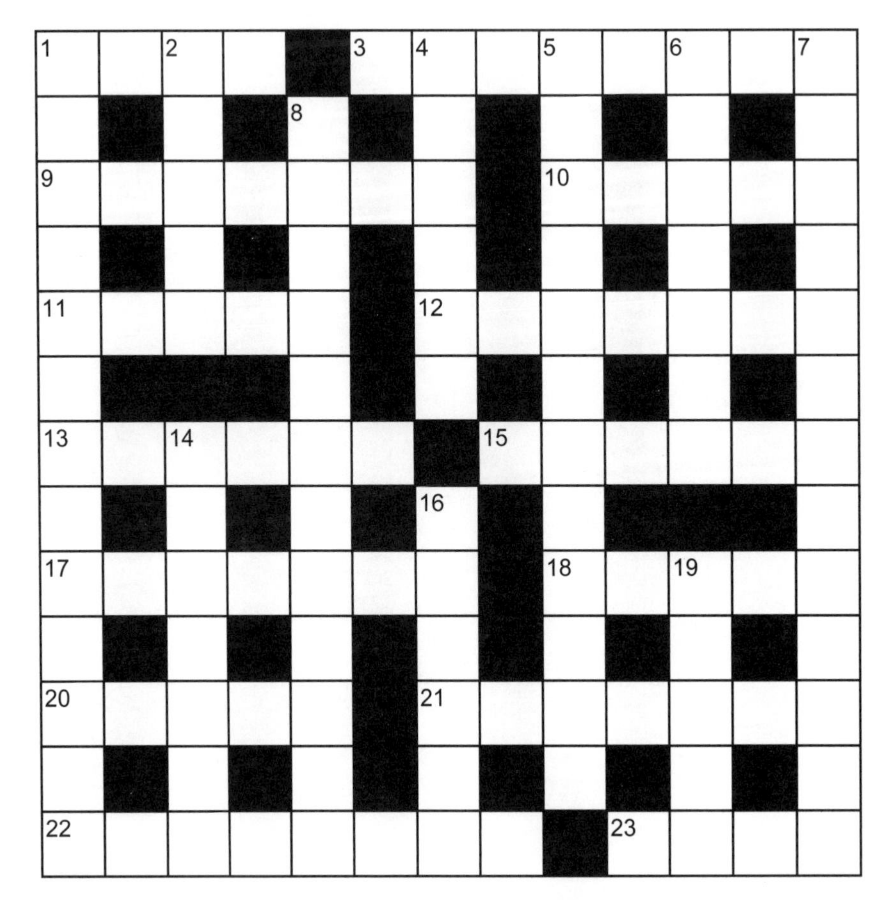

Across

1 Dice (anag) (4)
3 Bring together (8)
9 Increase the duration of (7)
10 Person who flies an aircraft (5)
11 Chris ___ : tennis champion (5)
12 Inspire with love (7)
13 Figure with four equal straight sides (6)
15 Afternoon nap (6)
17 Late (7)
18 Crime of burning something (5)
20 Country in southern Asia (5)
21 Surpass (7)
22 Relating to the Middle Ages (8)
23 Run at a moderate pace (of horses) (4)

Down

1 Style of painting (13)
2 Crumble (5)
4 Exhaled audibly (6)
5 Vehemently (12)
6 Roars (7)
7 Amusement (13)
8 Person studying after a first degree (12)
14 Overturned (7)
16 Former Spanish currency (6)
19 Brilliant (5)

Crossword

Puzzle 24

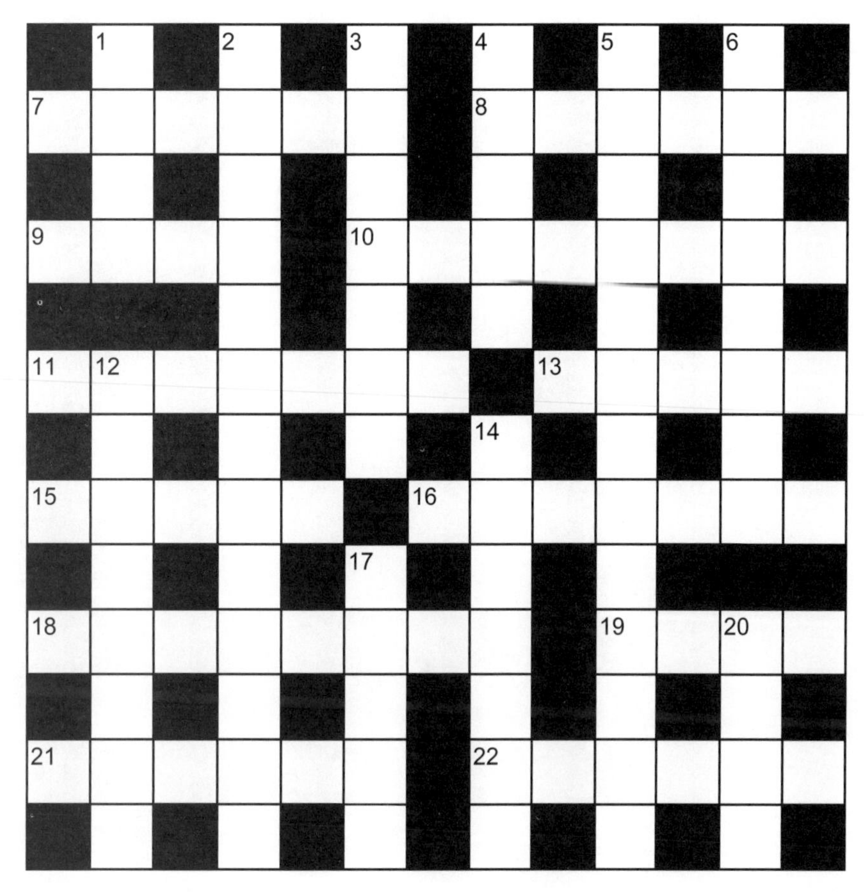

Across

7 Ostentatiously showy (6)
8 US state (6)
9 After the beginning of (4)
10 Baker's dozen (8)
11 Trembles (7)
13 Greenish-bronze fish (5)
15 Restraining straps (5)
16 Touches the skin of another lightly (7)
18 Aromatic shrub (8)
19 Body of water (4)
21 Involuntary spasm (6)
22 Mixes together (6)

Down

1 Clive ___ : Sin City actor (4)
2 Put to trouble (13)
3 Puzzle (7)
4 Of definite shape (5)
5 Fairground ride (6-7)
6 Not extreme (8)
12 Sacerdotal (8)
14 Bacterium (7)
17 Change (5)
20 Children (4)

Puzzle 25

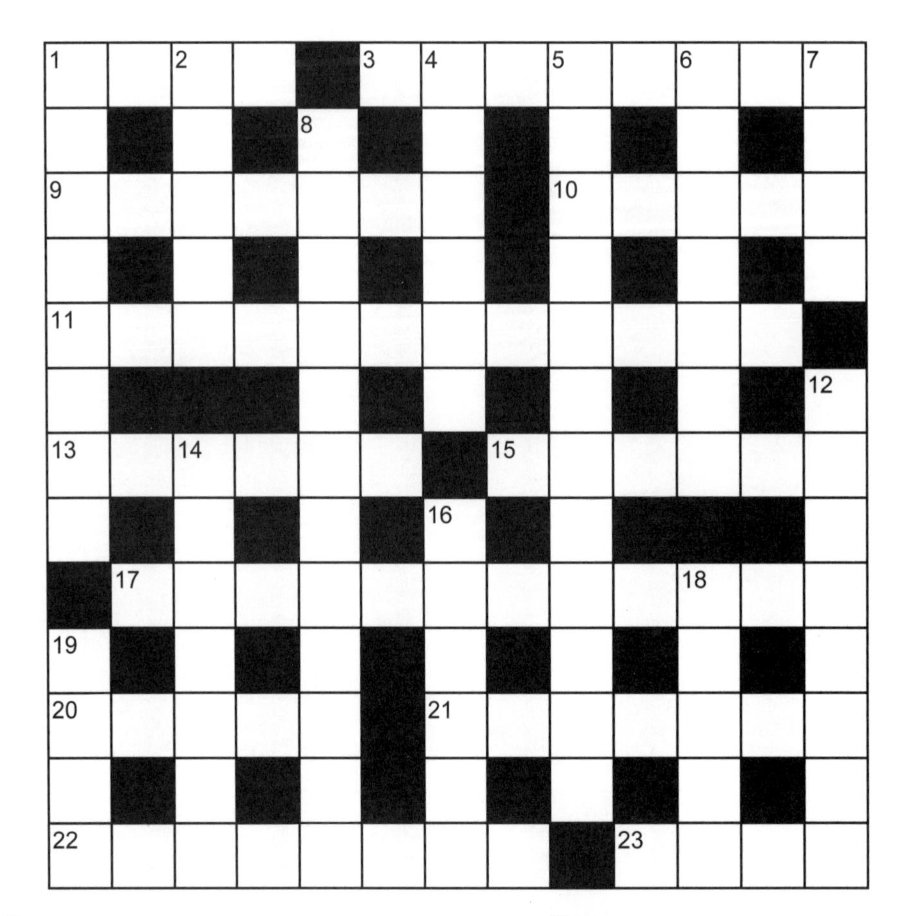

Across

- **1** Animal enclosure (4)
- **3** Three-hulled sailing boat (8)
- **9** Meaninglessness (7)
- **10** Entice to do something (5)
- **11** Ancient and old-fashioned (12)
- **13** Put down on paper (6)
- **15** Part of a motor (6)
- **17** Extremely harmful (12)
- **20** Lawful (5)
- **21** Discharge from a hole in a pipe (7)
- **22** Eg Gregorian or Julian (8)
- **23** Reasons; explanations (4)

Down

- **1** Medieval knightly system (8)
- **2** Huge mythical creature (5)
- **4** Casino ___ : James Bond film (6)
- **5** Inspiring action (12)
- **6** Remainder (7)
- **7** Nest (anag) (4)
- **8** School for young children (12)
- **12** Dry biscuits (8)
- **14** Part of a church near the altar (7)
- **16** ___ McCartney: fashion designer (6)
- **18** Sandy wasteland (5)
- **19** Group of countries in an alliance (4)

Crossword

Puzzle 26

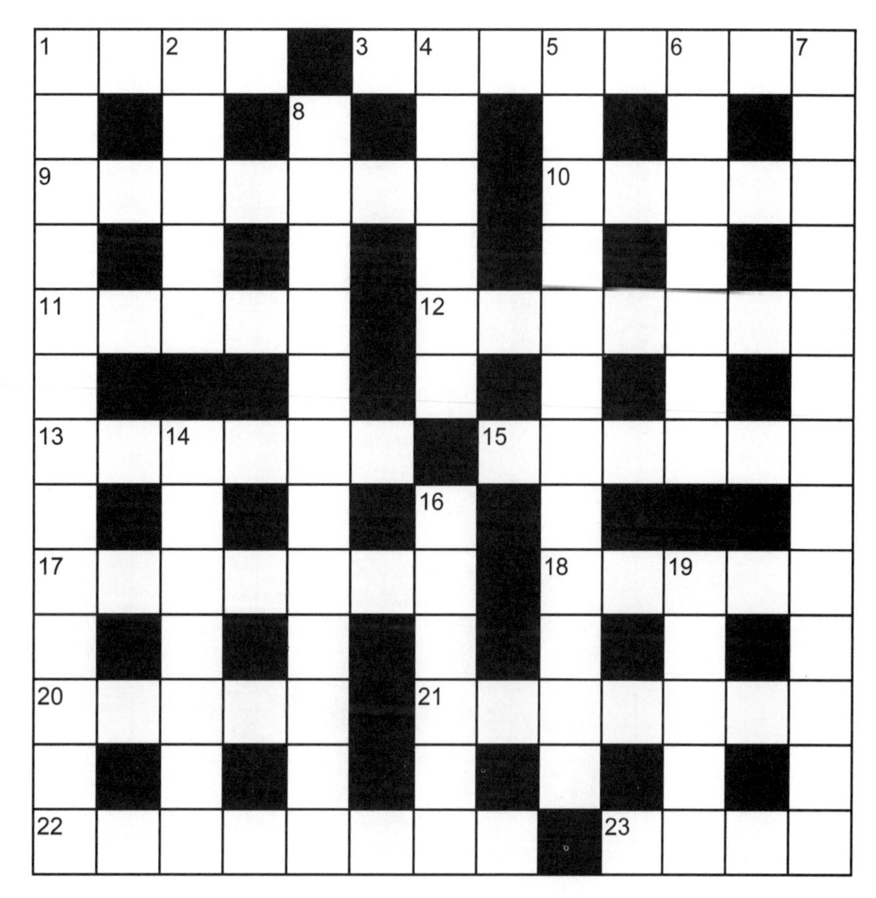

Across

1 Prod (4)
3 Elaborate (8)
9 Rowdy (7)
10 One who steals (5)
11 Not suitable in the circumstances (5)
12 Bring up; rear (7)
13 Cause to fall from a horse (6)
15 Steal (6)
17 Greed (7)
18 Unabridged (5)
20 Gold block (5)
21 Spiny egg-laying mammal (7)
22 Giving way under pressure (8)
23 ___ Campbell: actress (4)

Down

1 Quality of being individual (13)
2 Swedish monetary unit (5)
4 Relaxing (6)
5 An idea that is added later (12)
6 Time off (7)
7 Distinguish between (13)
8 Showed not to be true (12)
14 Spot of bright colour (7)
16 Within this context (6)
19 Get by begging (5)

Puzzle 27

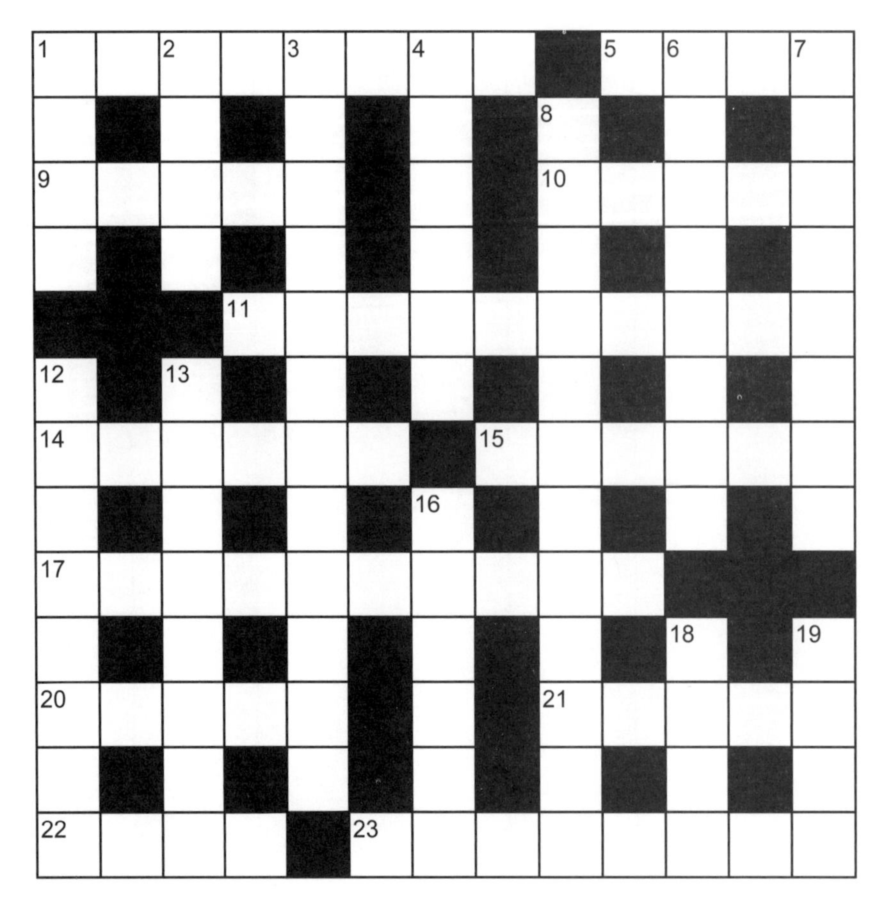

Across

1 Repudiate (8)
5 Goad on (4)
9 Helmet part for protecting the face (5)
10 Approaches (5)
11 Captivated (10)
14 Writer (6)
15 Wrestling hold (6)
17 Activist (10)
20 Tiny crustaceans (5)
21 Portable source of light (5)
22 Wise man (4)
23 Winch (8)

Down

1 Talk wildly (4)
2 Food (informal) (4)
3 Not guided by good sense (12)
4 Selection (6)
6 Apparition (8)
7 Living in (8)
8 Indifferent (12)
12 Crepes (8)
13 Franking (8)
16 Long-legged rodent (6)
18 Song for a solo voice (4)
19 ___ Priestland: Welsh rugby player (4)

Crossword

Puzzle 28

Across

1 Insurgents (6)
4 Housing (6)
9 Polish dance (7)
10 Lattice (7)
11 Promised (5)
12 Silly (5)
14 Uneven (of a surface) (5)
15 Means of mass communication (5)
17 Climb onto (5)
18 Hair-cleansing product (7)
20 Make ineffective (7)
21 Heart (slang) (6)
22 Climb (6)

Down

1 Take away (6)
2 Fashionable term (8)
3 Too bright in colour (5)
5 So soon (7)
6 Image of a god (4)
7 Slick and shiny (6)
8 Large fruits with red pulp (11)
13 Statuette (8)
14 Musical instrument (7)
15 Thing that brings good luck (6)
16 Steady (anag) (6)
17 Beasts of burden (5)
19 ___ Stewart: ex-England cricketer (4)

Puzzle 29

Across

1 Wear away (6)
5 Snappy dog (3)
7 Capital of South Korea (5)
8 Painkilling drug or medicine (7)
9 Silly action (5)
10 Devoted to a cause (8)
12 Sense of musical time (6)
14 Inferior (6)
17 Make-believe (8)
18 Loosen up (5)
20 Kind of abbreviation (7)
21 Requirements (5)
22 Cover with steam (of a glass surface) (3)
23 Proclamations (6)

Down

2 Below (7)
3 Illumination from the sun (8)
4 Hindu spiritual discipline (4)
5 Apparel (7)
6 Creator (anag) (7)
7 Flower part (5)
11 Put back (8)
12 Expression of blame (7)
13 Screaming (7)
15 Encode (7)
16 Killer whales (5)
19 Superhero film based on comic characters (1-3)

Crossword

Puzzle 30

Across

1 Eg pecan and cashew (4)
3 Enthusiasts (8)
9 Not subject to a levy (3-4)
10 Recipient of money (5)
11 Without equal (12)
14 At the present time (3)
16 Male bee (5)
17 Argument against something (3)
18 Male relation by marriage (7-2-3)
21 Prevent (5)
22 Woody plant (7)
23 Remedy to a poison (8)
24 Merriment (4)

Down

1 Substance that nourishes (8)
2 Poisonous (5)
4 Era (anag) (3)
5 Pertaining to letters (12)
6 Delightful (7)
7 Appear (4)
8 Planned in advance (12)
12 Home (5)
13 Not in a specific location (8)
15 Hottest (7)
19 Name applied to something (5)
20 Tibetan Buddhist monk (4)
22 Nevertheless (3)

Crossword

Puzzle 31

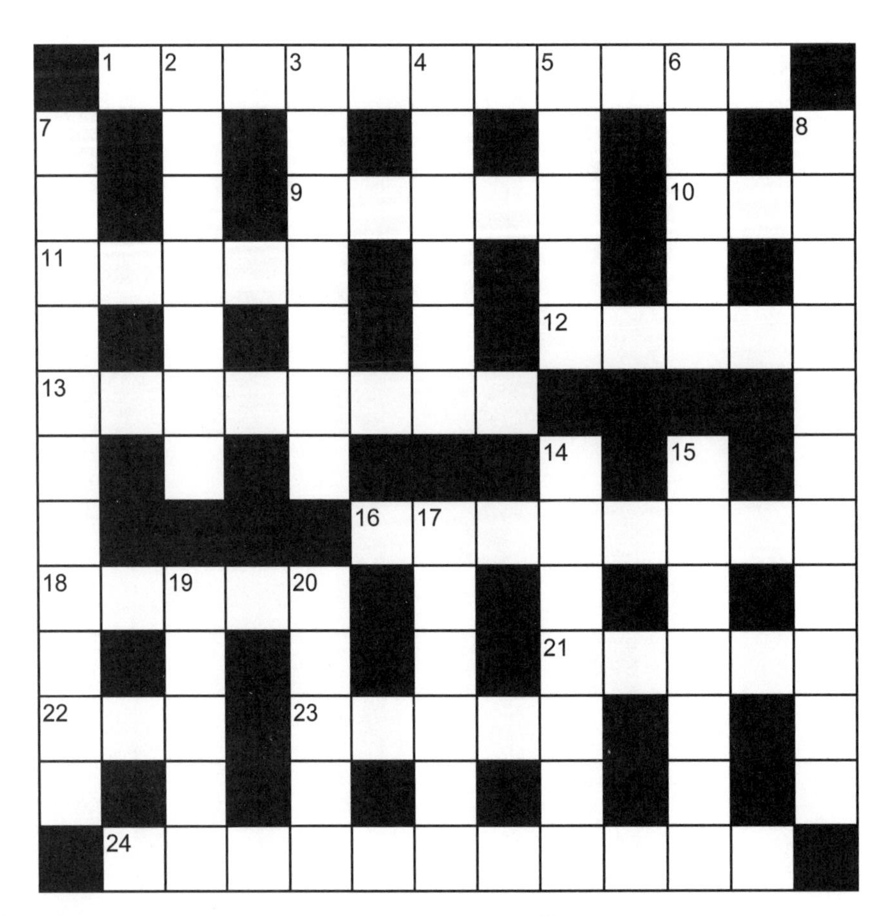

Across

1 Harmful and sneaky (11)
9 Slight error; oversight (5)
10 Golf peg (3)
11 Grips with the teeth (5)
12 Device used to sharpen razors (5)
13 Effusion (8)
16 Machines (8)
18 Fault (5)
21 One of the United Arab Emirates (5)
22 Long period of time (3)
23 Leaf of parchment (5)
24 Comprehends (11)

Down

2 Install (7)
3 Temperature scale (7)
4 Urges to do something (6)
5 Swerves off course (5)
6 Complete; absolute (5)
7 Needleworker (11)
8 Action of breathing (11)
14 Venetian boat (7)
15 Combined spear and battleaxe (7)
17 Male relatives (6)
19 Angry dispute (3-2)
20 Firearm (5)

Crossword

Puzzle 32

Across

1 Eventual outcome (6)
5 Assumes as a fact (6)
8 Anxiety; dread (4)
9 Hugging (8)
10 Garden tools (5)
11 Portable computers (7)
14 Intense fire (13)
16 Monumental Egyptian structure (7)
18 Cooked in hot fat (5)
20 Metrical analysis of verse (8)
22 Cereal grains used as food (4)
23 Wildcats (6)
24 Meagre (6)

Down

2 Rapacious (9)
3 Flesher (anag) (7)
4 Bloodsucking insect (4)
5 Chiropody (8)
6 Break apart forcibly (5)
7 Light brown colour (3)
12 Objector (9)
13 Happy ___ : card game (8)
15 Tumult (7)
17 Attach to (5)
19 Summit of a small hill (4)
21 Shed tears (3)

Puzzle 33

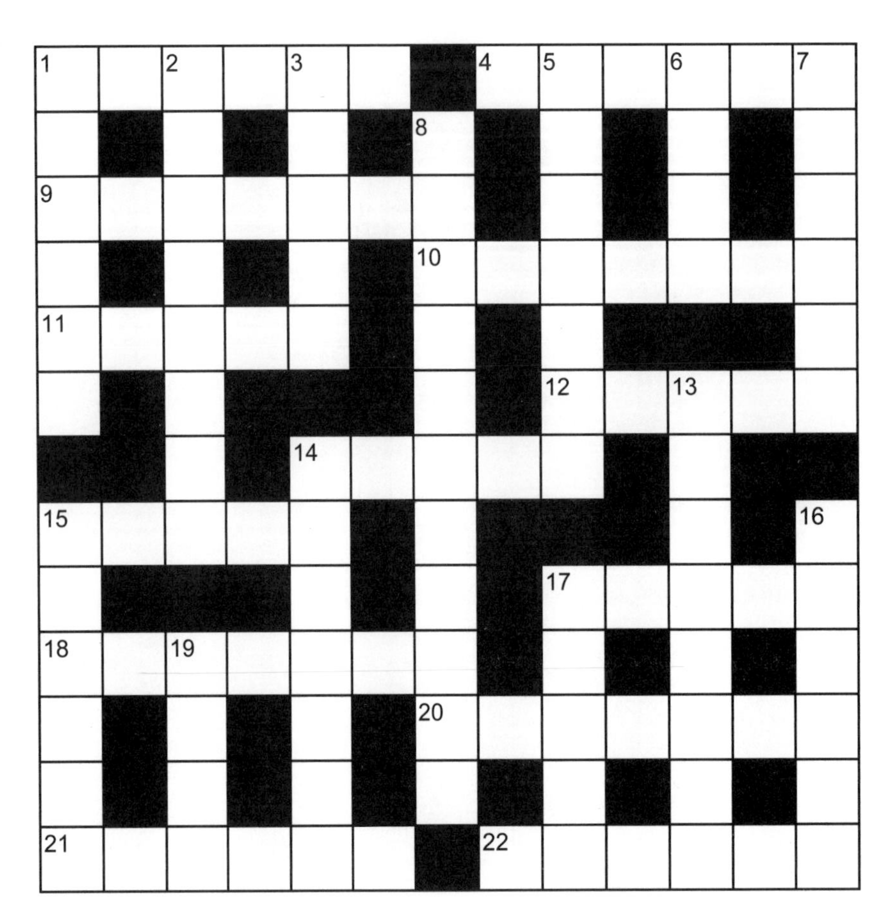

Across

1 End a dispute (6)
4 Items of value (6)
9 Liberate; release (7)
10 Sailing ship (7)
11 Retrieve (5)
12 Fertile spots in deserts (5)
14 ___ days: long ago (5)
15 Relating to the kidneys (5)
17 More ashen in appearance (5)
18 Male blaze fighters (7)
20 Ornamental stone openwork (7)
21 Exude (6)
22 Acquired money as profit (6)

Down

1 Fills up (6)
2 Not inclined to talk (8)
3 Drain away from soil (of a chemical) (5)
5 Rich white cheese (7)
6 Otherwise (4)
7 Portions of a play (6)
8 Component parts (11)
13 Most foolish (8)
14 Mountain in N Greece (7)
15 Safe place (6)
16 Made a request to God (6)
17 Stage (5)
19 Ridge of rock (4)

Crossword

Puzzle 34

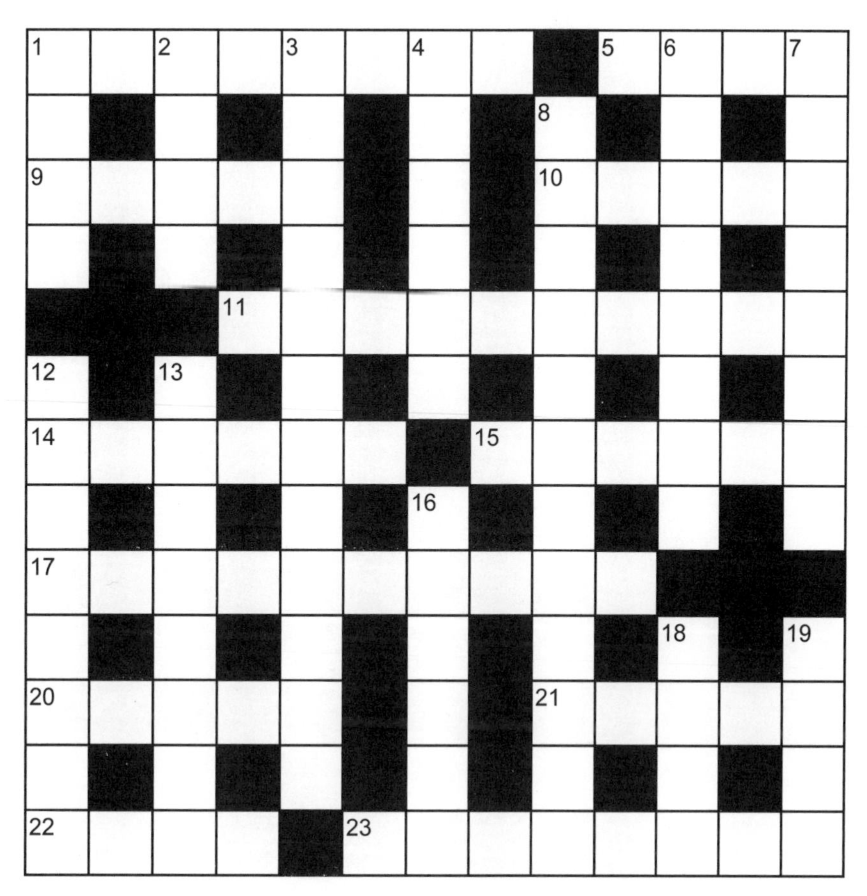

Across

1 Soccer (8)
5 Network of lines (4)
9 Floral leaf (5)
10 Words that identify things (5)
11 Making more palatable (10)
14 Giggles (6)
15 Fall quickly (6)
17 Raisable structure across a moat (10)
20 A satellite of Uranus (5)
21 Intimidate (5)
22 Eg perform karaoke (4)
23 Person of varied learning (8)

Down

1 Dandies (4)
2 Solemn promise (4)
3 Disregarding the rules (5,3,4)
4 Pantry (6)
6 Social gatherings for old friends (8)
7 Have a different opinion (8)
8 Understandably (12)
12 Dress clothes (4,4)
13 Length of time something lasts (8)
16 Japanese robe (6)
18 Earnest appeal (4)
19 Legendary story (4)

Puzzle 35

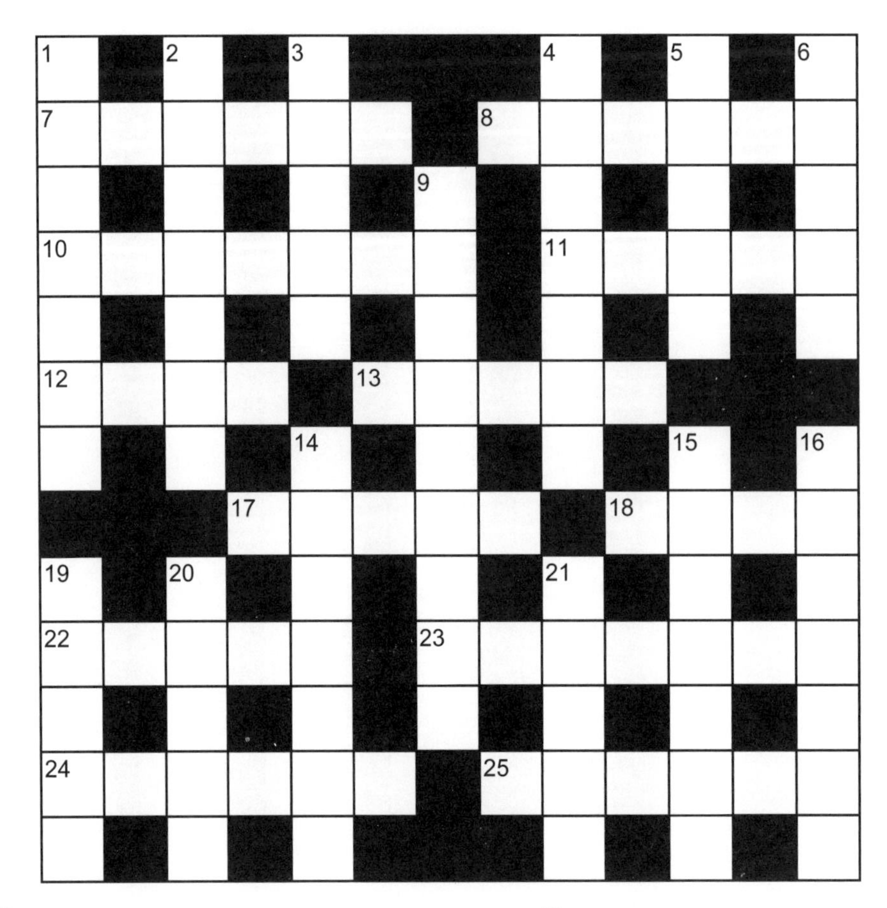

Across

7 Small hills (6)
8 Cause sudden excitement (6)
10 Lottery (7)
11 Light canoe (5)
12 Part of the foot (4)
13 Girls ___ : pop group (5)
17 Sends through the mail (5)
18 A performance by one person (4)
22 Discard; throw away (5)
23 Laurence ___ : English actor (7)
24 Restaurant (6)
25 Yells (6)

Down

1 Incomplete or lacking in detail (7)
2 More spacious (7)
3 Metallic compound (5)
4 Shock physically (5-2)
5 Type of plastic (5)
6 Man (informal) (5)
9 Powerful whirlpool (9)
14 Pennies (7)
15 Harmful (7)
16 Holiday visitor (7)
19 Trembling poplar (5)
20 Runs at a moderate pace (5)
21 Period of darkness (5)

Crossword

Puzzle 36

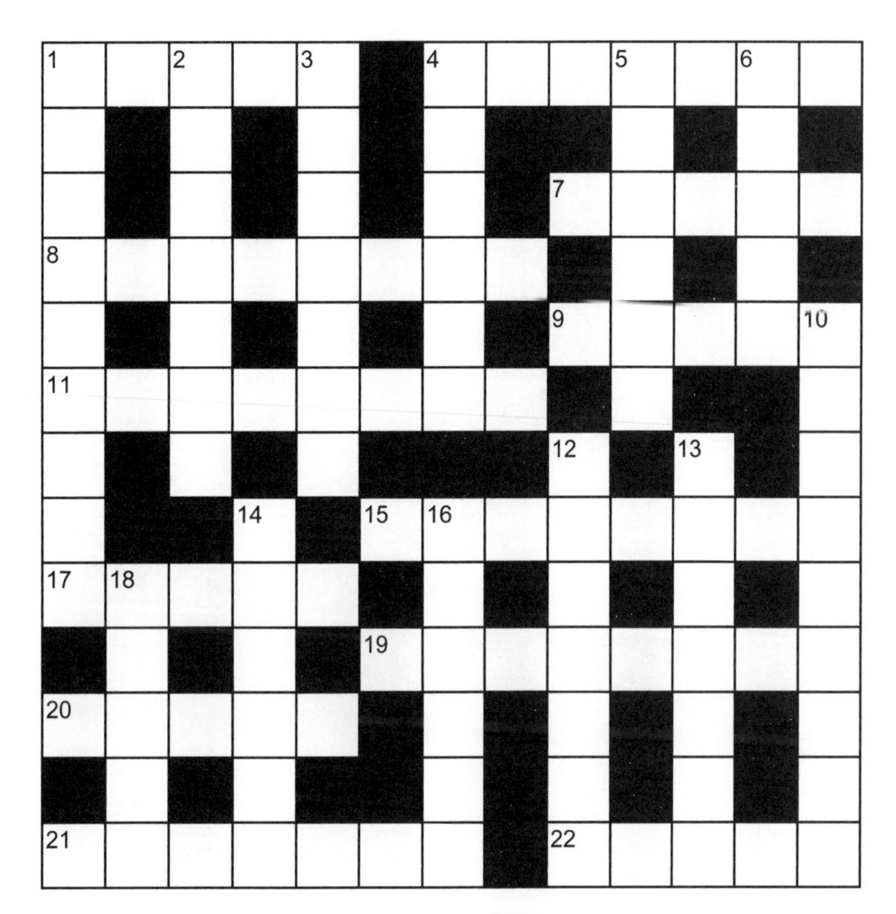

Across

1 Rapidity of movement (5)
4 Lie (7)
7 Body of rules (5)
8 Threatening (8)
9 Precious stone (5)
11 Official in football (8)
15 Opera texts (8)
17 Things to be done (5)
19 Malicious (8)
20 Cloud (anag) (5)
21 An oral communication (7)
22 Sudden forward thrust (5)

Down

1 Incentive; substance like caffeine (9)
2 Latter part of the day (7)
3 Bishop's jurisdiction (7)
4 Country in E Africa (6)
5 Brought up (6)
6 Store of hoarded wealth (5)
10 Make laws (9)
12 Visibly anxious (7)
13 Become more rigid (7)
14 Abilities; talents (6)
16 Enforce compliance with (6)
18 Higher than (5)

Puzzle 37

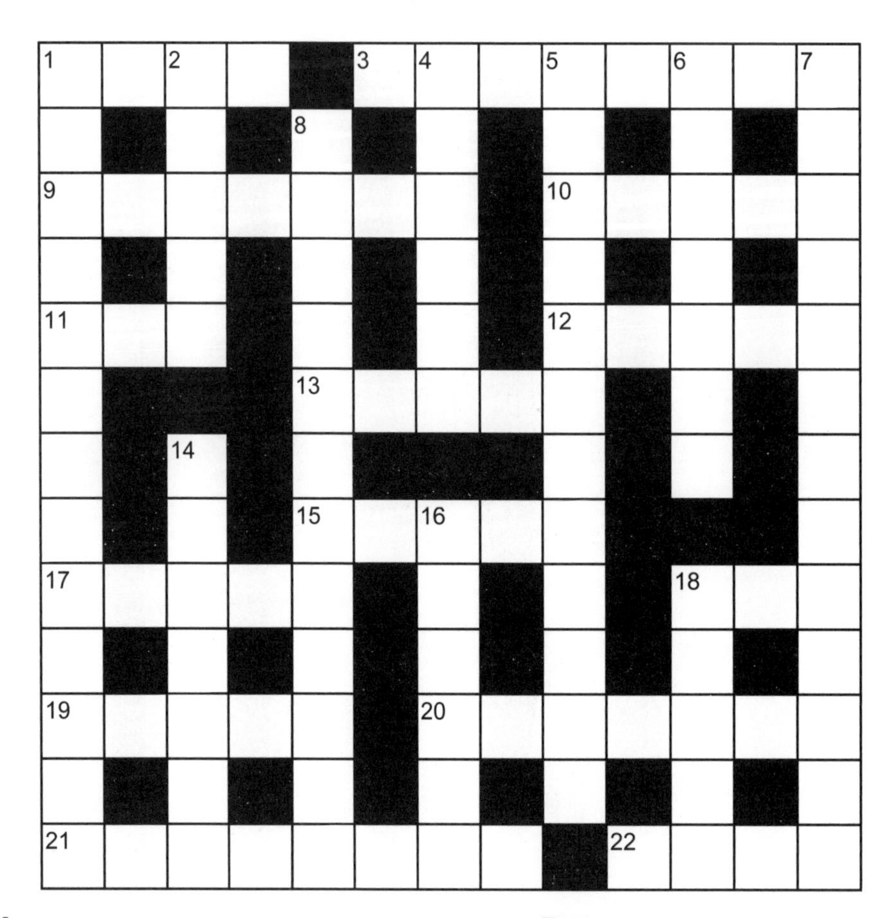

Across

1 On top of (4)
3 Tyrannical (8)
9 Alternative forms of genes (7)
10 Plant spike (5)
11 Dishonourable person (3)
12 Large bird of prey (5)
13 Show-off (5)
15 Venomous snake (5)
17 Making a knot in (5)
18 Additionally (3)
19 Sweeping implement (5)
20 Direct or control a machine (7)
21 Outpouring (8)
22 Streams of liquid or gas (4)

Down

1 Inexplicable (13)
2 Lubricated (5)
4 Follows (6)
5 Sound of quick light steps (6-6)
6 Mental process or idea (7)
7 Satisfaction (13)
8 International multi-sport event (7,5)
14 Incidental result of a larger project (4-3)
16 Pygmy chimpanzee (6)
18 Alert (5)

Crossword

Puzzle 38

Across

1 Send down a ball in cricket (4)
3 Etiquette (8)
9 Fail to care for (7)
10 Cool and distant (5)
11 Vain (12)
14 Involuntary spasm (3)
16 ___ Berry: actress (5)
17 Be in debt (3)
18 Renditions (12)
21 ___ Lavigne: Canadian singer (5)
22 Recording on tape (7)
23 Enclosed area in a farm (8)
24 Topical information (4)

Down

1 Piece of paper money (4,4)
2 Gamble (5)
4 Inform upon (3)
5 Capable of being moved (12)
6 Spicy Spanish sausage (7)
7 Attic (4)
8 Charmingly (12)
12 Pertaining to the sun (5)
13 Written communications (8)
15 Easier to understand (7)
19 ___ Woodward: rugby union coach (5)
20 Young sheep (4)
22 Coniferous tree (3)

Puzzle 39

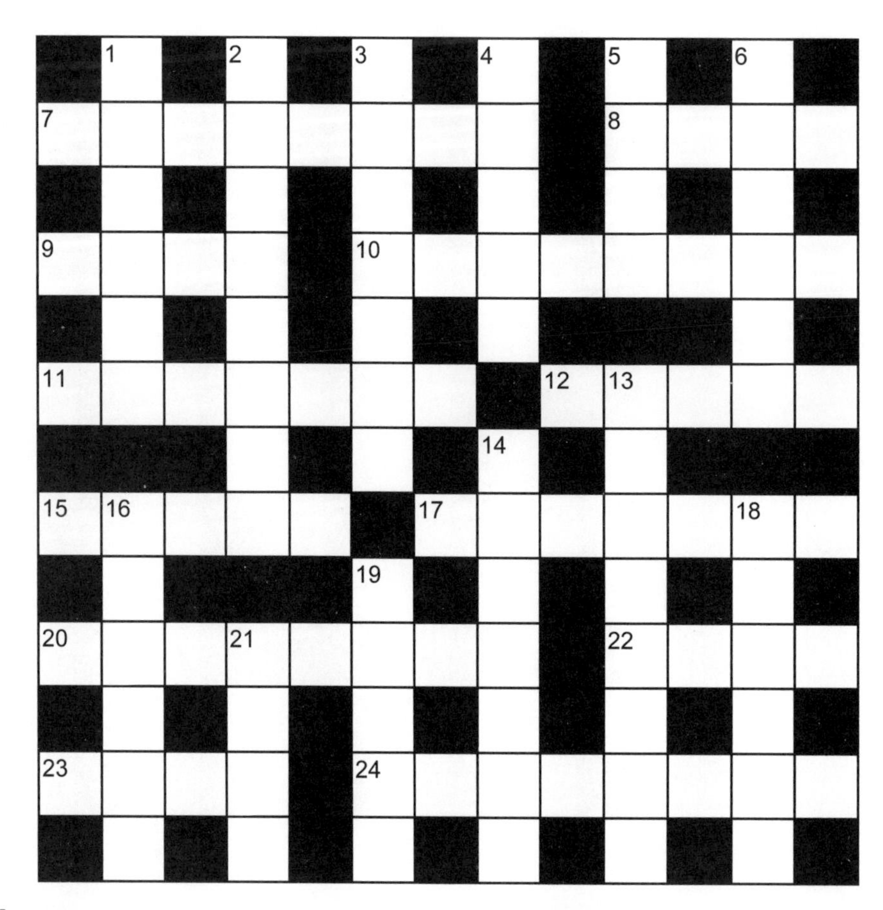

Across

7 Timetable (8)
8 Elan (anag) (4)
9 Worry about (4)
10 Acted with hesitation (8)
11 Distributing (7)
12 Bony structure in the head (5)
15 Animal skins; hurls missiles (5)
17 Panacea (4-3)
20 Inaccurate name (8)
22 Adds (4)
23 Dreadful (4)
24 Pinching sharply (8)

Down

1 Neck-warming garments (6)
2 Cause deliberate damage to (8)
3 Dull (7)
4 Eg incisors and molars (5)
5 Run away (4)
6 Imaginary (6)
13 Memento (8)
14 Hasty (7)
16 Evoke (6)
18 Thin layer of sedimentary rock (6)
19 Strike (5)
21 Negative votes (4)

Crossword

Puzzle 40

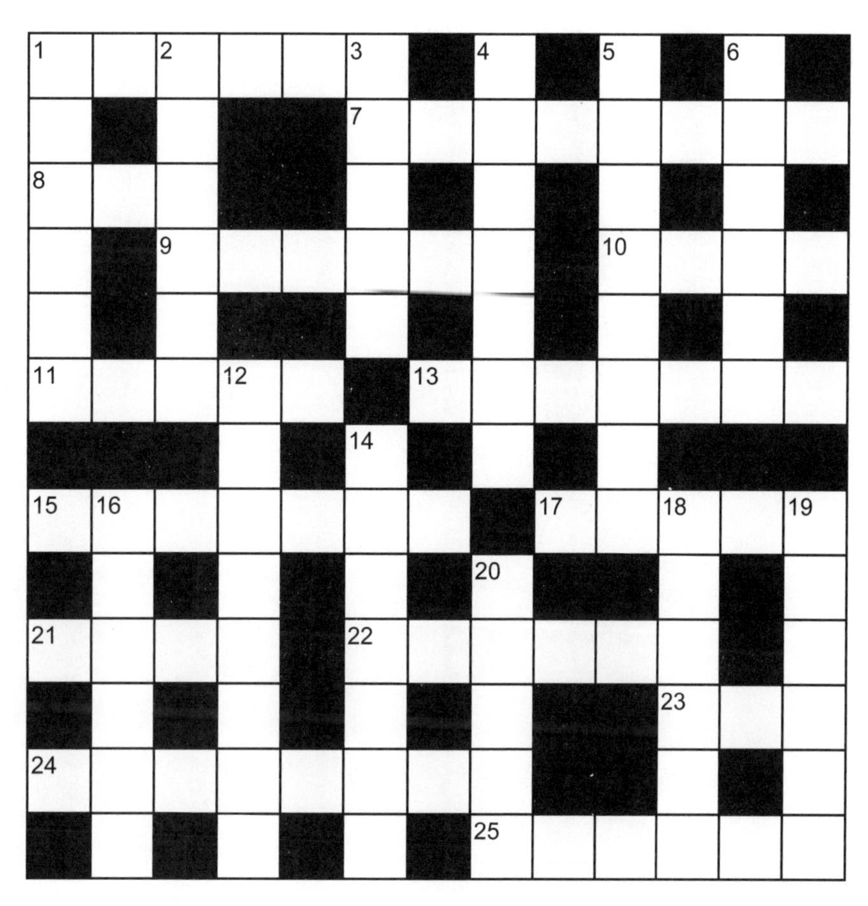

Across

1 Large lizard (6)
7 Sport (8)
8 22nd Greek letter (3)
9 Pilfers (6)
10 Centre (4)
11 ___ Els: golfing star (5)
13 Loving deeply (7)
15 Branch of maths (7)
17 Small venomous snake (5)
21 Short tail (4)
22 Dogs (6)
23 Sort; kind (3)
24 Loss of hearing (8)
25 Special ___ : film illusion (6)

Down

1 Provoke (6)
2 Agreement or concord (6)
3 Lion who rules over Narnia (5)
4 Illegally in advance of the ball (football) (7)
5 Partially hidden (8)
6 Former British coin (6)
12 Recognise (8)
14 Type of handicraft (7)
16 Hinged case hung from the neck (6)
18 Wish for (6)
19 Spacecraft (6)
20 Plain writing (5)

Puzzle 41

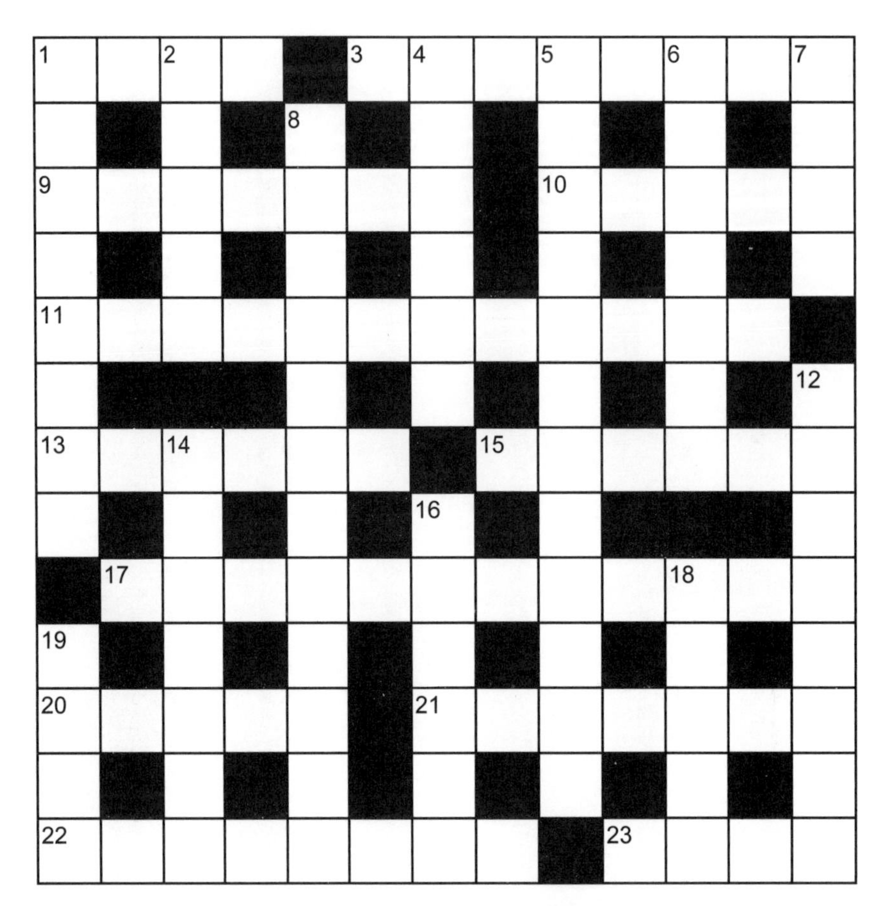

Across

1 Rough or harsh sound (4)
3 The act of swimming (8)
9 SI unit of electric charge (7)
10 Models for a photograph (5)
11 Adverse (12)
13 Frames used by artists (6)
15 Indicator on a computer screen (6)
17 Constantly; always (12)
20 Foot joint (5)
21 Stiff coarse hair (7)
22 Beneficial (8)
23 Money given to the poor (4)

Down

1 Hermits (8)
2 Cram (5)
4 Shady garden alcove (6)
5 Using letters and numbers (12)
6 Disparaging remarks (7)
7 Where a bird lays eggs (4)
8 Recovering from illness (of a person) (12)
12 Dreariness (8)
14 Breathing aid in water (7)
16 Line of equal pressure on a map (6)
18 Sum; add up (5)
19 Rodents (4)

Puzzle 42

Across

1 Marked effect (6)
5 Conceals with a cloth (6)
8 Spiritual teacher (4)
9 Plummet (8)
10 Chairs (5)
11 Capital of Indonesia (7)
14 Playful trick (9,4)
16 Elevate (7)
18 Lance (5)
20 Extreme audacity (8)
22 Tailless amphibian (4)
23 Course of a meal (6)
24 Bog (6)

Down

2 Device for catching rodents (9)
3 Living in water (7)
4 Melody (4)
5 Shipwrecked person (8)
6 Russian spirit (5)
7 Increase the running speed of an engine (3)
12 Fast food shops (9)
13 ___ Verdi: composer (8)
15 Largest planet (7)
17 Religious table (5)
19 ___ Yorke: Radiohead lead singer (4)
21 Female chicken (3)

Puzzle 43

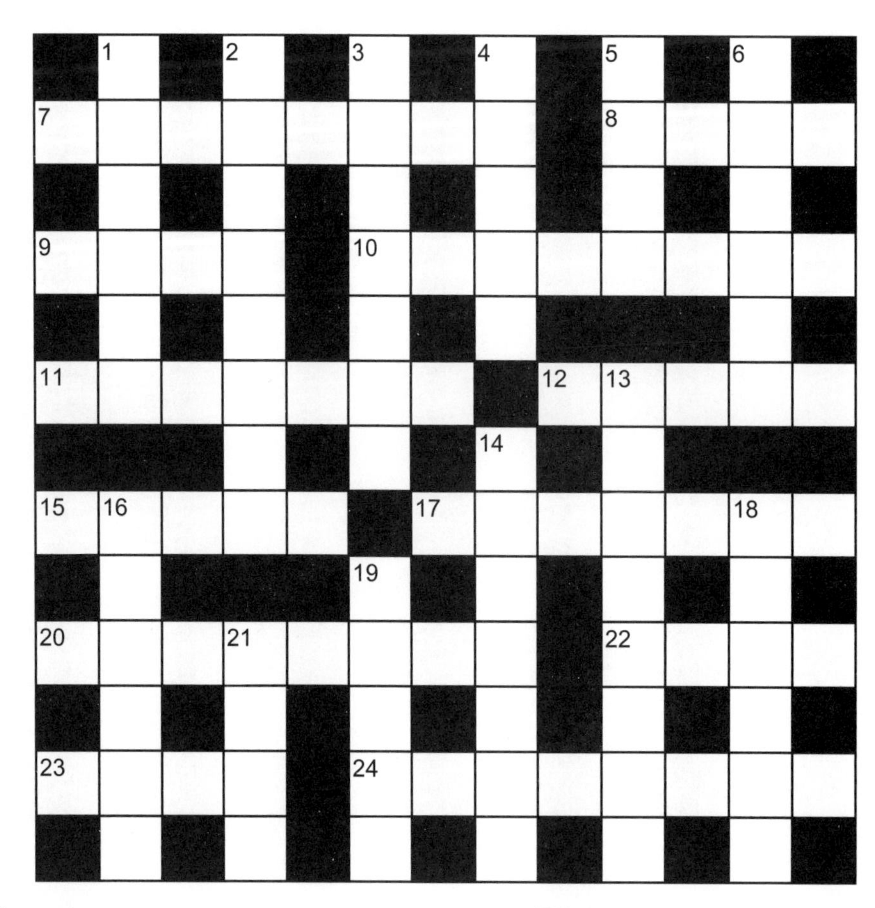

Across

7 Contents of the Mediterranean (8)
8 Method of learning by repetition (4)
9 Broken husks of seeds (4)
10 Clemency (8)
11 Helps (7)
12 Assumed appearance (5)
15 Arbiter (5)
17 Very small fish (7)
20 Without suffering any punishment (4-4)
22 Clarets (4)
23 Encircle or bind (4)
24 Drug that treats a disease (8)

Down

1 Jewels formed in oyster shells (6)
2 Moving from side to side (8)
3 Eg Paula Radcliffe (7)
4 Main stem of a tree (5)
5 Correct; accurate (4)
6 Adheres to; fastens (6)
13 Play a role with great restraint (8)
14 Sweetened citrus beverage (7)
16 Unwind (6)
18 Finish (6)
19 Felony (5)
21 Clean up (4)

Crossword

Puzzle 44

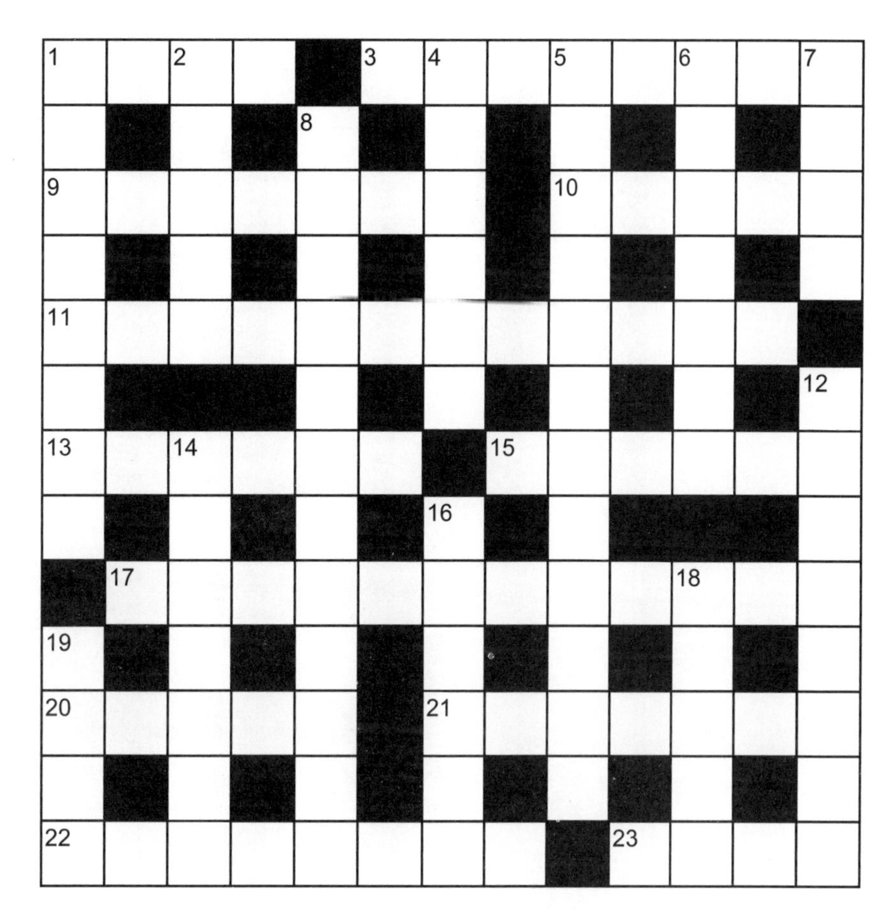

Across

1 Cleanse (4)
3 Removing from the premises (8)
9 Small Arctic whale (7)
10 Swells (5)
11 Advantageous; superior (12)
13 Appease (6)
15 Measure of how strongly an object reflects light (6)
17 Formal announcements (12)
20 Ravine (5)
21 Electronic retention of data (7)
22 Revealing a truth (8)
23 Barrels (4)

Down

1 Trachea (8)
2 Small loose stones (5)
4 Held in great esteem (6)
5 Surrender (12)
6 Catch fire (7)
7 Current of air (4)
8 Optimism (12)
12 Large edible marine crustaceans (8)
14 Tidy (5,2)
16 Prayer (6)
18 Egg-shaped (5)
19 Fever (4)

Puzzle 45

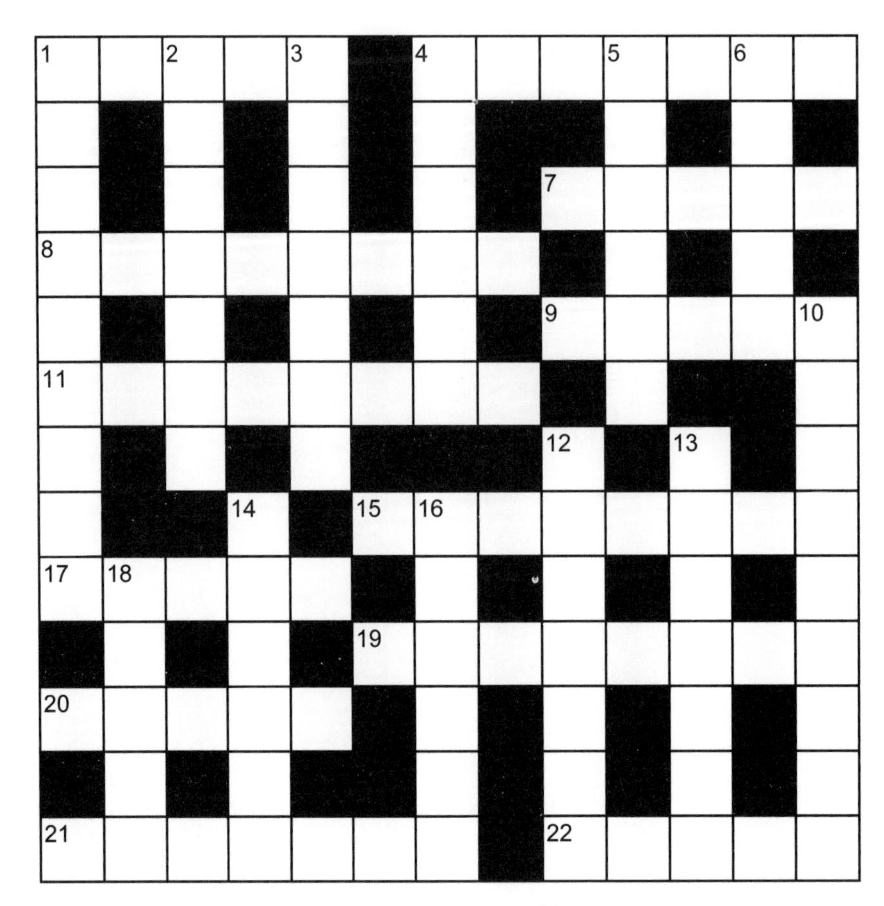

Across

1 Many times (5)
4 Shelter for a vehicle (7)
7 Large intestine (5)
8 Reassign (8)
9 Follows orders (5)
11 Water-resistant jacket (8)
15 Grandiosity of language (8)
17 Ring-shaped object (5)
19 US state (8)
20 Brings up (5)
21 Approve or support (7)
22 Reasoned judgement (5)

Down

1 Deficit in a bank account (9)
2 Slender stemlike plant appendage (7)
3 Quibble (7)
4 Gaseous envelope of the sun (6)
5 ___ Buffay: character in Friends (6)
6 Spacious (5)
10 Given to using irony (9)
12 Type of alcohol (7)
13 Deleting (7)
14 A size of book page (6)
16 Move with great speed (6)
18 Body of water (5)

Puzzle 46

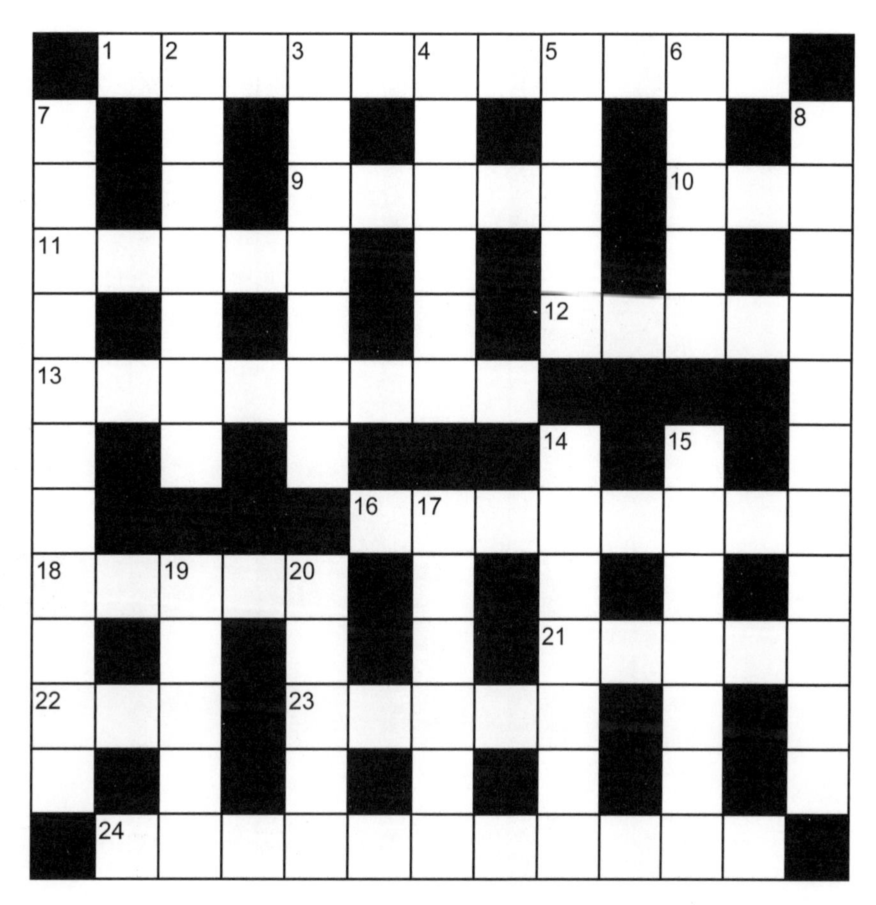

Across

1 Institute of higher education (11)
9 Vacillate (5)
10 Seventh Greek letter (3)
11 Bird claw (5)
12 Flatten on impact (5)
13 A lament (8)
16 An unwelcome person; invader (8)
18 Deducts (5)
21 ___ Sharapova: tennis player (5)
22 Nothing (3)
23 Individual things (5)
24 Lack of being (11)

Down

2 Stablemen (7)
3 Opening the mouth wide when tired (7)
4 Desired for oneself (6)
5 Throws (5)
6 Model; perfect (5)
7 Amazingly good (11)
8 Advance quickly (4-7)
14 Shade of red (7)
15 Speak to (7)
17 Country (6)
19 Stringed instrument (5)
20 Partly melted snow (5)

Puzzle 47

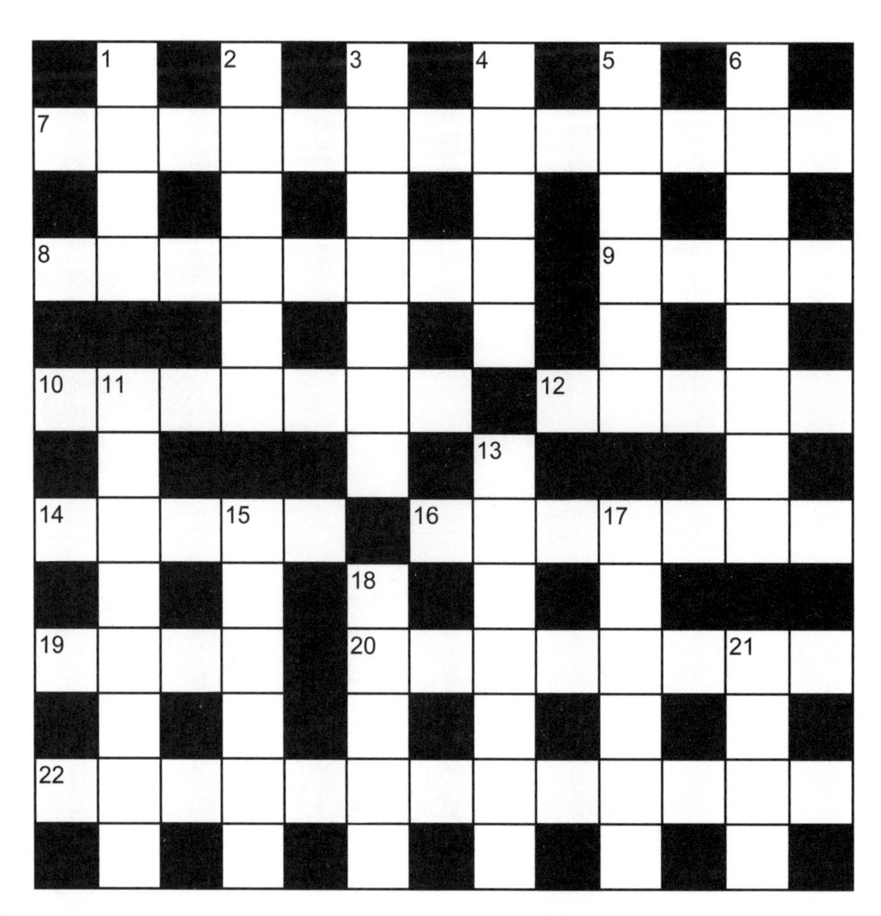

Across

7 Deceitful behaviour (6-7)
8 Includes (8)
9 Ancient city (4)
10 Praise formally (7)
12 Poetic verse (5)
14 Recycle (5)
16 White and lustrous (hair) (7)
19 Affirm with confidence (4)
20 Considers an option (8)
22 Congratulations (13)

Down

1 Urban area (4)
2 In flower (6)
3 Lifting with difficulty (7)
4 Believer in a supreme being (5)
5 Malfunction (6)
6 Mole (8)
11 Summary (8)
13 Exhibit (7)
15 Make an unusually great effort (6)
17 Stringed instrument (6)
18 Coiled curve (5)
21 Sea eagle (4)

Crossword

Puzzle 48

Across

1 Seabirds (4)
3 Well-rounded (8)
9 Not tense (7)
10 Edits (anag) (5)
11 Hopelessly (12)
14 Legal rule (3)
16 Rescues (5)
17 Pointed tool (3)
18 Skilled joiner (12)
21 Scoundrel (5)
22 Terms of office (7)
23 All people (8)
24 Proverbs (4)

Down

1 Large terrier (8)
2 Ovens (5)
4 Increase in amount (3)
5 Amazement (12)
6 Mark written under the letter c (7)
7 Fine powder (4)
8 Thoroughly (12)
12 Variety show (5)
13 Flower sellers (8)
15 Quarrel or haggle (7)
19 Destiny; fate (5)
20 Woody plant (4)
22 Unit of weight (3)

Puzzle 49

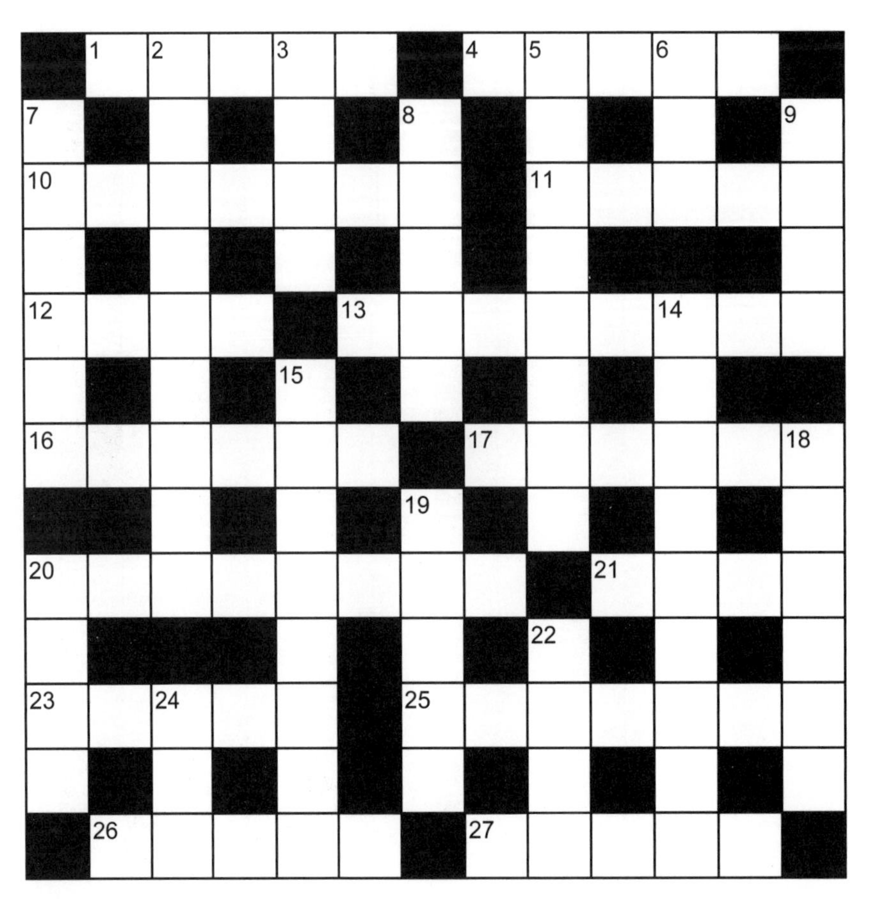

Across

1 Pleasantly warm (of weather) (5)
4 Submerged ridges of rock (5)
10 Satisfy; conciliate (7)
11 Major African river (5)
12 Roman god of war (4)
13 Eg resident of Cairo (8)
16 Crown (6)
17 In truth; really (6)
20 Monitors (8)
21 Fall vertically (4)
23 Cry out loudly (5)
25 An acted riddle (7)
26 Dull colours (5)
27 Outdoor fundraising events (5)

Down

2 Artificial sweetener (9)
3 Eg beef or pork (4)
5 Getting away from (8)
6 Wetland (3)
7 Heated up (6)
8 Pretend (5)
9 Fourth Gospel (4)
14 Intoxicate (9)
15 Honourably (8)
18 Put briefly into liquid (6)
19 Block of wood (5)
20 Opposite of fail (4)
22 Rank (4)
24 Blade for rowing a boat (3)

Crossword

Puzzle 50

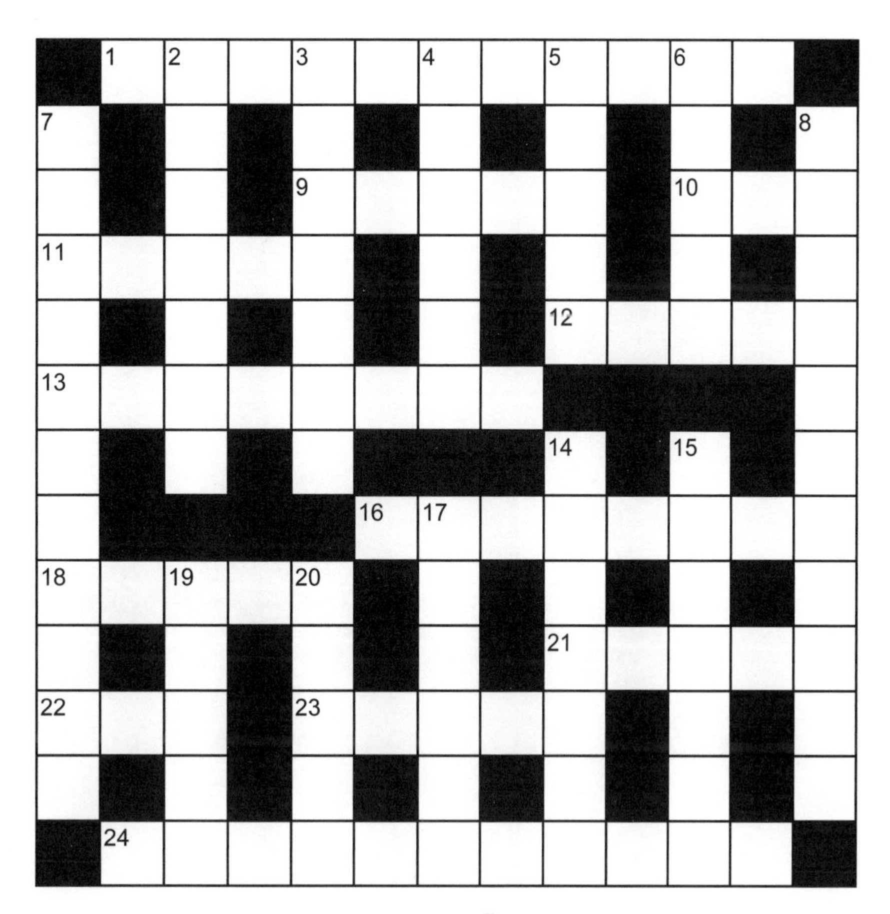

Across

1 Past performances (5,6)
9 Chaplain in the armed services (5)
10 Cereal grain (3)
11 Anxious (5)
12 Strong ringing sound (5)
13 Regnant (8)
16 Easy chair (8)
18 Small woody plant (5)
21 Cake decoration (5)
22 Towards the stern (3)
23 Ladies (5)
24 Acting out a part (4,7)

Down

2 Learn new skills (7)
3 Emulating (7)
4 Blush (6)
5 Fastening device (5)
6 Spanish wine (5)
7 US politician (11)
8 Fear in front of an audience (5,6)
14 Clearly (7)
15 Toxin in the body (7)
17 Hard tooth coating (6)
19 Imitative of the past (5)
20 Single-edged hunting knife (5)

Puzzle 51

Across

1 Publicity (8)
5 Light circle around the head of a saint (4)
8 Upright (5)
9 Scrunch up (7)
10 Slanted letters (7)
12 Portentous (7)
14 Elongated rectangles (7)
16 Catholic shrine in France (7)
18 Country in W Africa (7)
19 Move on ice (5)
20 Locate or place (4)
21 Wild prank (8)

Down

1 Days before major events (4)
2 Adjust in advance of its use (6)
3 Contented (9)
4 Pull back from (6)
6 Domestic assistant (2,4)
7 Abroad (8)
11 Inability to feel pain (9)
12 Sentiments (8)
13 Gold lump (6)
14 Academy Awards (6)
15 US state (6)
17 Your current location (4)

Crossword

Puzzle 52

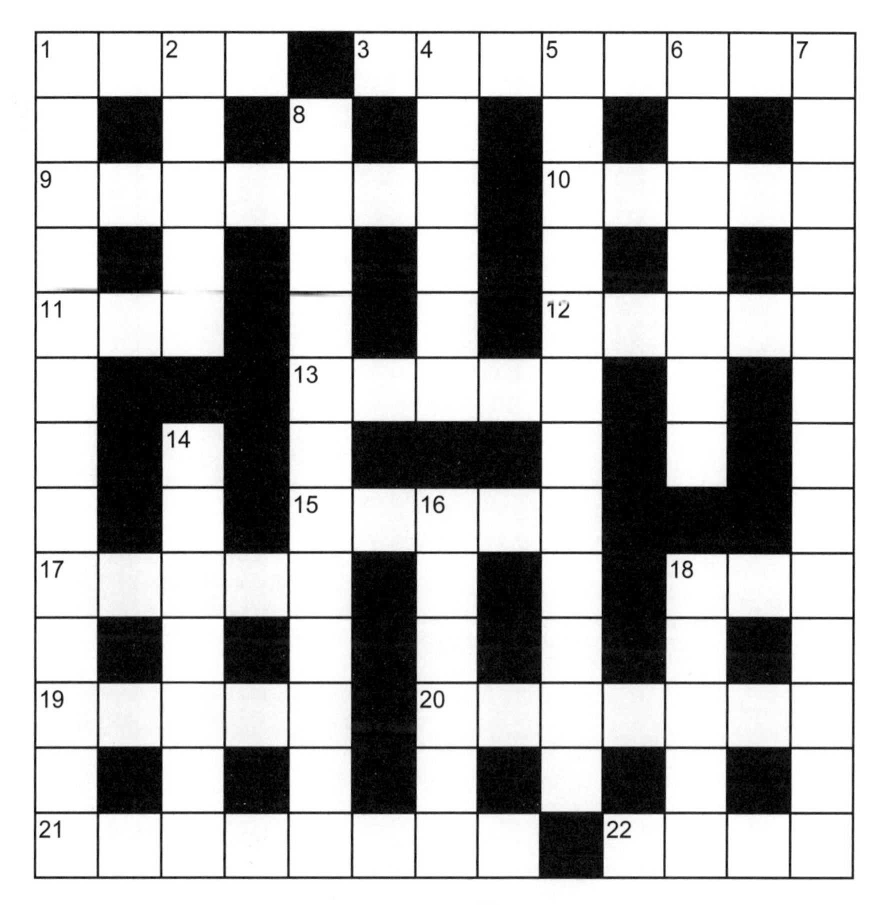

Across

- **1** Cried (4)
- **3** Elation (8)
- **9** Exclusion from the workplace (7)
- **10** A thing that measures (5)
- **11** Climbing shrub (3)
- **12** In a slow tempo (of music) (5)
- **13** Ski run (5)
- **15** Removes the lid (5)
- **17** Solid blow (5)
- **18** 21st Greek letter (3)
- **19** Public announcement officer (5)
- **20** Small bone (7)
- **21** Showering with liquid (8)
- **22** Antelopes (4)

Down

- **1** Supporting canes (7,6)
- **2** Finicky (5)
- **4** Speaks (6)
- **5** Vagrancy (12)
- **6** Comes back (7)
- **7** Fitness to fly (13)
- **8** Repository for misplaced items (4,8)
- **14** Messenger (7)
- **16** Urge to do something (6)
- **18** Brown nut (5)

Puzzle 53

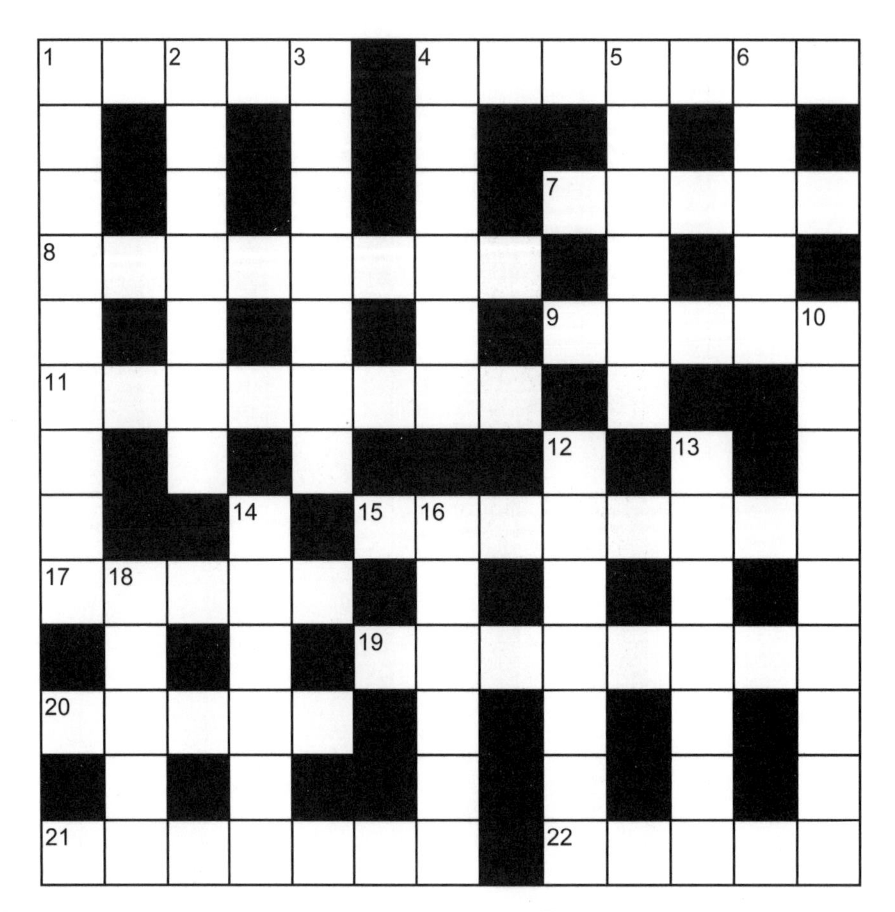

Across

1 Not a winner (5)
4 Homilies (7)
7 Ballroom dance (5)
8 Came to light (8)
9 Turns over and over (5)
11 Not guilty (8)
15 Altercation (8)
17 Twenty (5)
19 Food enhancer (8)
20 Regard highly (5)
21 Sharp no (anag) (7)
22 Expanse of grass (5)

Down

1 Cosmetics (9)
2 Frightening (7)
3 Love; genre of fiction (7)
4 Television surface (6)
5 Piece of grassland (6)
6 Pertaining to birth (5)
10 Broke into pieces (9)
12 Day trips (7)
13 ___ Carlisle: US singer (7)
14 Bend down low (6)
16 Long narrow hilltops (6)
18 Seat (5)

Crossword

Puzzle 54

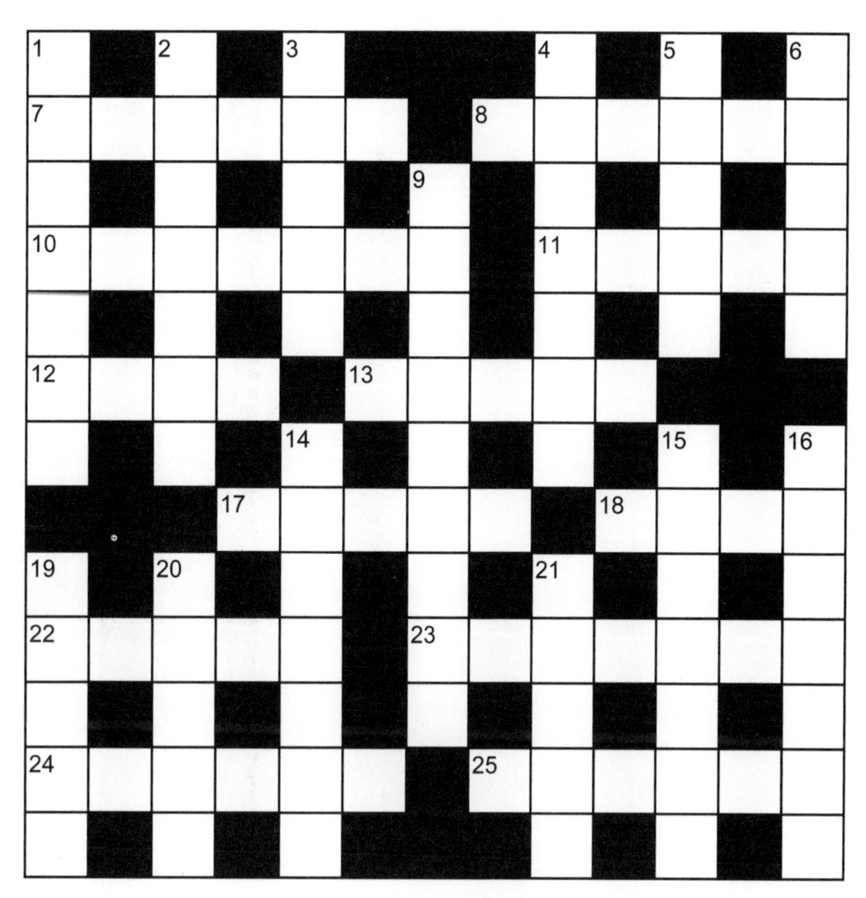

Across

7 Juicy citrus fruit (6)
8 Very brave and courageous (6)
10 Appease; placate (7)
11 Ballroom dance (5)
12 ___ off: falls asleep (4)
13 Young male horses (5)
17 Bags (5)
18 Desert in northern China (4)
22 Pointed part of a fork (5)
23 Makes certain of (7)
24 Shining with light (6)
25 Remember (6)

Down

1 Making; constructing (7)
2 Slow romantic songs (7)
3 Once more (5)
4 Ear test (anag) (7)
5 Shared by two or more people (5)
6 Exclusive newspaper story (5)
9 Something that is revealing (3-6)
14 Insulating material (7)
15 Bouncer (7)
16 Primarily (7)
19 Be relevant (5)
20 Compel (5)
21 Small island (5)

Puzzle 55

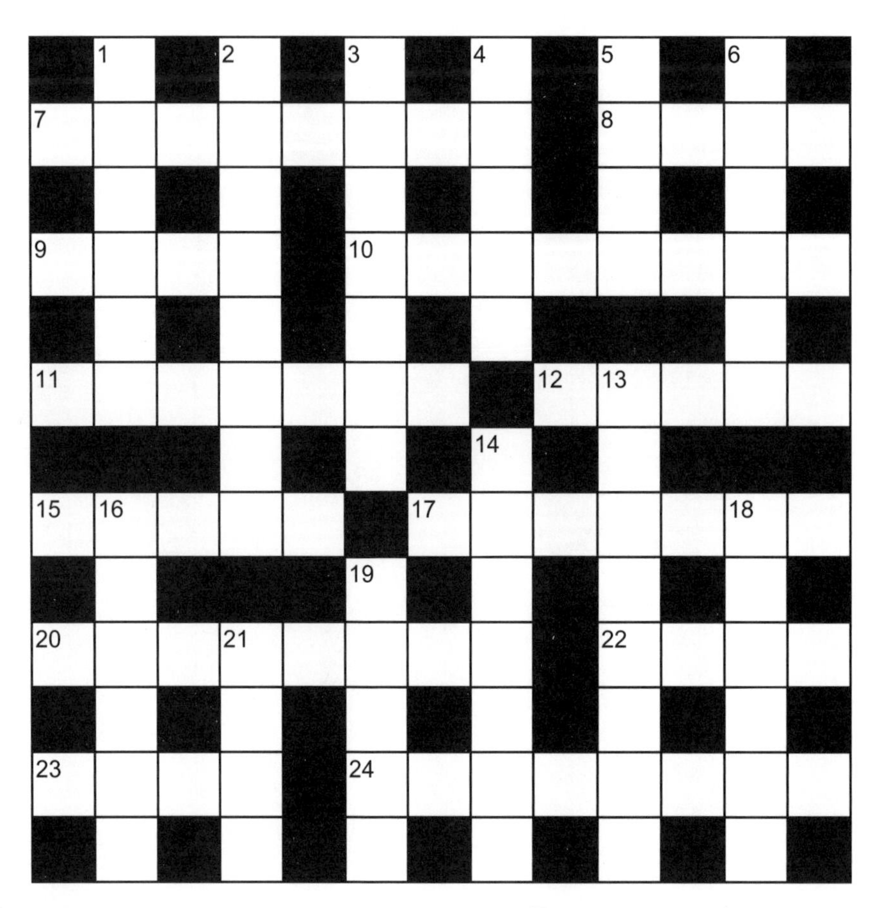

Across

7 Stir dust (anag) (8)
8 Breezy (4)
9 Standard (4)
10 Sudden forceful recoil (8)
11 Type of ship (7)
12 Cruel or severe (5)
15 Salma ___ : actress (5)
17 Define clearly (7)
20 Renounce (8)
22 Tim ___ : English lyricist (4)
23 Sci-fi film with Jeff Bridges (4)
24 In a shrewd manner (8)

Down

1 Boneless piece of meat (6)
2 Stop progressing (8)
3 Gives way under pressure (7)
4 Slender piece of wood (5)
5 Clothing (4)
6 Vestiges (6)
13 Free from error (8)
14 Alcoholic drinks (7)
16 Love affairs (6)
18 Easily done (6)
19 Started (5)
21 Having a sound mind (4)

Crossword

Puzzle 56

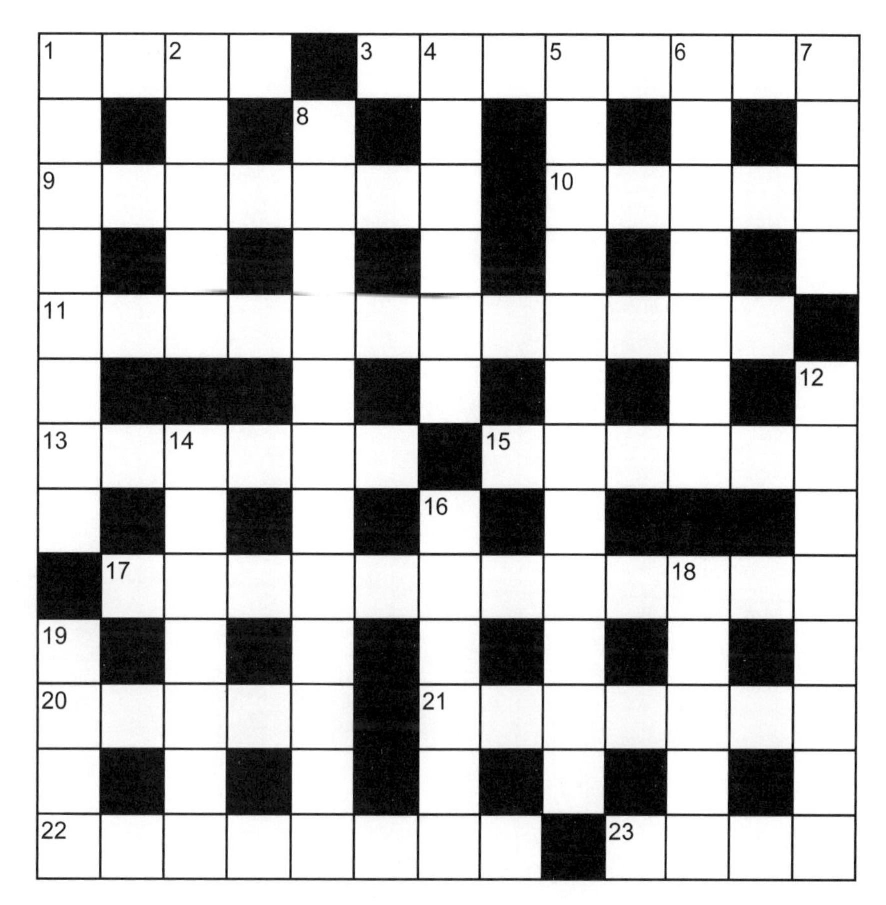

Across

1 Administrative district (4)
3 Rubbed with the hands (8)
9 Newness (7)
10 Dry biscuits used as baby food (5)
11 Relating to numbers (12)
13 Finally (6)
15 Israeli monetary unit (6)
17 Overstatement (12)
20 Bring into a line (5)
21 Mechanical keyboard (7)
22 Inn (8)
23 Stringed instrument (4)

Down

1 Soft toffees (8)
2 Implied (5)
4 Regardless (6)
5 Immediately (12)
6 Bird of prey found in the UK (7)
7 Shallow food container (4)
8 Ability to acquire and apply knowledge (12)
12 Lengthen (8)
14 Decade from 1960 - 1969 (7)
16 Aide (6)
18 Creamy-white colour (5)
19 Hit hard (4)

Puzzle 57

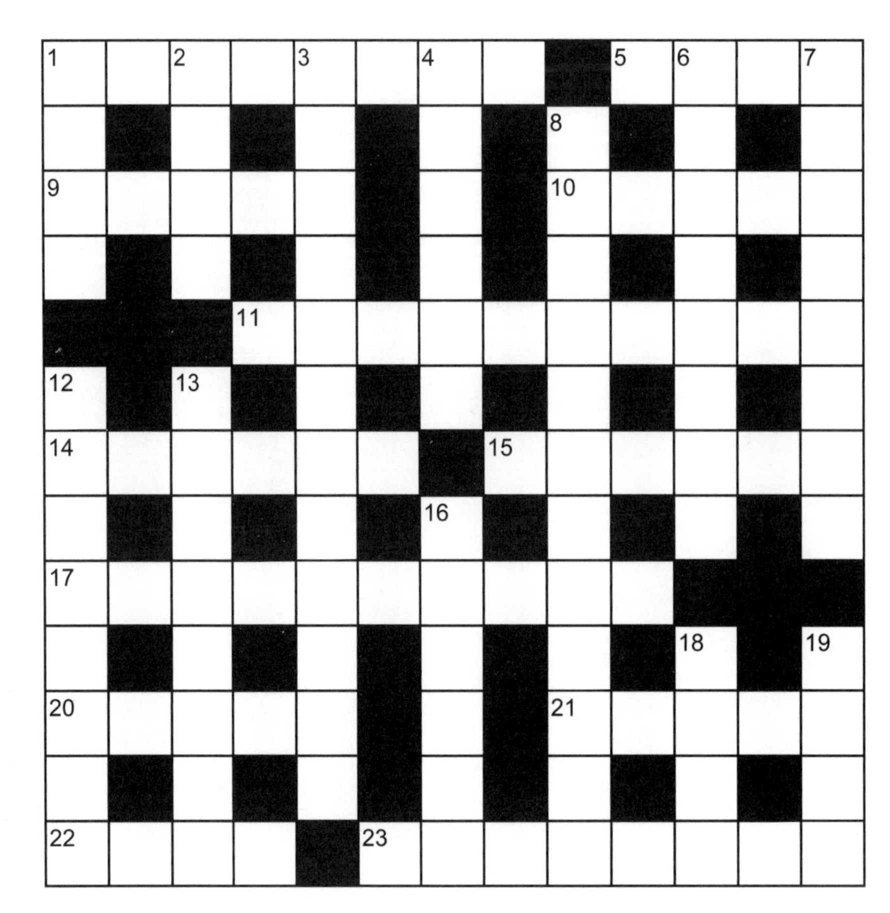

Across

1 Burning (8)
5 Large US feline (4)
9 Ciphers (5)
10 Inhales open-mouthed when sleepy (5)
11 Unable to talk (10)
14 Bow and arrow expert (6)
15 Snow vehicle with runners (6)
17 Machine used to spin things (10)
20 Warning noise (5)
21 Church singers (5)
22 Narrow opening (4)
23 Great adulation (8)

Down

1 Unwell (4)
2 Helper; assistant (4)
3 Vanishing (12)
4 Required (6)
6 Difficult to move because of its size (8)
7 Aided (8)
8 Based on legend (12)
12 Political meetings (8)
13 Plot outline for a play (8)
16 Have sufficient money to pay for (6)
18 Not hard (4)
19 Donkey noise (4)

Crossword

Puzzle 58

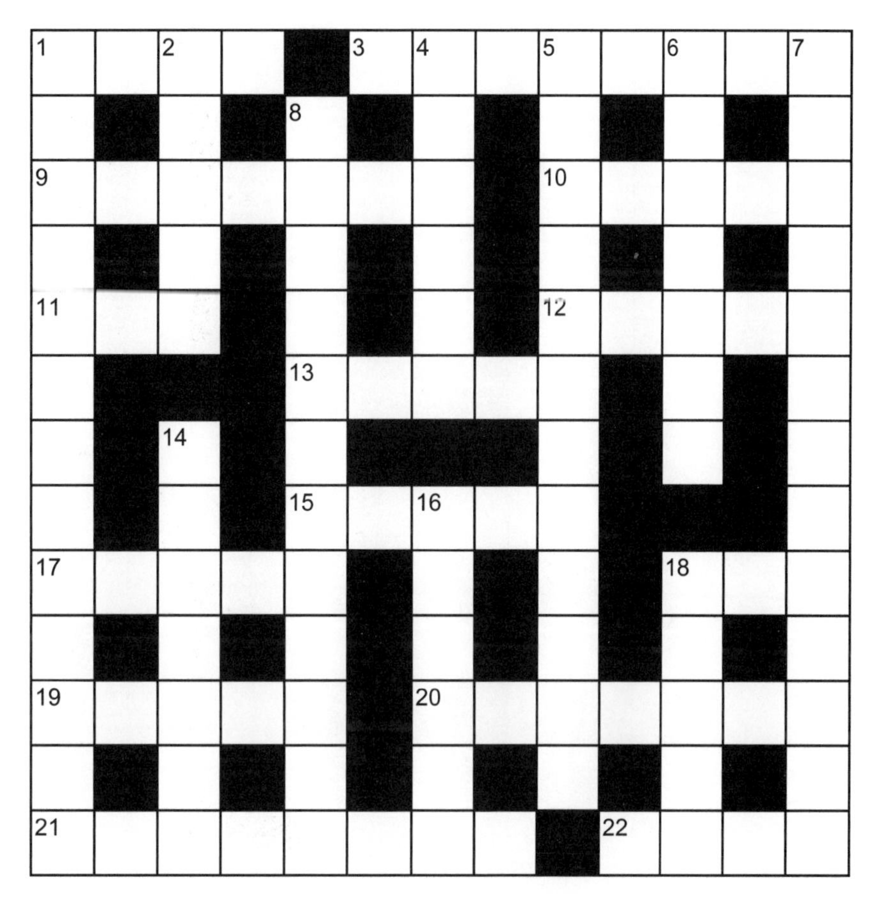

Across

1 Particles around a comet (4)
3 Felon (8)
9 Tranquil (7)
10 Swagger (5)
11 Secret agent (3)
12 Jewel from an oyster shell (5)
13 Touch on; mention (5)
15 Implant (5)
17 Golf course sections (5)
18 Pro (3)
19 Cereal plant (5)
20 Pause in a line of verse (7)
21 Dull (8)
22 Pay close attention to (4)

Down

1 Plant with bright flowers (13)
2 Untidy (5)
4 Respite (6)
5 Made in bulk (4-8)
6 Perfect happiness (7)
7 The ___ / ___ : Fairy tale by Hans Christian Andersen (6,7)
8 Bubbling (12)
14 One thousand million (7)
16 Visible warning device (6)
18 Wind instrument (5)

Puzzle 59

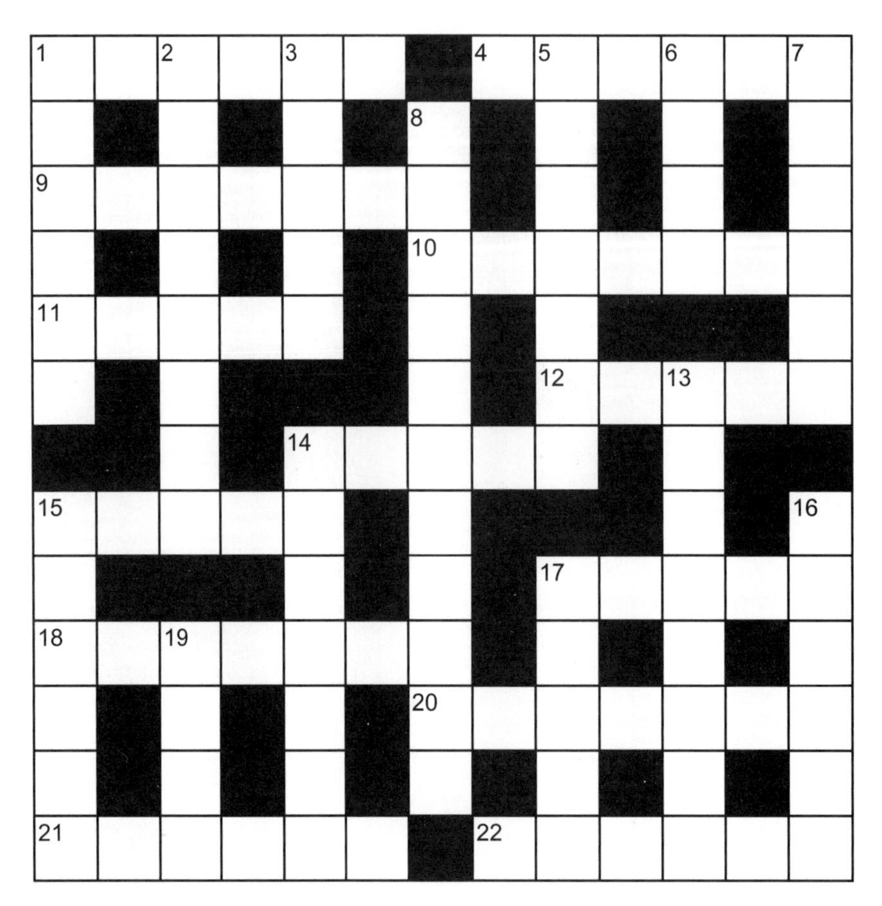

Across

1 Lumberjack (6)
4 Contaminate (6)
9 Body of troops (7)
10 Drop sharply (7)
11 Bits of meat of low value (5)
12 Small insect (5)
14 Out of fashion (5)
15 Verse form (5)
17 Rustic (5)
18 Sign of the zodiac (7)
20 Serviettes (7)
21 Short track for storing trains (6)
22 Complex problem (6)

Down

1 Subatomic particle such as an electron (6)
2 Unauthorised writing on walls (8)
3 Electronic message (5)
5 Interstellar gas clouds (7)
6 School test (4)
7 Coloured (6)
8 Sayings (11)
13 Moving at speed (8)
14 Gourd-like squash (7)
15 Makes a sibilant sound (6)
16 State of matter (6)
17 Become ready to eat (of fruit) (5)
19 Still to be paid (4)

Crossword

Puzzle 60

Across

1 Built (11)
9 Moderate and well-balanced (5)
10 Midge ___ : Ultravox musician (3)
11 Surprise result (5)
12 Scheme intended to deceive (3-2)
13 Close familiarity (8)
16 Plantation producing grapes (8)
18 Opposite one of two (5)
21 Denise van ___ : English actress (5)
22 Mouth (informal) (3)
23 Peak (5)
24 Compassionate (11)

Down

2 State of being overweight (7)
3 Complex wholes (7)
4 Heading on a document (6)
5 Flexible insulated cables (5)
6 Explode (5)
7 Famous cabaret in Paris (6,5)
8 Dejection (11)
14 Avid follower (7)
15 Type of vermouth (7)
17 Overrun in large numbers (6)
19 Married man (informal) (5)
20 Repeat something once more (5)

Puzzle 61

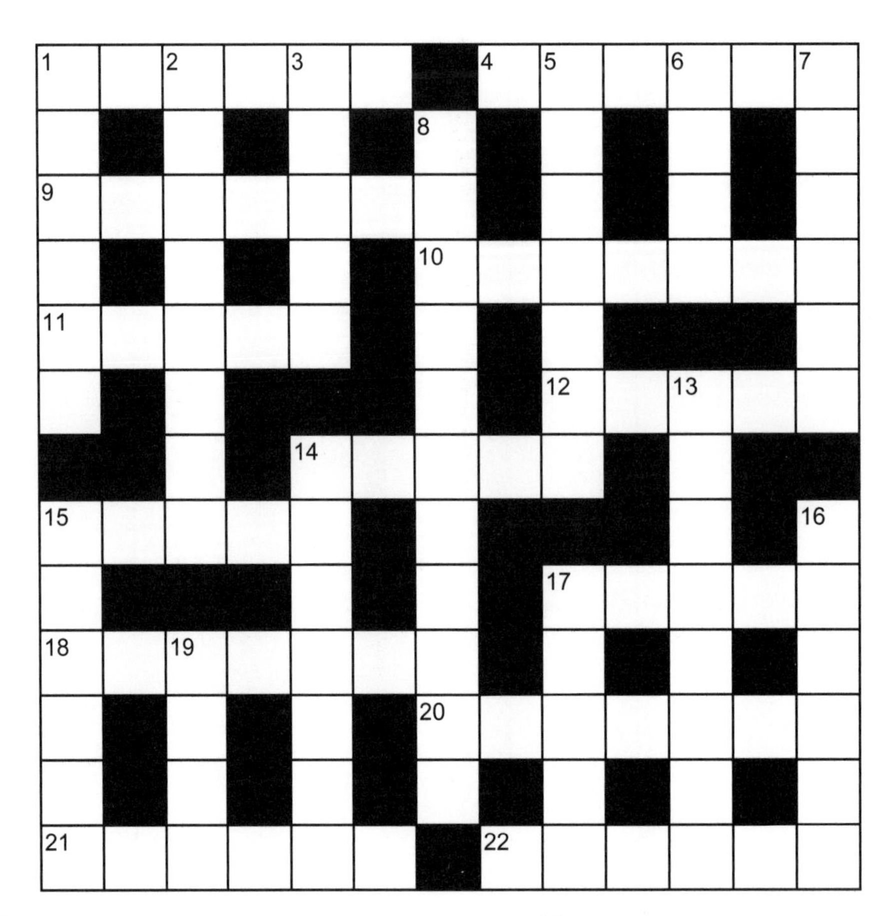

Across

1 Divide into two parts (6)
4 Request made to God (6)
9 Japanese warriors (7)
10 Allowing (7)
11 Reside (5)
12 Seethed with anger (5)
14 Biter (anag) (5)
15 Stratum (5)
17 Brief appearance (5)
18 Epicure (7)
20 Envelops (7)
21 Very much (6)
22 Robinson ___ : novel (6)

Down

1 Next to (6)
2 Regularity of nature (8)
3 Christmas song (5)
5 Reinstate (7)
6 ___ Berra: baseball player (4)
7 Having a rough surface (of terrain) (6)
8 In a state of disrepair (11)
13 Complains (8)
14 Restrict (7)
15 Molecule that binds to another (6)
16 Whipped cream dessert (6)
17 Cylinder of smoking tobacco (5)
19 Bone of the forearm (4)

Crossword

Puzzle 62

Across

1 Climbs (6)
5 Tell off severely (6)
8 Business (4)
9 Unseemly (8)
10 Manipulate dough (5)
11 Gnarled (7)
14 Presentation on how to use something (13)
16 Person with auburn hair (7)
18 Empty spaces (5)
20 Aromatic herb (8)
22 Cry of a goose (4)
23 Strangest (6)
24 Prison officer (6)

Down

2 Customers collectively (9)
3 Back pain (7)
4 Propel the body through water (4)
5 Exterior of a motor vehicle (8)
6 Moves back and forth (5)
7 Nine plus one (3)
12 Fluent use of language (9)
13 Edible snail (8)
15 Instructor (7)
17 Vast multitude (5)
19 Was aware of; understood (4)
21 Assist (3)

Puzzle 63

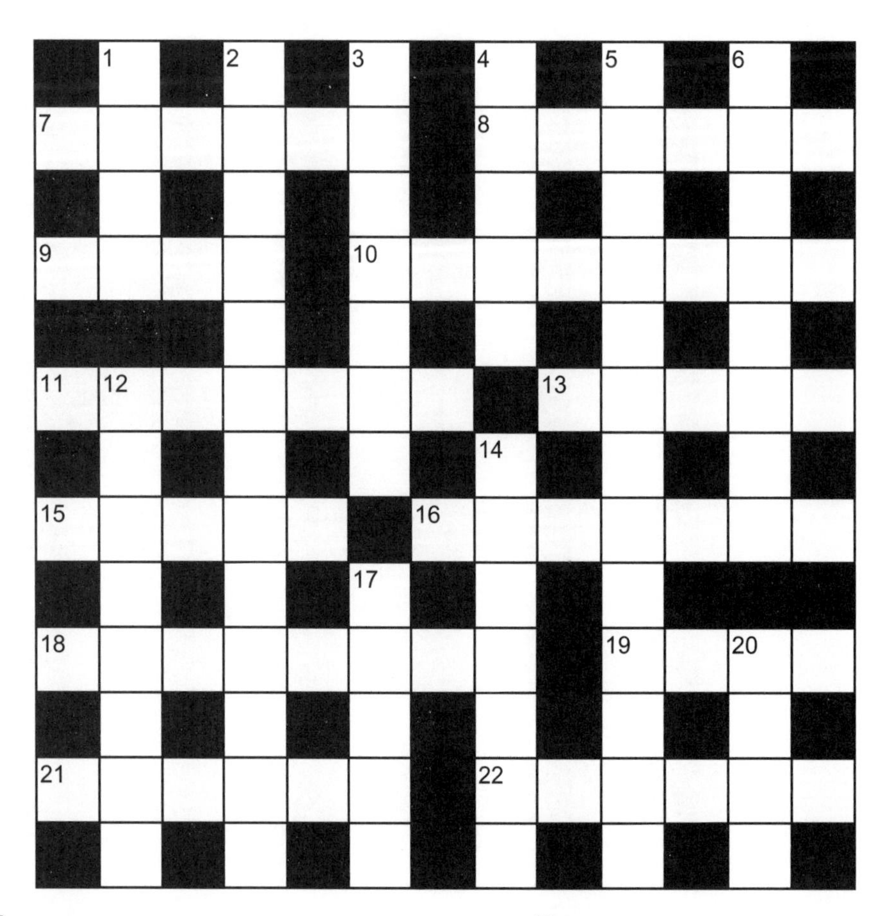

Across

7 Easy victory (4-2)
8 Indefinitely large number (6)
9 Quartz-like gem (4)
10 Supplication (8)
11 Nonsense (7)
13 Roman cloaks (5)
15 Sense of seeing (5)
16 In an unspecified manner (7)
18 Suave; stylish (8)
19 Targets (4)
21 Scorched (6)
22 Contract of insurance (6)

Down

1 Hit with a lash (4)
2 Continue a stroke in tennis (6,7)
3 Ardent (7)
4 Not containing anything (5)
5 Irretrievable (13)
6 Capital of Chile (8)
12 Common salad dressing (5,3)
14 Willing to act dishonestly (7)
17 Overly showy (5)
20 Small rodents (4)

Crossword

Puzzle 64

Across

1 Loose scrum (rugby) (4)
3 Conspicuous (8)
9 Imprecise (7)
10 ___ Maradona: footballer (5)
11 Surface upon which one walks (5)
12 Desist from (7)
13 Artefacts (6)
15 Take into the body (of food) (6)
17 Shut in (7)
18 ___ Milan: Italian football club (5)
20 Leaves (5)
21 Foolish person (7)
22 Delaying (8)
23 Remain in the same place (4)

Down

1 Action of strengthening (13)
2 Doctrine; system of beliefs (5)
4 Teachers (6)
5 Not capable of justification (12)
6 Do repeatedly (7)
7 Amiably (4-9)
8 Unpredictably (12)
14 More fortunate (7)
16 Heavy (6)
19 Short treatise (5)

Puzzle 65

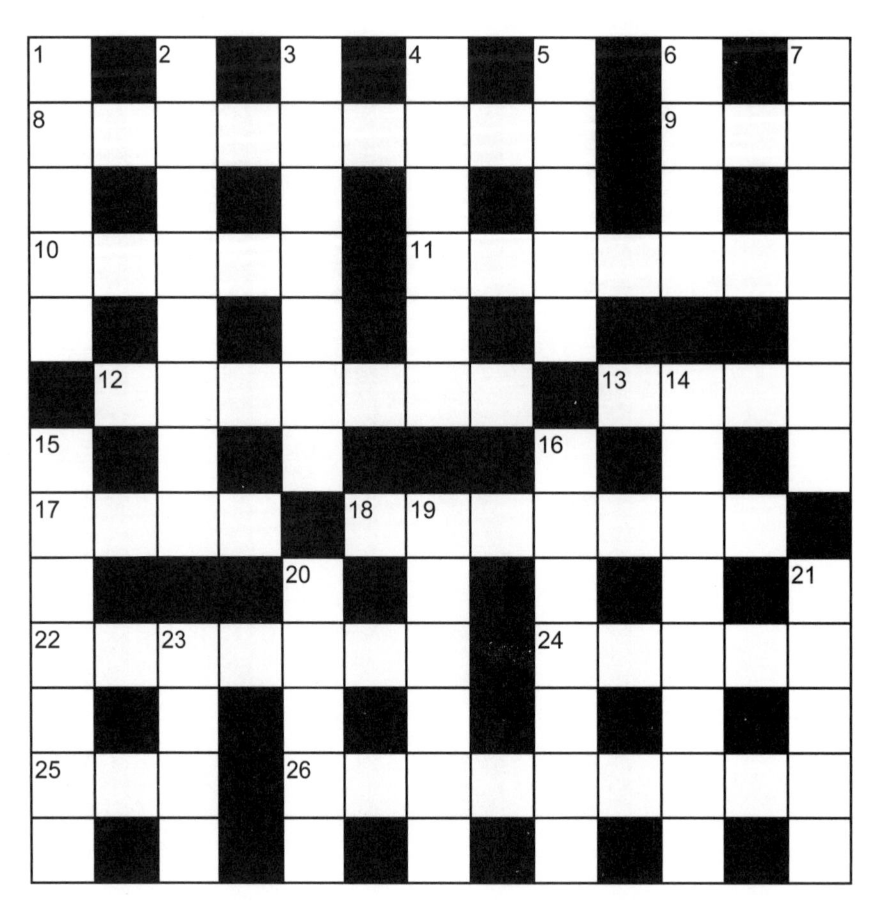

Across

- **8** Geri ___ : Spice Girl (9)
- **9** ___ de Cologne: perfume (3)
- **10** Liquid essential for life (5)
- **11** Imparts knowledge (7)
- **12** Fishing (7)
- **13** Leave out (4)
- **17** TV award (4)
- **18** Spend lavishly (7)
- **22** Spanish beverage (7)
- **24** Type of tooth (5)
- **25** Strong drink (3)
- **26** Vehicles (9)

Down

- **1** Displays (5)
- **2** Precious metallic element (8)
- **3** Govern badly (7)
- **4** Large military unit (6)
- **5** Divided into two (5)
- **6** Edible fruit with a distinctive shape (4)
- **7** Throb (7)
- **14** Ferdinand ___ : Portuguese navigator (8)
- **15** Sweet course (7)
- **16** Precis (7)
- **19** Puts in the soil (6)
- **20** Stage play (5)
- **21** Alloy of copper and zinc (5)
- **23** Deprived of sensation (4)

Puzzle 66

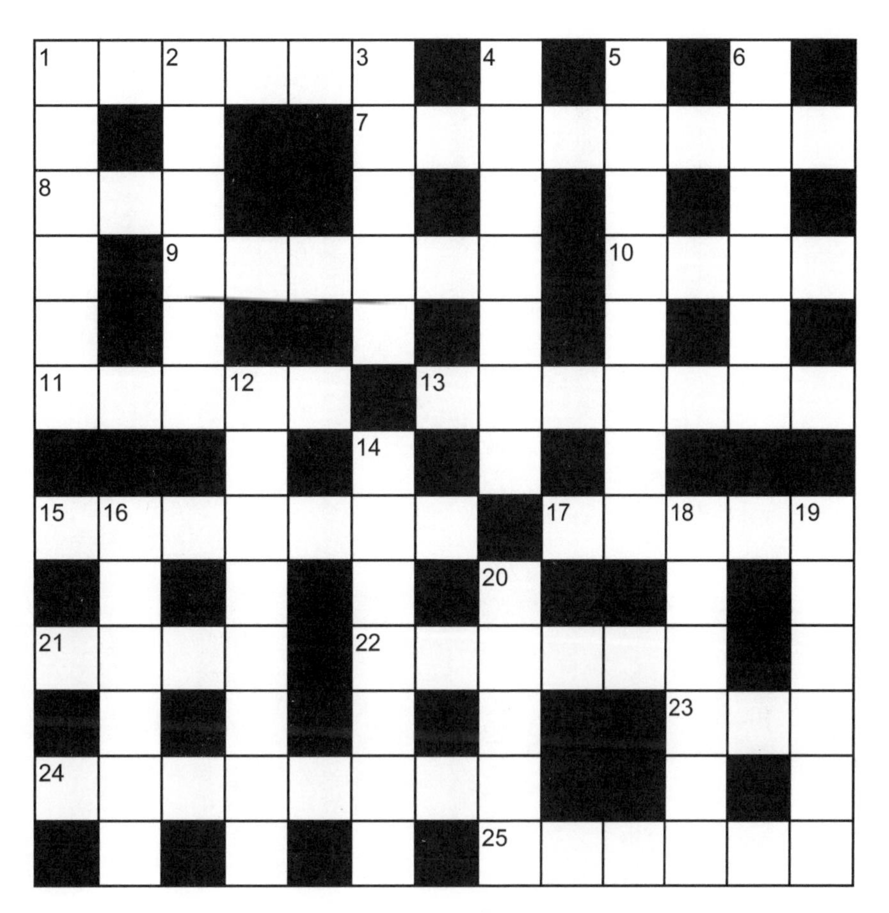

Across

1 Soft felt hat (6)
7 Card game (8)
8 Grey-brown colour (3)
9 Maiden (6)
10 Double-reed instrument (4)
11 Microorganisms (5)
13 ___ harp: musical instrument (7)
15 Iron attractors (7)
17 Declared solemnly (5)
21 Agitate a liquid (4)
22 From what place (6)
23 Thee (3)
24 Individual properties (8)
25 Displayed freely (6)

Down

1 Growing dimmer (6)
2 Flakes of skin in an animal's fur (6)
3 Embarrass (5)
4 Burnt (7)
5 Church rules (5,3)
6 Eastern temple (6)
12 Opposite of majority (8)
14 Person who looks after the passengers on a ship (7)
16 Deer horn (6)
18 Complied with a command (6)
19 Followed (6)
20 Compact (5)

Puzzle 67

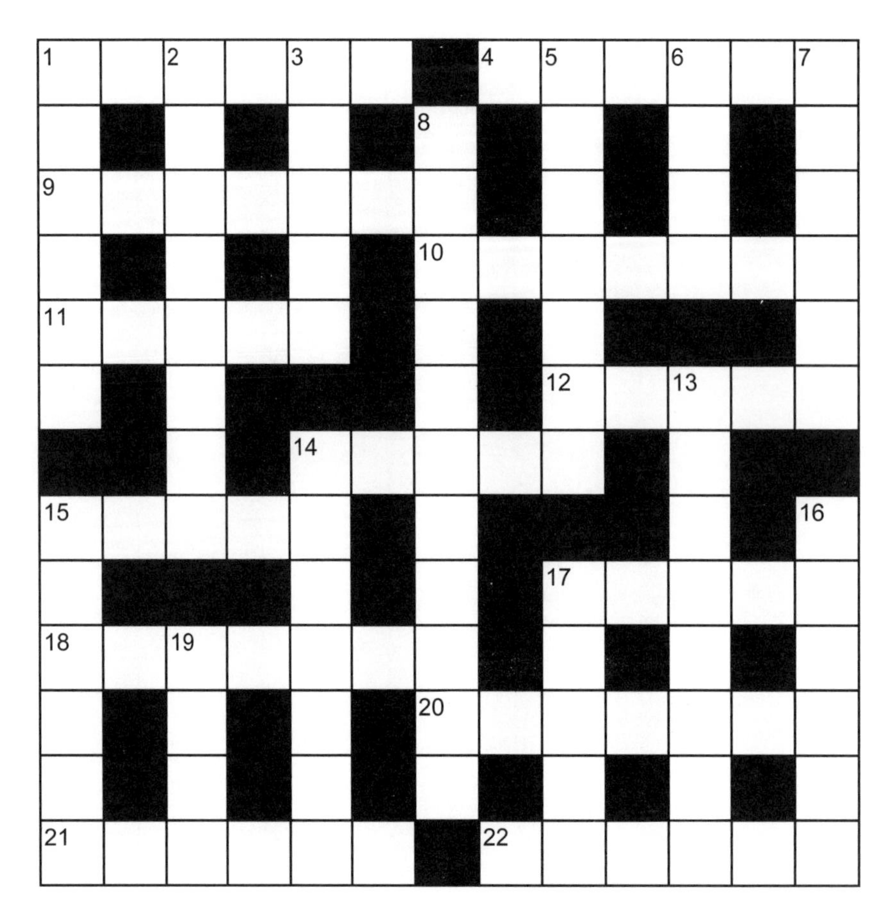

Across

1 Large enclosed space; grotto (6)
4 Stretch prior to exercise (4-2)
9 Sustain with food (7)
10 Type of optician (7)
11 Unfasten (5)
12 Tall and slim (5)
14 Popular sport (5)
15 Molten rock (5)
17 Stadium (5)
18 Tomato sauce (7)
20 Accommodation (7)
21 Excessively bright (6)
22 Liam ___ : Schindler's List actor (6)

Down

1 Agree (6)
2 Leaping up or over (8)
3 Increment (5)
5 Insurance calculator (7)
6 The wise men (4)
7 To some extent (6)
8 Images recorded on film (11)
13 The decade from 1990 - 1999 (8)
14 Pieces of bacon (7)
15 Creating (6)
16 Edge (6)
17 Entertain (5)
19 Logical division; rank (4)

Crossword

Puzzle 68

1	■	2	■	3	■	■	■	4	■	5	■	6
7						■	8					
	■		■		■	9	■		■		■	
10							■	11				
	■		■		■		■		■		■	
12				■	13					■	■	■
	■		■	14	■		■		■	15	■	16
■	■	■	17					■	18			
19	■	20	■		■		■	21	■		■	
22					■	23						
	■		■		■		■		■		■	
24						■	25					
	■		■		■	■	■		■		■	

Across

7 Firmly established (6)
8 Shelter; place of refuge (6)
10 Break a rule (7)
11 US musician (5)
12 Hit with the foot (4)
13 Russian monarchs (5)
17 Plentiful (5)
18 Colours or tints (4)
22 Scoop (5)
23 Confused struggle (7)
24 Perennial flowering plant (6)
25 Orange vegetable (6)

Down

1 Stimulate a reaction (7)
2 Country in NW Africa (7)
3 Royal (5)
4 Title appended to a man's name (7)
5 Hawaiian greeting (5)
6 Hurt; clever (5)
9 Incessant (9)
14 Momentum (7)
15 Experiences pain (7)
16 Characteristics (7)
19 Prevent access to something (5)
20 Supplementary component (3-2)
21 Sweetener (5)

Puzzle 69

Across

1 Catholic leader (4)
3 Solids with regularly ordered atoms (8)
9 Rise again (7)
10 Easy (of a job) (5)
11 Intended to attract notice (12)
14 Sound that a cow makes (3)
16 Clean spiritually (5)
17 Bitumen (3)
18 Lacking tolerance or flexibility (6-6)
21 Negatively charged ion (5)
22 A bird's feathers collectively (7)
23 Stocky (8)
24 Midge (4)

Down

1 Acts in a play (8)
2 Suggest (5)
4 Fish eggs (3)
5 Blasphemous (12)
6 Attack (7)
7 Utters (4)
8 Clearness (12)
12 Pointed projectile (5)
13 Slope (8)
15 Musical wind instrument (7)
19 Draw off liquid from (5)
20 Route (4)
22 Type of statistical chart (3)

Crossword

Puzzle 70

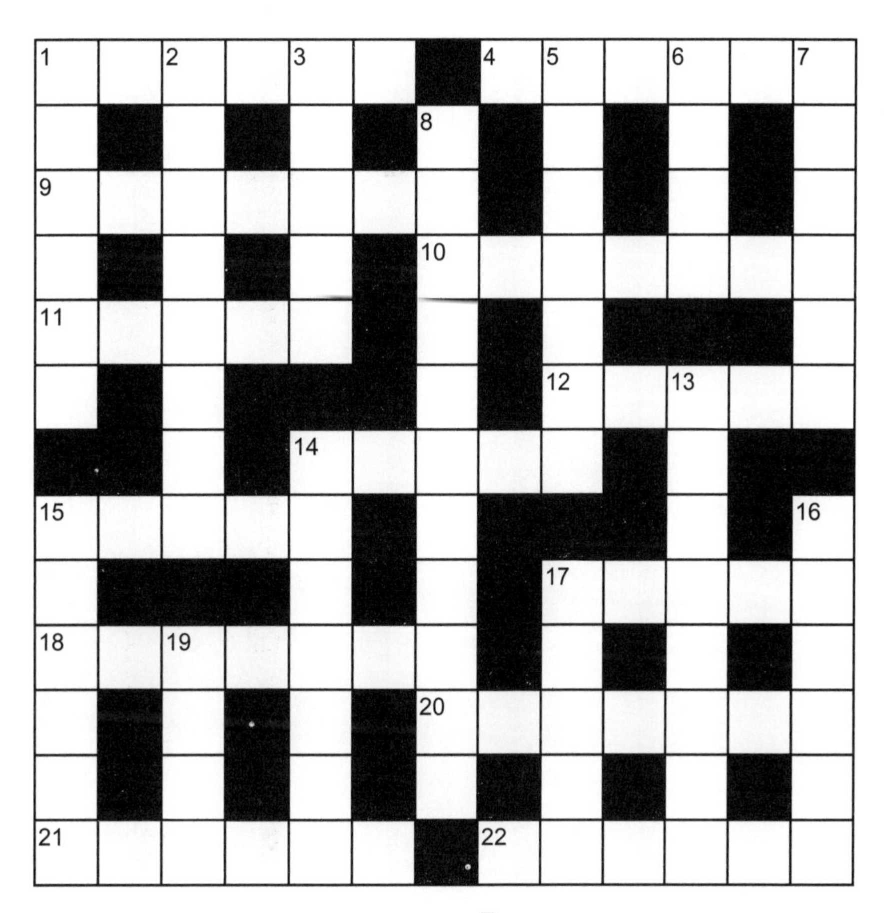

Across

1 Select (6)
4 Unseated by a horse (6)
9 Width (7)
10 Last longer than (of clothes) (7)
11 Part of a church tower (5)
12 Landowner (5)
14 Smooth transition (5)
15 Spread by scattering (5)
17 Student (5)
18 Sudden outburst of something (5-2)
20 Number of years in a century (7)
21 Hankers after (6)
22 Frank (6)

Down

1 Style and movement in art (6)
2 Short joke (3-5)
3 Move sideways (5)
5 Not friendly (7)
6 Where darts players throw from (4)
7 Approached (6)
8 The art of taking photos (11)
13 Made another excited about (8)
14 Cause to taste more sugary (7)
15 Security (6)
16 Dodged (6)
17 Mammal that eats bamboo (5)
19 Continent (4)

Puzzle 71

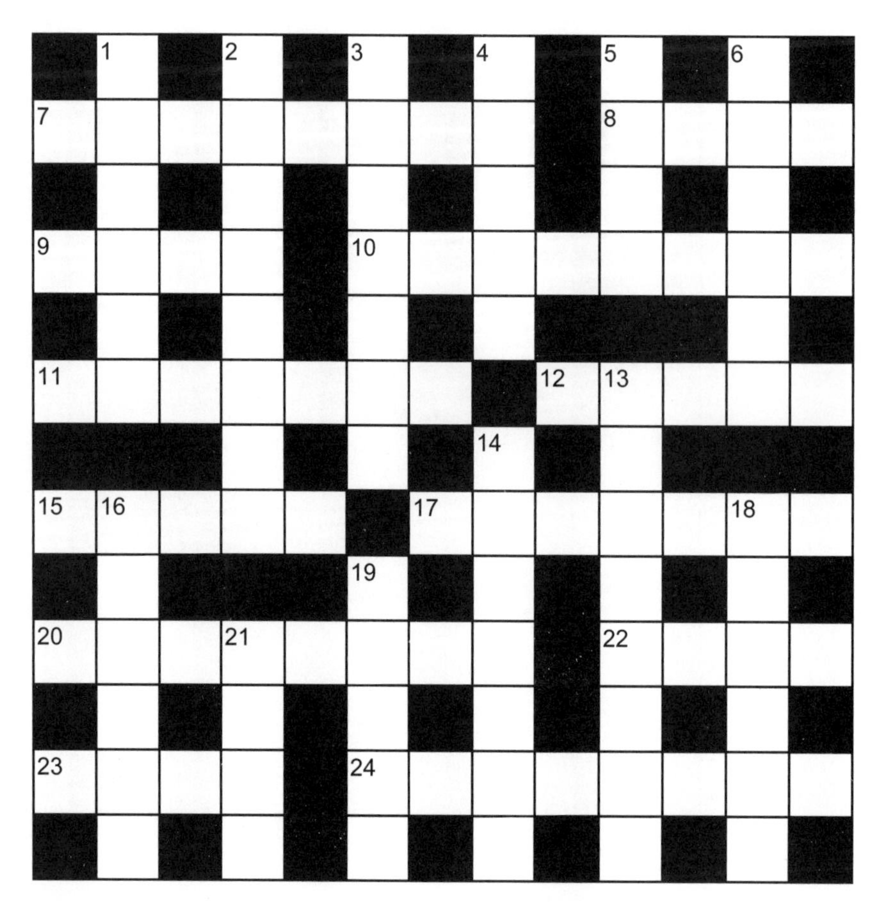

Across

7 Surpass (8)
8 Close by (4)
9 Eat at a restaurant (4)
10 Extreme reproach (8)
11 Options (7)
12 Female servants (5)
15 Male elephants (5)
17 Zephyrs (7)
20 Drawing templates (8)
22 Opposite of light (4)
23 Damage from continuous use (4)
24 Playhouses (8)

Down

1 Subject to a penalty (6)
2 Exceptional (8)
3 Broken; split (7)
4 Used up (5)
5 A single time (4)
6 Uttered coarsely (6)
13 Short account of an incident (8)
14 Traversed (7)
16 Undoes (6)
18 Nearer (anag) (6)
19 Foggy (5)
21 Standard (4)

Crossword

Puzzle 72

Across

1 Inert gaseous element (6)
7 Lifts up (8)
8 Small truck (3)
9 Cordial (6)
10 Attack at speed (4)
11 Sages (anag) (5)
13 Wrap in garments (7)
15 Single-handed (7)
17 Ordered arrangement (5)
21 Eg Shrek (4)
22 Covering a roof with thin slabs (6)
23 Bustle (3)
24 Country in NE Africa (8)
25 Explanation (6)

Down

1 Owning (6)
2 Sudden forward thrusts (6)
3 Doctor (5)
4 Eg primrose and lemon (7)
5 Breed of retriever (8)
6 Antenna (6)
12 Large outbreak of a disease (8)
14 Excessive bureaucracy (3,4)
16 Periods of darkness (6)
18 Legal entitlements (6)
19 Servant in a royal household (6)
20 Lucid (5)

Puzzle 73

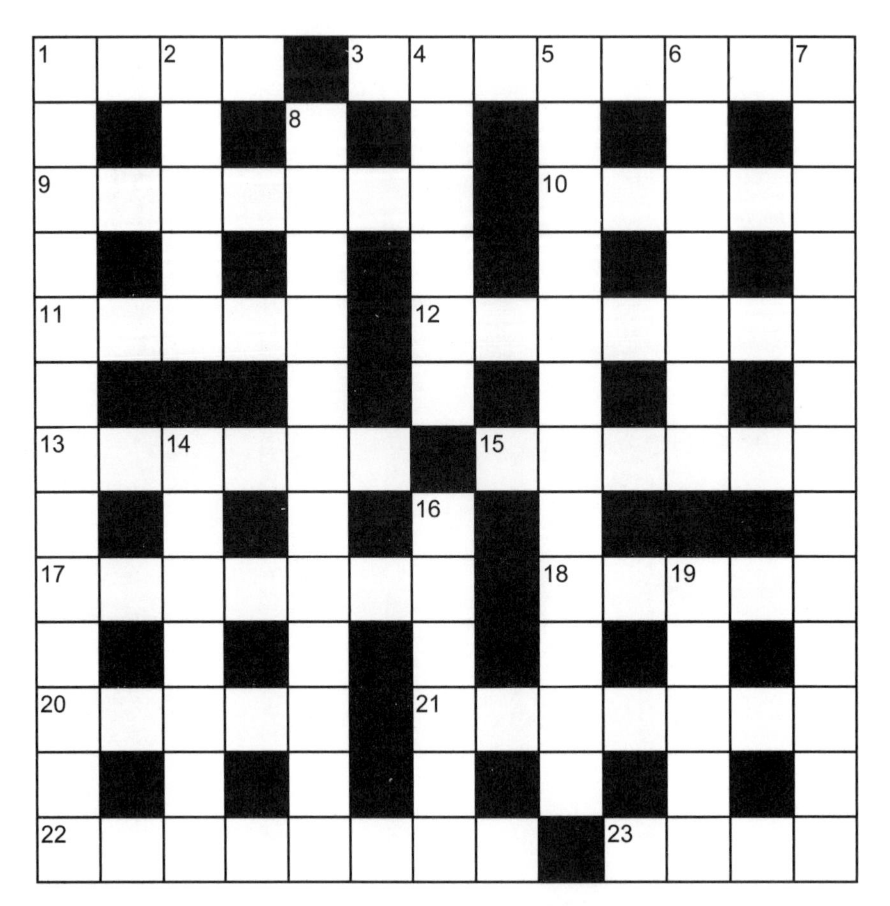

Across

1 Poker stake (4)
3 Device controlling flow of fuel to an engine (8)
9 Lively; cheerful (7)
10 Andrew Lloyd Webber musical (5)
11 Agreeable sound or tune (5)
12 Enduring (7)
13 Overseas (6)
15 Marble (anag) (6)
17 Inner parts of things (7)
18 Franz ___ : Hungarian composer (5)
20 Furnish or supply (5)
21 Stated the meaning of (7)
22 Sharpness (of taste) (8)
23 Hunted animal (4)

Down

1 Supporting musical part (13)
2 Attempts (5)
4 Barely (6)
5 Omit too much detail (12)
6 Insignificant (7)
7 In an inflated manner (13)
8 Spotless (5-3-4)
14 Saviour (7)
16 Incidental remarks (6)
19 Acoustic detection system (5)

Crossword

Puzzle 74

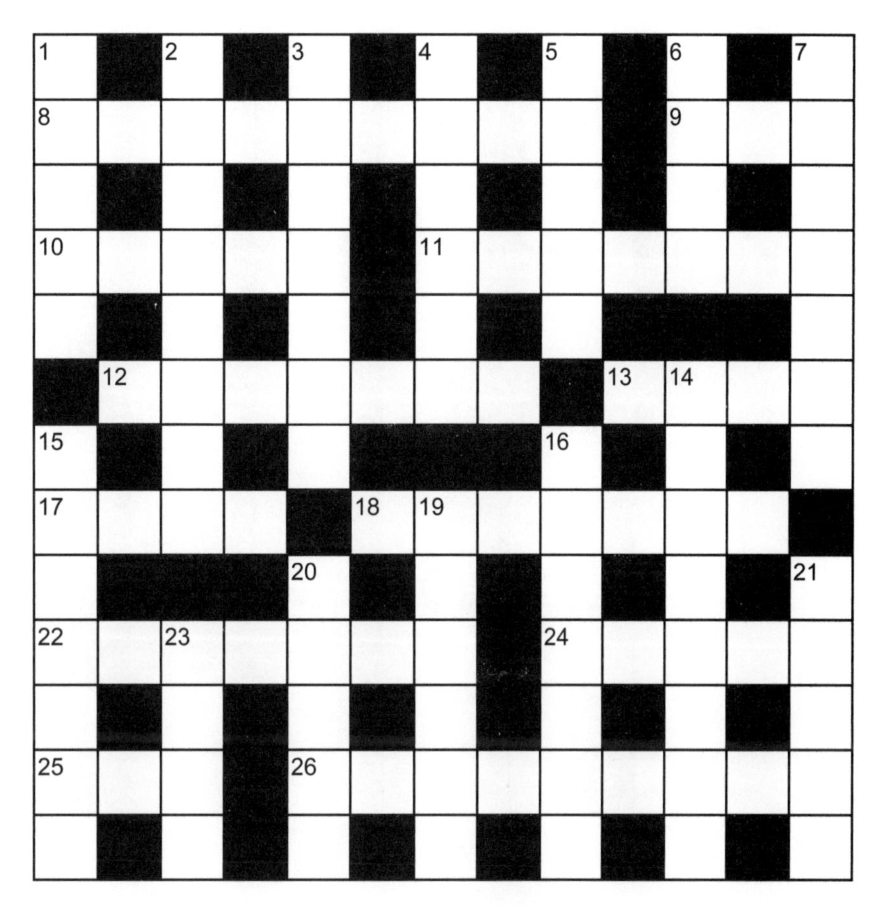

Across

8 At hand (9)
9 ___ de Janeiro: Brazilian city (3)
10 Discuss an idea casually (5)
11 Unit of sound intensity (7)
12 Sickness (7)
13 Throb; dull pain (4)
17 Government tax (4)
18 Drawout (anag) (7)
22 Tapering stone pillar (7)
24 Find an answer to (5)
25 Fix the result in advance (3)
26 Medicinal creams (9)

Down

1 Roadside area (3-2)
2 Strong glove (8)
3 Taking part in a game (7)
4 Homes (6)
5 Therefore (5)
6 Insect larva (4)
7 Large rock (7)
14 Forming a ring around (8)
15 Postpone (7)
16 Couple (7)
19 Mean (6)
20 Spike used by a climber (5)
21 Make fun of someone (5)
23 ___ bread: French toast (4)

Puzzle 75

Across

1 Come up ___ : do better than expected (6)
5 Small social insect (3)
7 Trimmed (5)
8 Generally; in summary (7)
9 Immature insects (5)
10 Final (8)
12 Medical treatment place (6)
14 Make beloved (6)
17 Knock down (8)
18 ___ Halfpenny: Welsh rugby player (5)
20 Bloodsucking creature (7)
21 Expulsion (5)
22 Thing that fails to work properly (3)
23 Fit for consumption (6)

Down

2 Restoration to life (7)
3 Starchy banana-like fruit (8)
4 Snare (4)
5 Fatty tissue (7)
6 Small loudspeaker (7)
7 Prayers (5)
11 Knowledgeable (8)
12 Cooled down (7)
13 Caused to burn (7)
15 Coming from the south (7)
16 Tennis stroke (5)
19 Inheritor (4)

Puzzle 76

Across

1 Having only magnitude (6)
5 Deceive (6)
8 Extreme point (4)
9 Moored (8)
10 Bungle (5)
11 Ate and drank sumptuously (7)
14 Way of saying a word (13)
16 Got away (7)
18 Faint (5)
20 Bendy (8)
22 Liquid precipitation (4)
23 Sharp pain (6)
24 Throws a coin in the air (6)

Down

2 Storage spaces (9)
3 Vocabulary list (7)
4 Quantity of paper (4)
5 Dilapidated (8)
6 Views; observes (5)
7 Expected at a certain time (3)
12 Reduce one's expenditure (9)
13 Group of musicians (8)
15 In the direction of (7)
17 Plant hormone (5)
19 Departed (4)
21 Opposite of high (3)

Puzzle 77

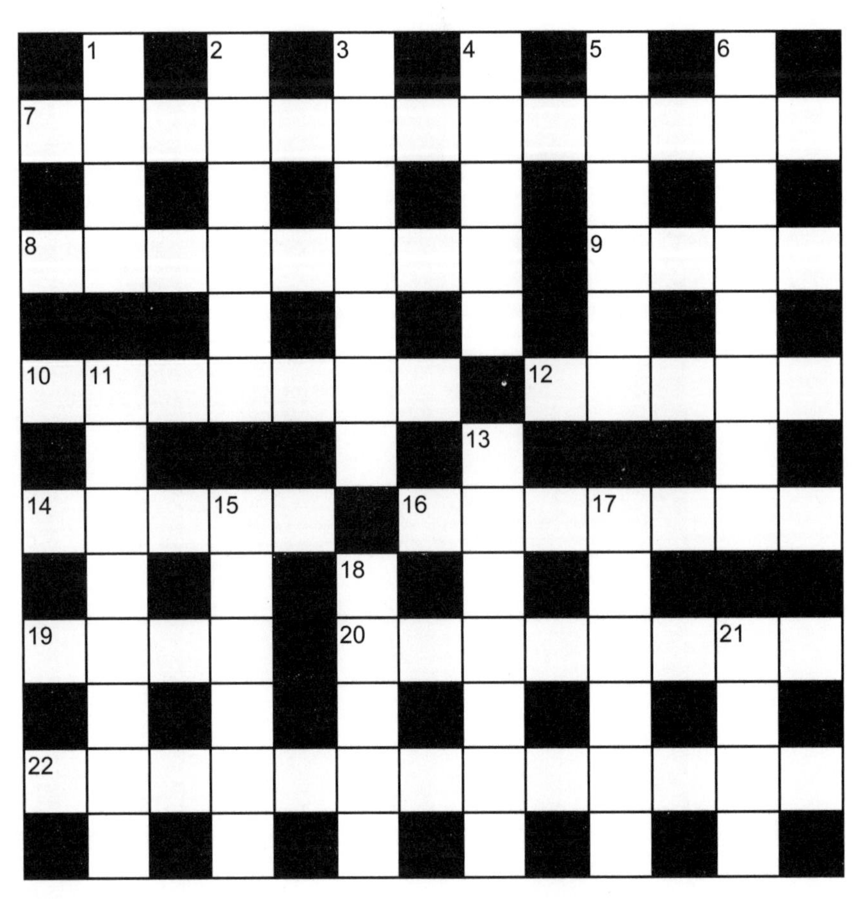

Across

7 Unemotional (13)
8 Scope for freedom (8)
9 An individual thing (4)
10 Restaurant in a workplace (7)
12 Trivial (5)
14 Confusion (3-2)
16 Shows again (7)
19 Sharp bristle (4)
20 Egg-laying mammal (8)
22 Copious abundance (13)

Down

1 ___ Simone: US singer (4)
2 Thin strip of wood (6)
3 Confident (7)
4 Broaden (5)
5 Damage (6)
6 Rigidly; sternly (8)
11 One who stirs up trouble (8)
13 Reduce the worth of (7)
15 Straightened (6)
17 Putting down carefully (6)
18 Small branch (5)
21 ___ Major: the Great Bear (4)

Crossword

Puzzle 78

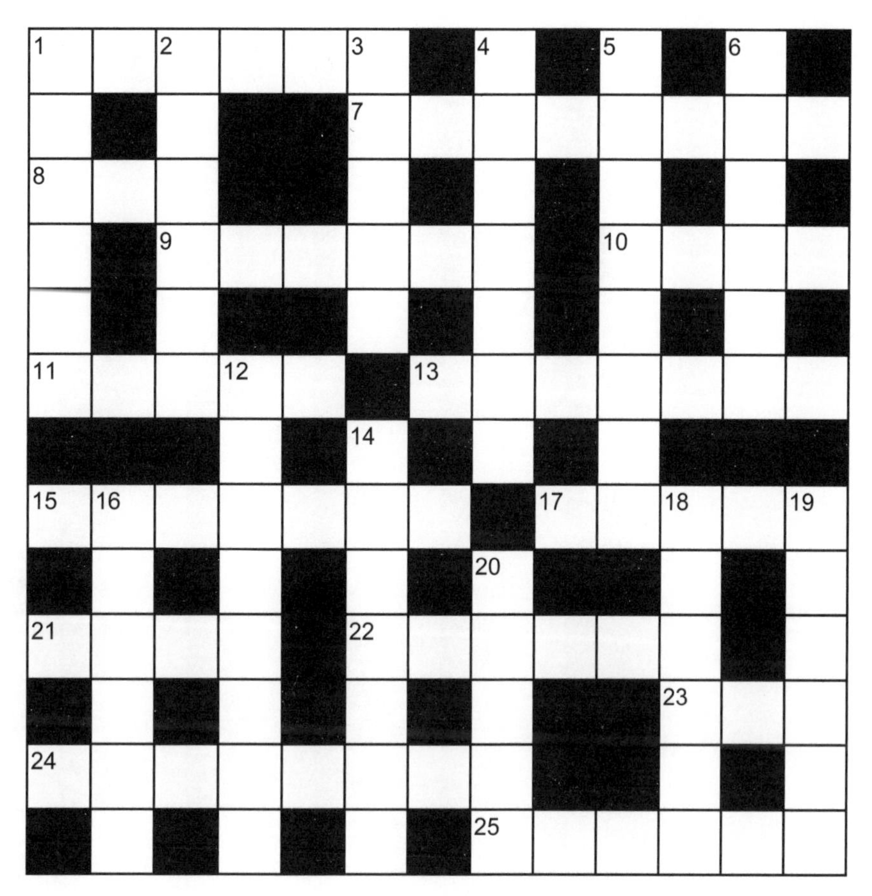

Across

1 Type of ski race (6)
7 Changing gradually (8)
8 Flightless bird (3)
9 Gag; silence (6)
10 Suggestion (4)
11 Wander aimlessly (5)
13 Satisfy (7)
15 As fast as possible (4,3)
17 Concur (5)
21 Adult male deer (4)
22 Lilo and ___ : Walt Disney animated film (6)
23 Exclamation of surprise (3)
24 Whole; complete (8)
25 Heavy metal weight used by a ship (6)

Down

1 Cooked slowly in liquid (6)
2 Former pupils (6)
3 ___-soprano: singing voice (5)
4 Collection of sheets of paper (7)
5 Evading (8)
6 Turn upside down (6)
12 Weary (8)
14 Scholarship (7)
16 Hidden (6)
18 Recycle old material (6)
19 Book of the Bible (6)
20 Roman country house (5)

Puzzle 79

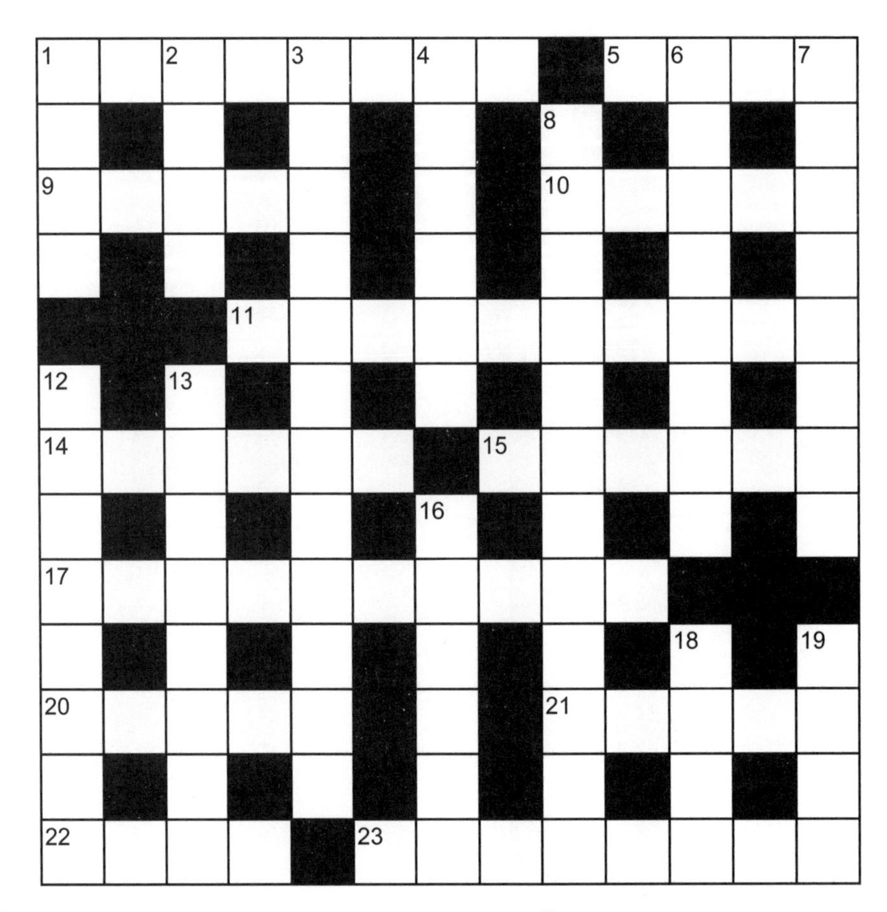

Across

1 Person skilled in languages (8)
5 Liquefy (4)
9 Stomach exercise (3-2)
10 Collection of songs (5)
11 Rival contestant (10)
14 Frederic ___ : Polish composer (6)
15 Religious minister (6)
17 Lift secrecy restrictions on (10)
20 ___ Streep: Mamma Mia! actress (5)
21 Wide open (of the mouth) (5)
22 Dove sounds (4)
23 Sewed together (8)

Down

1 Get beaten (4)
2 Memo (4)
3 Making no money (12)
4 Morsels of food (6)
6 Cause resentment (8)
7 Audacity (8)
8 Unemotional and practical (6-2-4)
12 Pertaining to education (8)
13 Musical composition (8)
16 Classify (6)
18 Thin strip of wood (4)
19 Fight off (4)

Crossword

Puzzle 80

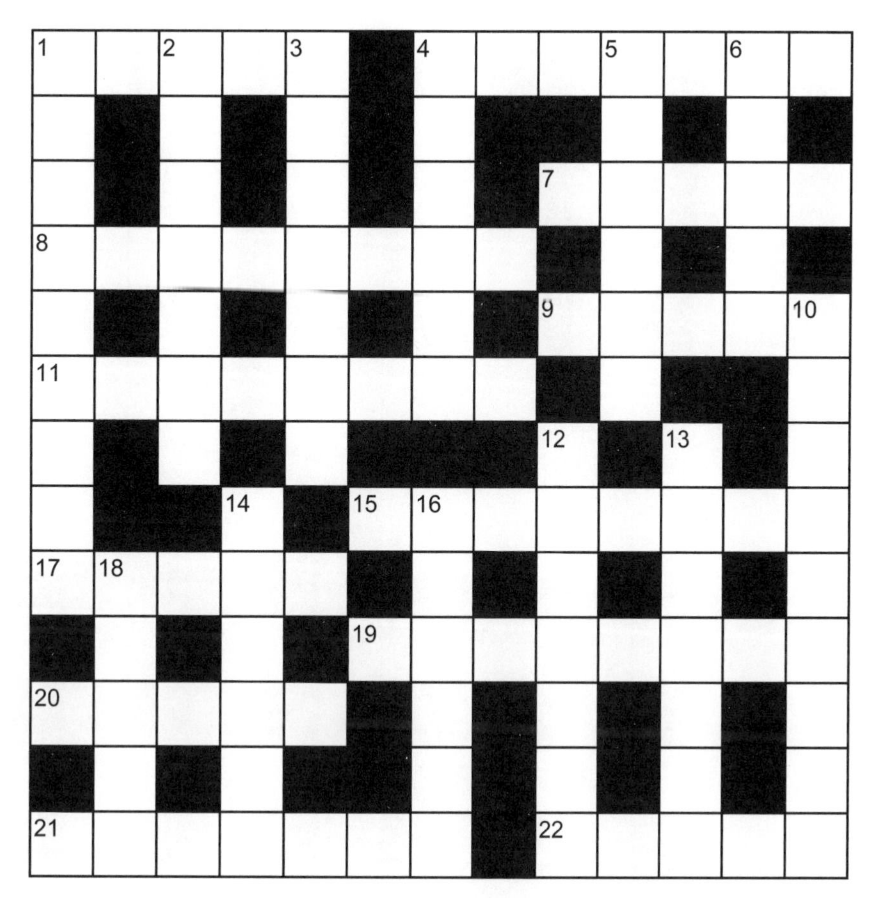

Across

1 Hits high up in the air (5)
4 Business matters (7)
7 Tie; snag (5)
8 On the outer side (8)
9 Supernatural skill (5)
11 Approximate (8)
15 Highly critical remark (8)
17 Steps of a ladder (5)
19 Playful (8)
20 Summed together (5)
21 ___ in: restricting the movement of (7)
22 Harsh and grating in sound (5)

Down

1 Financial inducement (9)
2 Copy; mimic (7)
3 Person in overall charge (7)
4 Nimble (6)
5 Type of living organism (6)
6 Christina ___ : actress (5)
10 Cranky (9)
12 Disperse (7)
13 Compels to do something (7)
14 Shining (6)
16 Gathering up leaves in the garden (6)
18 Unwarranted (5)

Puzzle 81

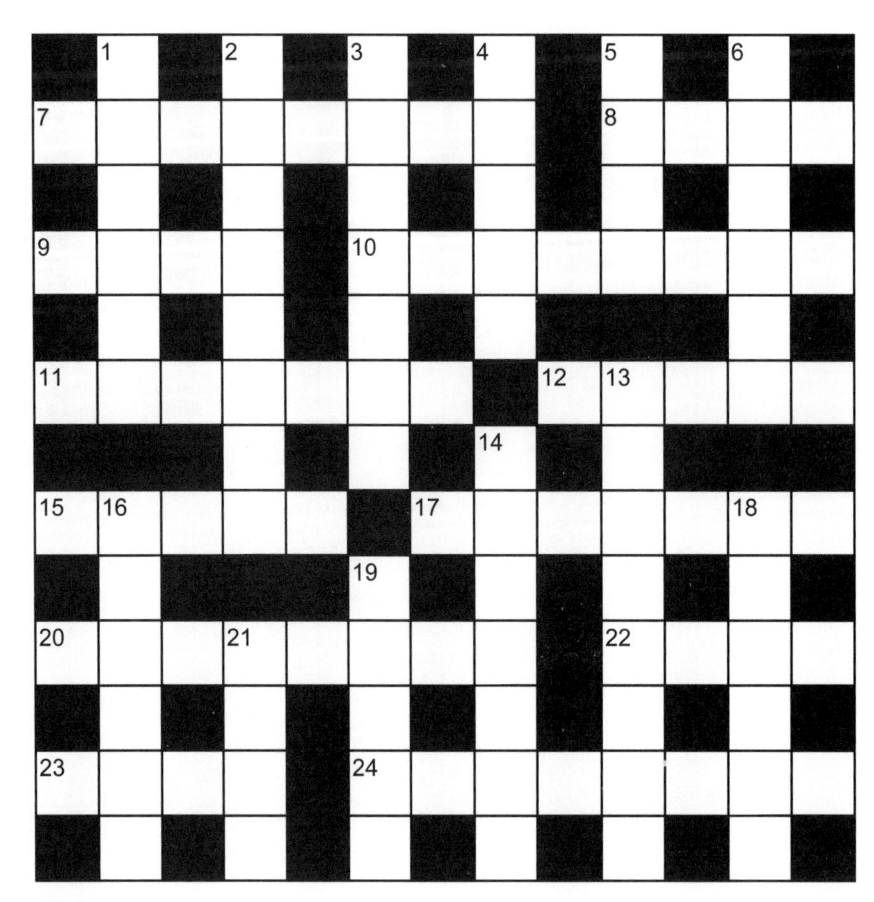

Across

7 Cut across (8)
8 Chemical salt used in dyeing (4)
9 This covers your body (4)
10 Decorate; adorn (8)
11 Obsequious person (7)
12 Merchandise (5)
15 Pursue in order to catch (5)
17 Temporary camp (7)
20 Creatures with one horn (8)
22 Helps (4)
23 Retain (4)
24 Coerces into doing something (8)

Down

1 Buyer and seller (6)
2 Things we are not familiar with (8)
3 Very loyal; dedicated (7)
4 Smart; ache (5)
5 Heat up (4)
6 Subtle variation (6)
13 Pear-shaped fruits (8)
14 Blood relation (7)
16 ___ Mahan: US golfer (6)
18 Fervent (6)
19 Assess; rank (5)
21 Drinking vessels (4)

Crossword

Puzzle 82

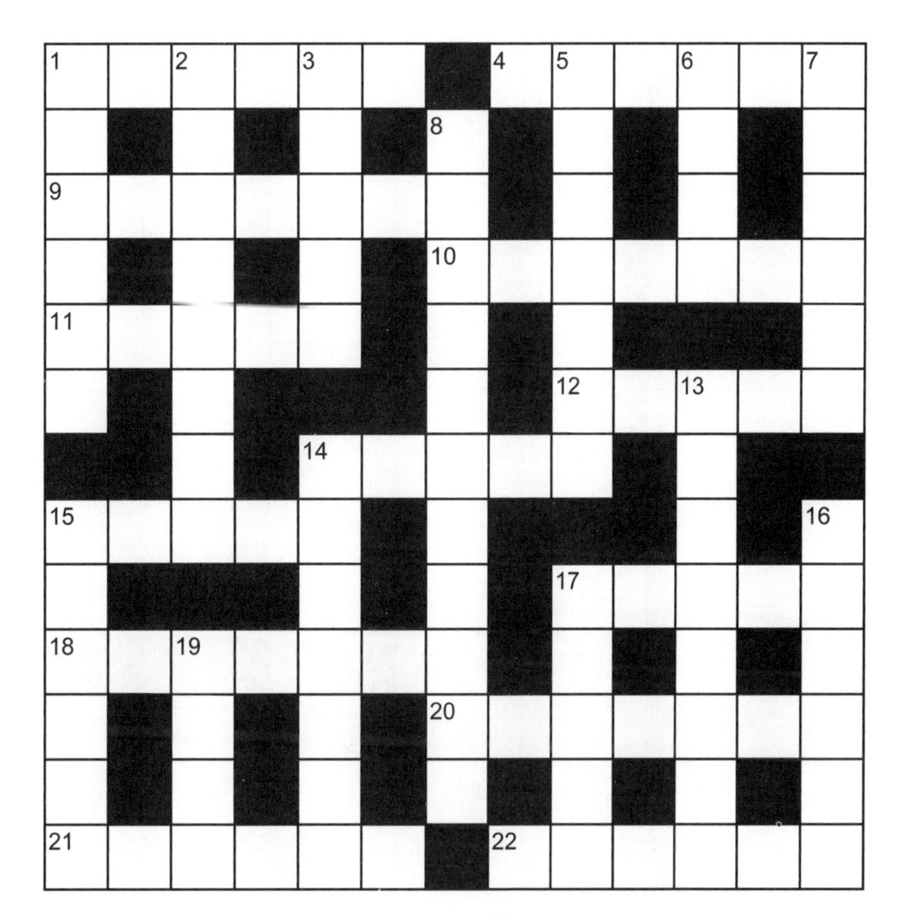

Across

1 Expose as being false (6)
4 Competitive games (6)
9 Fear of heights (7)
10 Scarf (7)
11 Hang with cloth (5)
12 Stinging insects (5)
14 Aromatic herb (5)
15 Genuflect (5)
17 Capital of Ghana (5)
18 Opposes (7)
20 Granite (anag) (7)
21 Throwing at a target (6)
22 Wealthy person in business (6)

Down

1 Separate into pieces (6)
2 Small crustacean (8)
3 Foolishly credulous (5)
5 Type of pheasant (7)
6 Move like a wheel (4)
7 Trousers that end above the knee (6)
8 Metabolic equilibrium (11)
13 Form of musical articulation (8)
14 Char or burn (7)
15 Bumps into (6)
16 Collapse (4,2)
17 Annoyed (5)
19 Young kangaroo (4)

Puzzle 83

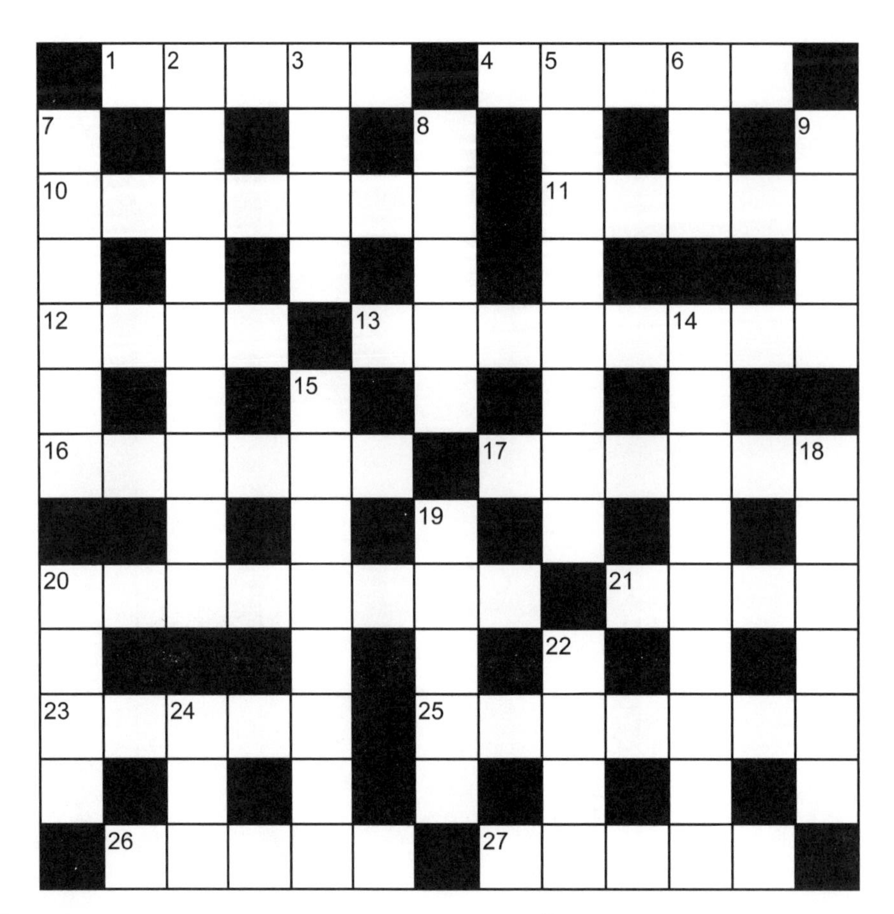

Across

1 Understands; realises (5)
4 Talked audibly (5)
10 Thief (7)
11 Evade (5)
12 Clock face (4)
13 Fraudster (8)
16 Grabbed (6)
17 Commercial aircraft (6)
20 Dark reddish-brown colour (8)
21 Contact by phone (4)
23 Shady spot under trees (5)
25 Reviewers (7)
26 Ales (5)
27 Animal restraint (5)

Down

2 Pertaining to a standard (9)
3 Legal document (4)
5 Overly concerned with detail (8)
6 Child (3)
7 Dwells in (6)
8 Gets larger (5)
9 Rip up (4)
14 Book depositories (9)
15 University teacher (8)
18 Spatter in small drops (6)
19 Sound a duck makes (5)
20 Taxis (4)
22 Financial penalty (4)
24 Very small (3)

Crossword

Puzzle 84

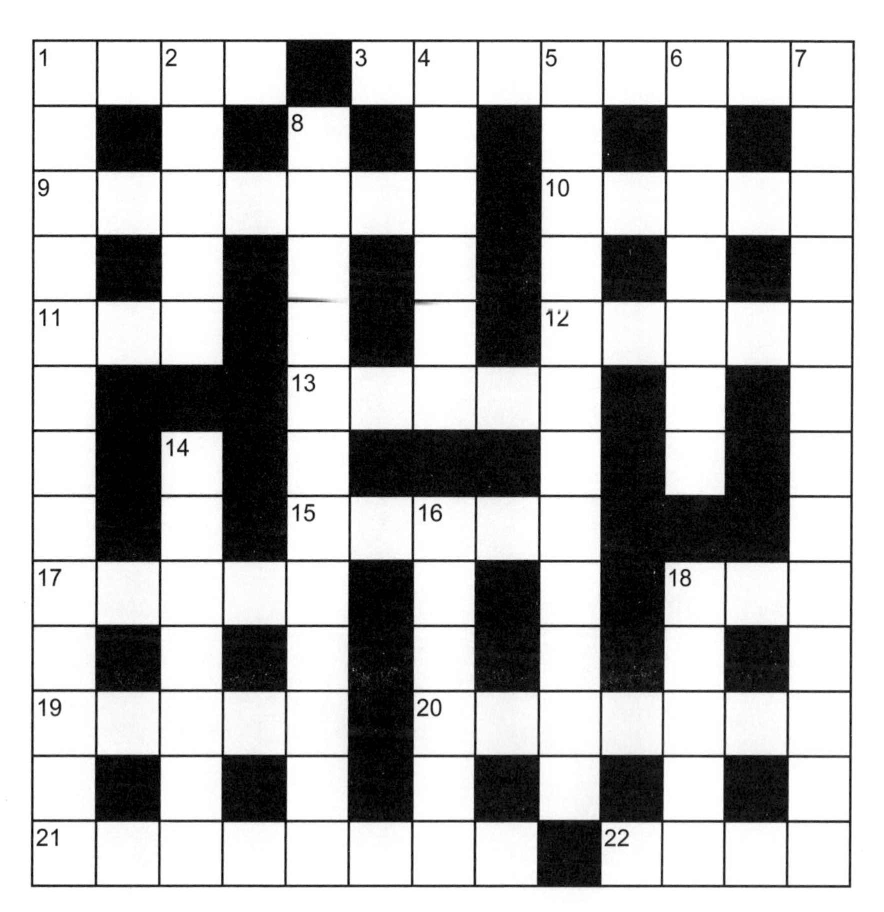

Across

1 Gain deservedly (4)
3 Creature that eats both meat and plants (8)
9 Cries for (7)
10 Commerce (5)
11 Sticky substance (3)
12 Outstanding (of a debt) (5)
13 Competed in a speed contest (5)
15 Having three dimensions (5)
17 Between eighth and tenth (5)
18 Ant and ___ : British presenting duo (3)
19 Join together; merge (5)
20 Disentangle (7)
21 Rocked (8)
22 Dull colour (4)

Down

1 The ___ : intellectual movement (13)
2 Lover of Juliet (5)
4 Believer in the occult (6)
5 Preliminary (12)
6 Formal speech (7)
7 Vigorously (13)
8 Perform below expectation (12)
14 Prisoner (7)
16 Bewilder; puzzle (6)
18 Person who goes underwater (5)

Puzzle 85

Across

- **1** Use these to row a boat (4)
- **3** Calling out (8)
- **9** Russian tea urn (7)
- **10** Short-tempered; ardent (5)
- **11** Graphical (12)
- **14** Every (3)
- **16** Viewpoint (5)
- **17** Range of knowledge (3)
- **18** Author of screenplays (12)
- **21** A Fish Called ___ : film (5)
- **22** A rich mine; big prize (7)
- **23** Small N Atlantic fish (8)
- **24** Unit of heredity (4)

Down

- **1** Glass-like volcanic rock (8)
- **2** Cuban folk dance (5)
- **4** Female pronoun (3)
- **5** Uncomplimentary (12)
- **6** Tool for the Arctic (3,4)
- **7** Men (4)
- **8** Make a guess that is too high (12)
- **12** Intended (5)
- **13** Grow in number (8)
- **15** Terse (7)
- **19** Colour lightly (5)
- **20** Moved through water (4)
- **22** Farewell remark (3)

Crossword

Puzzle 86

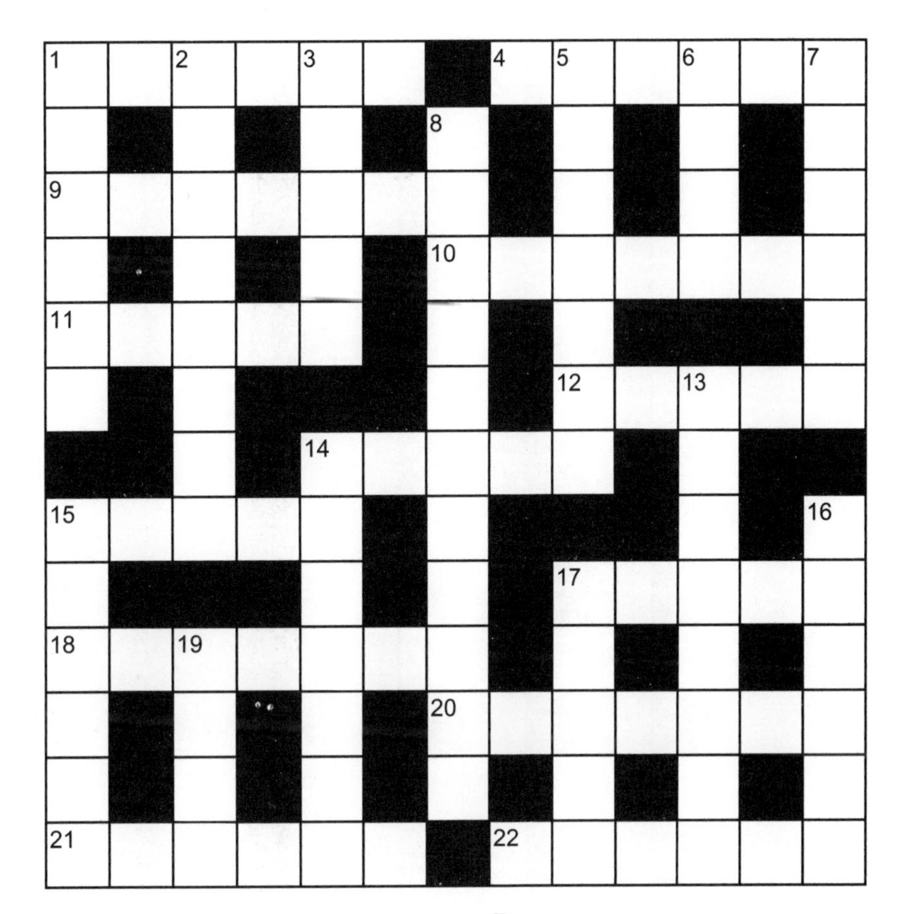

Across

1 Misplace (6)
4 Physical item (6)
9 Group of figures representing a scene (7)
10 Hawker (7)
11 Epic poem ascribed to Homer (5)
12 Water container; sink (5)
14 Allow in (5)
15 Sea duck (5)
17 Reproach (5)
18 Knoll (7)
20 Large retail stores (7)
21 Person after whom a discovery is named (6)
22 Grown-ups (6)

Down

1 Array of numbers (6)
2 Became less intense (8)
3 In front (5)
5 Unrecoverable sum of money one is owed (3,4)
6 Morally wicked (4)
7 Charlize ___ : South African actress (6)
8 Large shop (11)
13 Bushy-tailed rodent (8)
14 Arsenal (7)
15 Breathe out (6)
16 Layers (anag) (6)
17 Managed to deal with (5)
19 Not stereo (4)

Puzzle 87

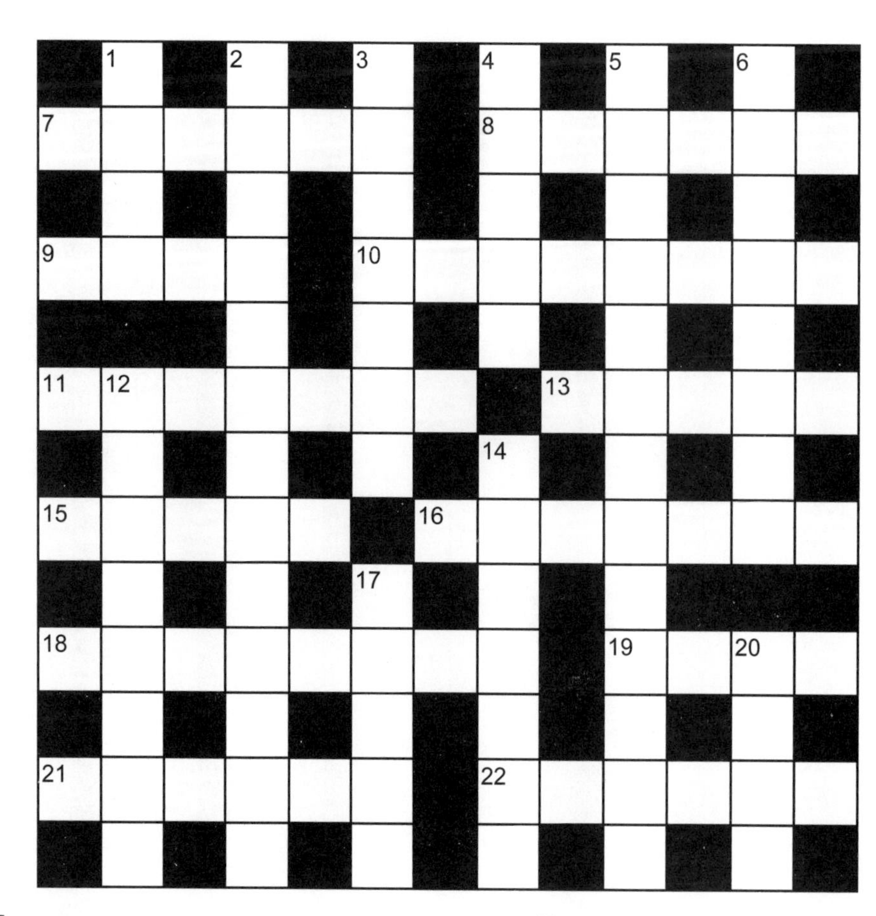

Across

7 Sharp bend in a road (3-3)
8 Quantum of electromagnetic energy (6)
9 Opposing (4)
10 Sanctity (8)
11 Curved structure forming a passage (7)
13 Start (5)
15 Go swiftly (5)
16 Capital of Northern Ireland (7)
18 Confused mixture (8)
19 ___ Novello: Welsh composer and actor (4)
21 John ___ : one of the Beatles (6)
22 Give satisfaction (6)

Down

1 Ripped (4)
2 Legerdemain (7,2,4)
3 Intellectual (7)
4 Gemstones (5)
5 Forger (13)
6 European primulas (8)
12 Part of a telephone apparatus (8)
14 Fashion anew (7)
17 Stamping ground (5)
20 Expel; drive out (4)

Puzzle 88

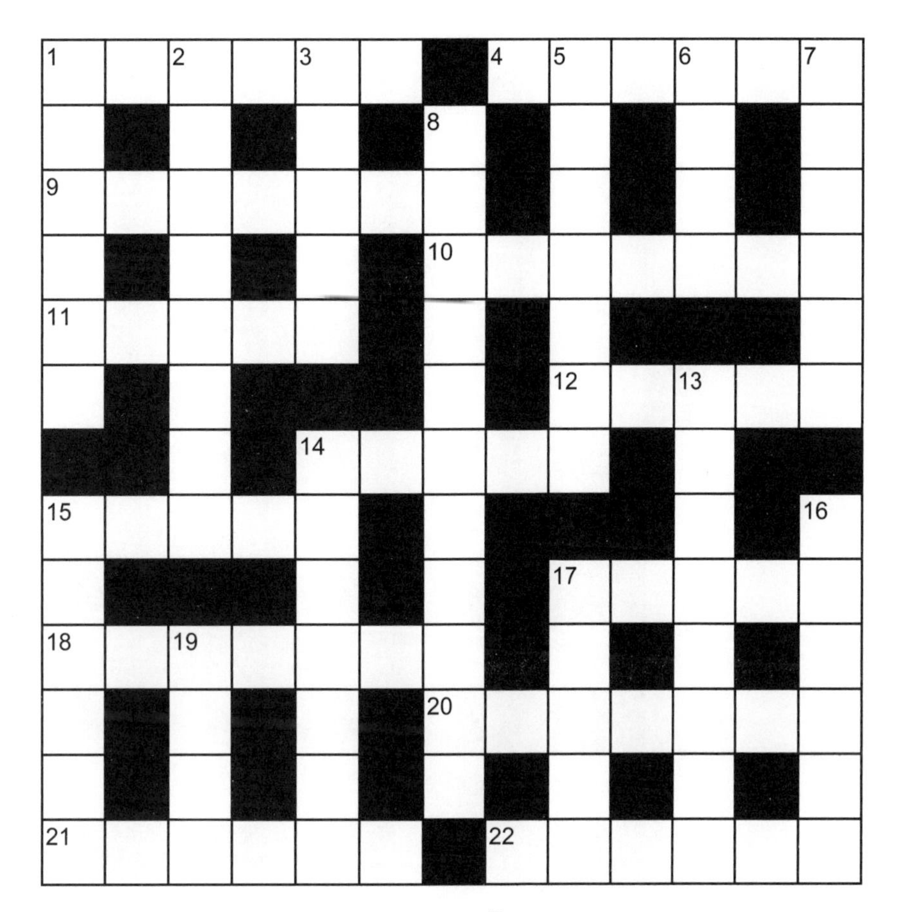

Across

1 Least young (6)
4 Flexible (6)
9 Colourless liquid hydrocarbon (7)
10 Help the progress of (7)
11 Measures duration (5)
12 Descend rapidly (5)
14 Eats like a bird (5)
15 Punctuation mark (5)
17 Mexican tortilla wraps (5)
18 Motivate (7)
20 Film directed by Stephen Gaghan (7)
21 Ready ___ : flavour of crisps (6)
22 ___ and Gretel: fairy tale (6)

Down

1 Paths of electrons around nuclei (6)
2 Great energy; vitality (8)
3 Plant stalks (5)
5 Remove clothes (7)
6 Luxurious; stylish (4)
7 Catch or snare (6)
8 Helpless (11)
13 Surpass in excellence (8)
14 Short moral story (7)
15 Pursues; runs after (6)
16 Attack (6)
17 ___ firma: dry land (5)
19 Small freshwater duck (4)

Puzzle 89

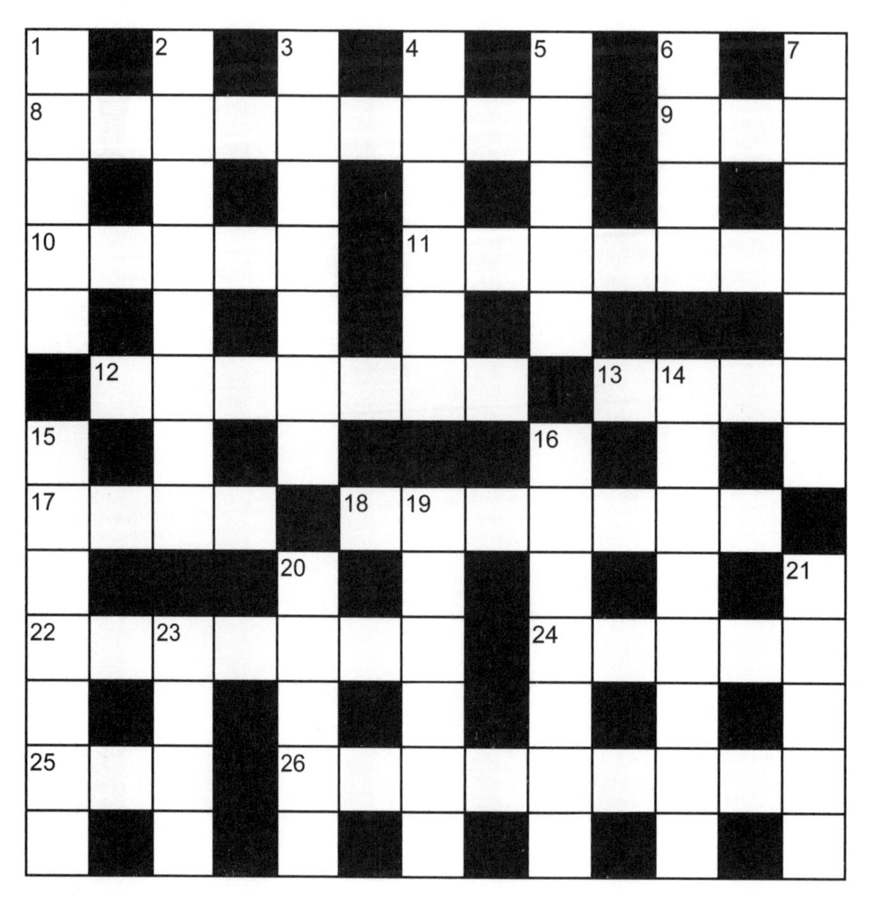

Across

8 Femur (5,4)
9 Came across (3)
10 Book leaves (5)
11 From now on (7)
12 Cup (7)
13 Hew (4)
17 Bites sharply (4)
18 Dome-shaped tents (7)
22 Perform in an exaggerated manner (7)
24 Cattle-breeding farm (5)
25 And not (3)
26 Gathered ripened crops (9)

Down

1 Paces (5)
2 Position of a male monarch (8)
3 Spiky weed (7)
4 Picture produced from many small pieces (6)
5 Precious stone (5)
6 Eg bullets (abbrev) (4)
7 Try (7)
14 Compassion; benevolence (8)
15 Not attached or tied together (7)
16 Rotated quickly (7)
19 Confine as a prisoner (6)
20 Russian country house (5)
21 Area sheltered from the sun (5)
23 British nobleman (4)

Crossword

Puzzle 90

Across

1 Charged particles (4)
3 Exhaustive (8)
9 Most healthy (7)
10 Small game bird (5)
11 Of the nose (5)
12 Statement of commemoration (7)
13 However (6)
15 Swiss city (6)
17 Orbs (7)
18 Praise highly (5)
20 Large fruit with pulpy flesh (5)
21 Emerged from an egg (7)
22 A period of 366 days (4,4)
23 Movement of water causing a small whirlpool (4)

Down

1 Extremely small (13)
2 Memos (5)
4 Towards this place (6)
5 Demands or needs (12)
6 Ignorant of something (7)
7 Unenthusiastically (4-9)
8 Hostility (12)
14 Character in Hamlet (7)
16 Respiratory condition (6)
19 Hankered after (5)

Puzzle 91

Across

1 Burrowing long-eared mammal (6)
4 Expels (6)
9 Mythical bird (7)
10 Juicy fruits (7)
11 Carer (anag) (5)
12 Short crowbar (5)
14 Port-au-Prince is the capital here (5)
15 Sound (5)
17 Dance club (5)
18 The Windy City (7)
20 Dig out of the ground (7)
21 Crazy (6)
22 Stableman (6)

Down

1 ___ Everett: English actor (6)
2 Green vegetable (8)
3 Opposite of outer (5)
5 Film about a magical board game (7)
6 Money in notes or coins (4)
7 Sloppy (6)
8 Done efficiently (11)
13 Medieval musician (8)
14 Six-sided shape (7)
15 Central parts of cells (6)
16 Pester (6)
17 Judges (5)
19 Egyptian goddess (4)

Crossword

Puzzle 92

Across

1 Well known for some bad deed (8)
5 Nocturnal birds of prey (4)
8 Fills a suitcase (5)
9 Plant with bright flowers (7)
10 Chemical element with atomic number 33 (7)
12 Guilty person (7)
14 Persuasive relevance (7)
16 Relating to heat (7)
18 Regain strength (7)
19 Capital of Japan (5)
20 Neither good nor bad (2-2)
21 Solid with straight sides and a circular section (8)

Down

1 Mischievous fairies (4)
2 Cosmetic treatment (6)
3 Hypnotism (9)
4 In an optimistic mood (6)
6 ___ and dining: entertaining well (6)
7 Barely (8)
11 Type of pasta (9)
12 Tanks for storing water (8)
13 Barriers between houses (6)
14 Body of all ordained people (6)
15 Cut slightly (6)
17 Having no money (4)

Puzzle 93

Across

1 Grammatical mistake (8)
5 Engage in argument (4)
9 Assembly of witches (5)
10 Musical instrument (5)
11 Bad luck (10)
14 Pictures (6)
15 Make something new (6)
17 Infectious (10)
20 Uproarious party or fight (5)
21 Question intensely (5)
22 ___ Fitzgerald: famous jazz singer (4)
23 Blushed (8)

Down

1 Religious group (4)
2 Deep affection (4)
3 Significantly (12)
4 Conflict (6)
6 Manufacturer (8)
7 Sergeant (anag) (8)
8 Ate excessively (12)
12 Capable of being conquered (8)
13 Precipitation (8)
16 Hit a snooker ball incorrectly (6)
18 Indication (4)
19 Pleased (4)

Crossword

Puzzle 94

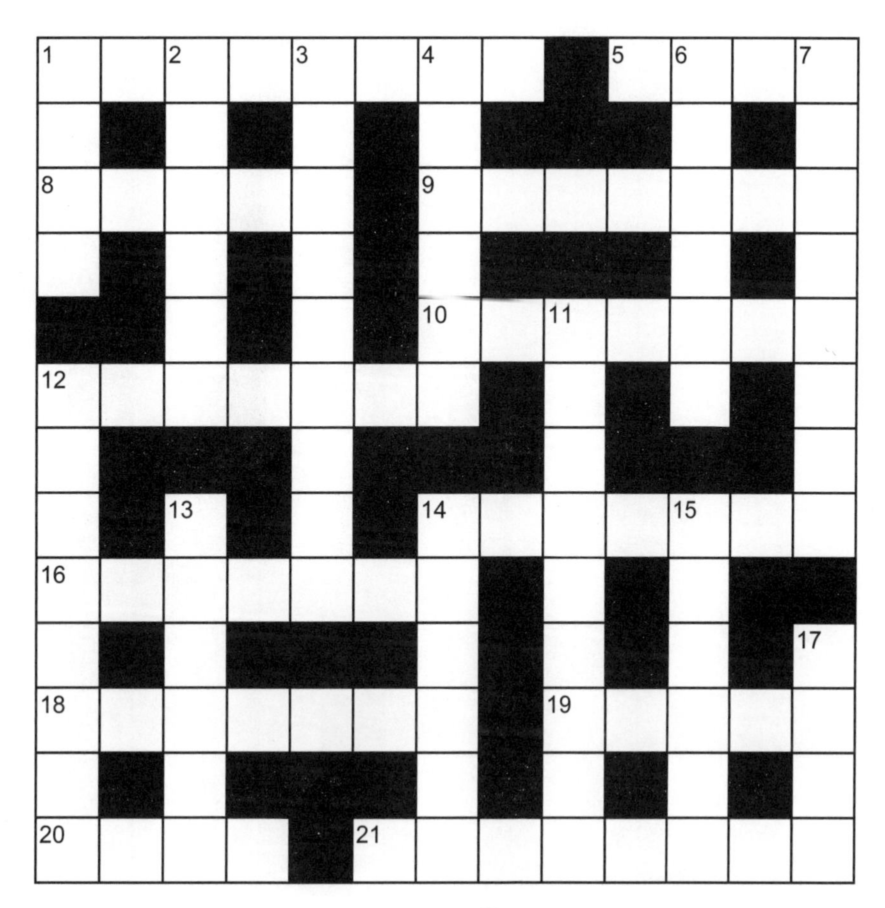

Across

1 Wounding (8)
5 Dutch cheese (4)
8 Strangely (5)
9 Service; state of being useful (7)
10 ___ seat: aircraft safety device (7)
12 Written record (7)
14 Takes a firm stand (7)
16 Prepared for an exam (7)
18 Satisfy a desire (7)
19 Avoided by social custom (5)
20 Finishes (4)
21 Rush of animals (8)

Down

1 Type of golf club (4)
2 Arbiters (6)
3 Monarchists (9)
4 Gender of nouns in some languages (6)
6 Moves slowly and aimlessly (6)
7 Female head of a town (8)
11 Biological community (9)
12 Cervine (8)
13 Eluded (6)
14 Season of the Church year (6)
15 Mob (6)
17 Plant stem part from which a leaf emerges (4)

Puzzle 95

Across

1 Spread out and apart (of limbs or fingers) (5)
4 High-pitched cries (5)
10 Cigar (7)
11 Male parent (5)
12 Caustic calcium compound (4)
13 Too bright to look at (8)
16 Turning armatures (6)
17 Humans in general (6)
20 Large Eurasian maple (8)
21 Push; poke (4)
23 Not asleep (5)
25 Glitz; allure (7)
26 Travelled on snow runners (5)
27 Conflict (5)

Down

2 Operated by air under pressure (9)
3 Very long period of time (4)
5 Grew in size (8)
6 Deep hole in the ground (3)
7 Of the eye (6)
8 Steps over a fence (5)
9 Boast (4)
14 Dictatorial; arrogant (9)
15 First public performance (8)
18 Undergo a hardship (6)
19 Narcotics (5)
20 Absorbent pad (4)
22 Frozen rain (4)
24 Ancient boat (3)

Puzzle 96

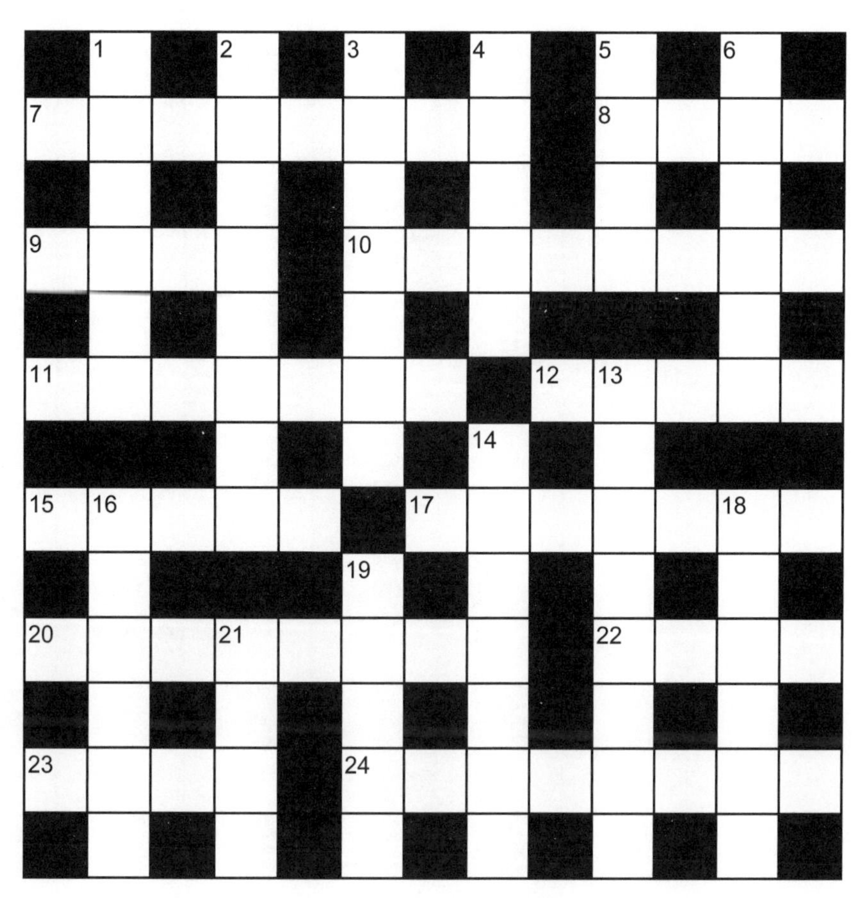

Across

7 Perhaps (8)
8 Cooking appliance (4)
9 Luxurious car (abbrev) (4)
10 Applauding (8)
11 People (7)
12 Types (5)
15 Acer tree (5)
17 Old (7)
20 Utopian (8)
22 Repose (4)
23 Princess ___ : Star Wars character (4)
24 Includes (8)

Down

1 Easily handled (6)
2 Marriage ceremony (8)
3 Leave quickly and in secret (7)
4 Local authority rule (2-3)
5 Liquid food (4)
6 Inclined at an angle (6)
13 Frozen dessert (3,5)
14 Typewriter rollers (7)
16 Mixed up or confused (6)
18 Failing to win (6)
19 A sure thing; easy task (5)
21 Not at home (4)

Puzzle 97

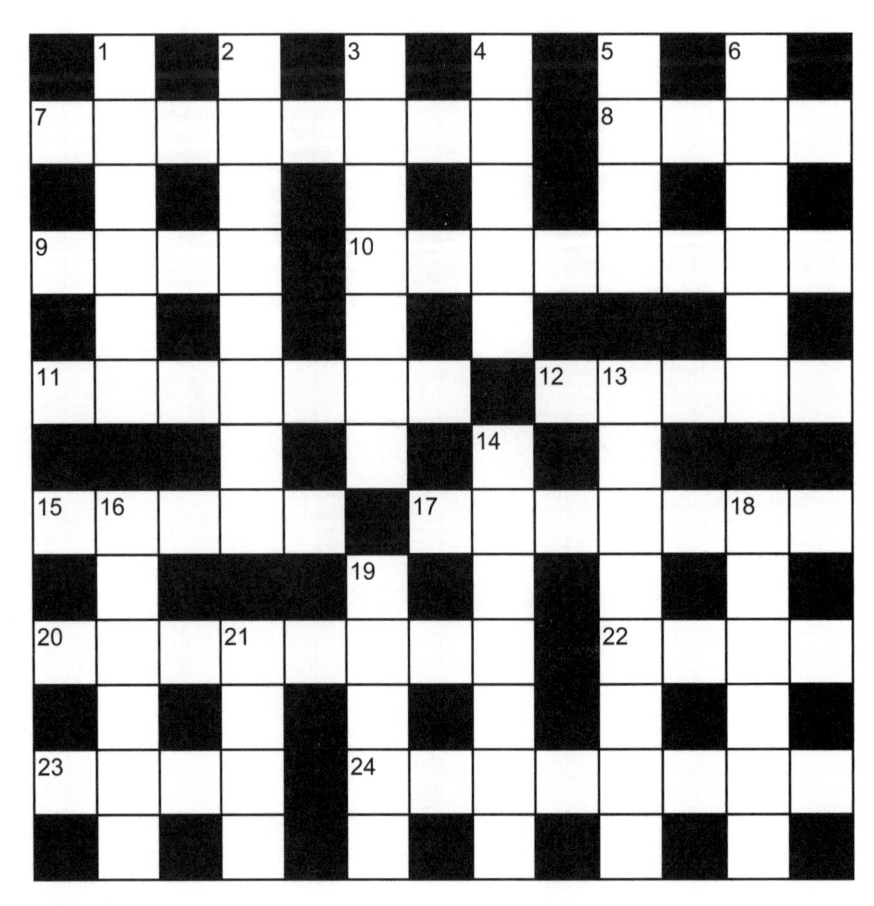

Across

7 Food poisoning (8)
8 Jump (4)
9 Desire; hope for (4)
10 Protruding rotund stomach (8)
11 Seize and take custody of (7)
12 Walks awkwardly (5)
15 Frightening (5)
17 Adding together (7)
20 Wedge to keep an entrance open (8)
22 Hollow cylinder (4)
23 Meat from a calf (4)
24 Small falcons (8)

Down

1 Reactive metal (6)
2 Busiest time on the roads (4,4)
3 Giving money in recognition of good service (7)
4 Friendship (5)
5 Adhesive (4)
6 Ride a horse at pace (6)
13 Not ripe (of fruit) (8)
14 Goal (7)
16 Shuts (6)
18 Take small bites out of (6)
19 Sum of money wagered (5)
21 Small stream (4)

Crossword

Puzzle 98

Across

1 Chicken (4)
3 First-year university student (US) (8)
9 Building (7)
10 Remains somewhere (5)
11 Supporting cane (7,5)
14 Ignited (3)
16 Connection; link (3-2)
17 Spoil (3)
18 Very determined (6-6)
21 Longest river in Europe (5)
22 Of great size (7)
23 Made less bright (8)
24 Weapons (4)

Down

1 Ability to act as one wishes (4,4)
2 Spin around (5)
4 Fish eggs (3)
5 Strengthen; confirm (12)
6 Small amount (7)
7 Prying; overly curious (4)
8 Break up into pieces (12)
12 Church farmland (5)
13 Foretells (8)
15 Flirter (anag) (7)
19 Serbian monetary unit (5)
20 Roman poet (4)
22 Foot extremity (3)

Puzzle 99

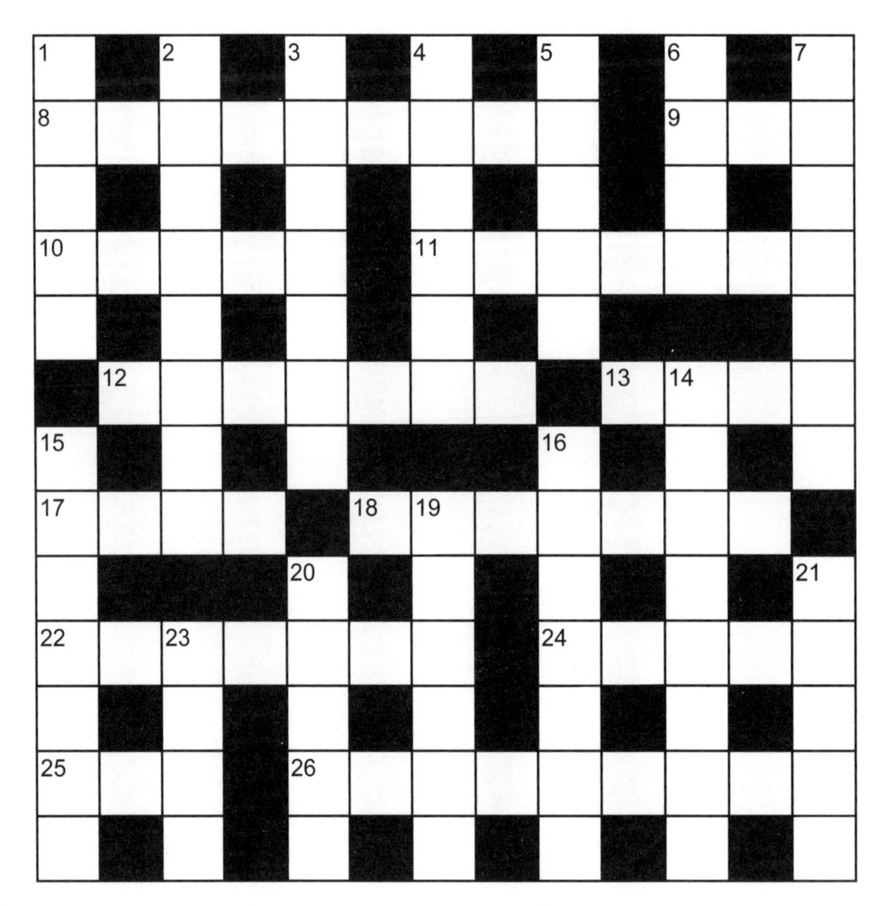

Across

8 Tending to get in the way (9)
9 Court (3)
10 Vaulted (5)
11 Squirm (7)
12 Unsurpassed (3-4)
13 Encourage in wrongdoing (4)
17 Ill-mannered (4)
18 Contentedly (7)
22 Greedy drinker (7)
24 Dwarfish creature (5)
25 Eg English Breakfast (3)
26 Elucidated (9)

Down

1 Semiconductor (5)
2 Tripped (8)
3 Experts (7)
4 Type of tent (6)
5 Give a false notion of (5)
6 Drink greedily (4)
7 Cornmeal (7)
14 Increases rapidly (8)
15 Warship (7)
16 Witty saying (7)
19 Sudden (6)
20 Ice masses (5)
21 Studies a subject at university (5)
23 Fervour (4)

Crossword

Puzzle 100

Across

1 Snug (4)
3 Decade from 1920 - 1929 (8)
9 European deer (7)
10 Pale orange tropical fruit (5)
11 Not in good physical condition (5)
12 Stylishly (7)
13 Squall of snow (6)
15 Quick look (6)
17 Refills (7)
18 Unspecified object (5)
20 Flaring stars (5)
21 Serving no purpose (7)
22 Put at risk (8)
23 Surprise; amaze (4)

Down

1 Line that bounds a circle (13)
2 Projecting horizontal ledge (5)
4 Becomes alert after sleep (6)
5 Garments worn in bed (12)
6 Eg a resident of Rome (7)
7 Black Eyed Peas star (5,8)
8 Underground (12)
14 Friendless (7)
16 Guarantee (6)
19 Maladroit (5)

Puzzle 101

Across

1 Concealed from view (6)
4 Fill a balloon with air (4,2)
9 Massage technique (7)
10 Tall stand used by a preacher (7)
11 ___ Trott: Olympic gold medallist in cycling (5)
12 Tries out (5)
14 Yearns for (5)
15 Type of bandage (5)
17 Stomach (informal) (5)
18 Surface layer of earth (7)
20 20th letter of the Greek alphabet (7)
21 Emperor of Japan (6)
22 Contemptibly small (6)

Down

1 Jostle (6)
2 Cocktail (8)
3 Excess (5)
5 Surgical knives (7)
6 Ewer (anag) (4)
7 Keyboard instruments (6)
8 Prevent from continuing (4,3,4)
13 Impetus (8)
14 Stuck on the bottom (of a ship) (7)
15 Humorous television drama (6)
16 Capital of New South Wales (6)
17 Sense experience (5)
19 Eat like a bird (4)

Puzzle 102

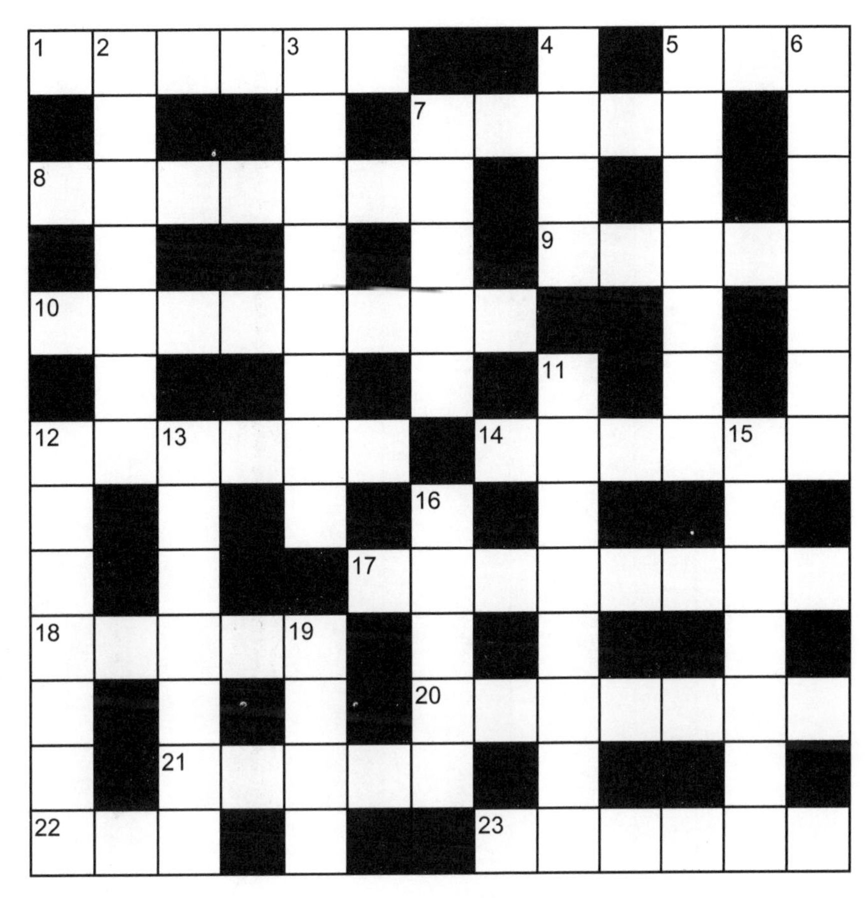

Across

1 Entertained (6)
5 Writing fluid (3)
7 Tests (5)
8 Gift (7)
9 Defect (5)
10 Red fruits eaten as vegetables (8)
12 Large dark cloud bearing rain (6)
14 Water diviner (6)
17 Instalments of a TV series (8)
18 Make inoperative (5)
20 Sceptical (7)
21 Trail (5)
22 17th Greek letter (3)
23 Deceives; finest (anag) (6)

Down

2 Guglielmo ___ : radio pioneer (7)
3 Full of interesting happenings (8)
4 Stick with a hook (4)
5 Dispensers (7)
6 Needleworker (7)
7 Nice-smelling colourless volatile liquid (5)
11 Gibberish (8)
12 One who eats a bit at a time (7)
13 Film starring Guy Pearce (7)
15 Graceful in form (7)
16 Small spot (5)
19 ___ Egan: Westlife singer (4)

Puzzle 103

Across

1 Lower (8)
5 Boxing match (4)
9 Short choral composition (5)
10 Observed (5)
11 Dilapidated (10)
14 Abominable (6)
15 Takes the place of (6)
17 Current of air near a moving car (10)
20 Seemingly (combining form) (5)
21 Scowl (5)
22 Pitcher (4)
23 Circumspection (8)

Down

1 Honoured lady (4)
2 Baby beds (4)
3 Eager (12)
4 Woody plants (6)
6 In the open air (8)
7 Orderliness (8)
8 Inadequately manned (12)
12 Bodily form (8)
13 Water (8)
16 Author (6)
18 Silly person (4)
19 Paul ___ : former England football captain (4)

Crossword

Puzzle 104

Across

1 Soak (6)
5 Snip (3)
7 Dark wood (5)
8 Used to one's advantage (7)
9 Litre (anag) (5)
10 Destroy in large numbers (8)
12 Egyptian god (6)
14 Sweltering (6)
17 Glue (8)
18 Melts (5)
20 Any part of the face (7)
21 Thermosetting resin (5)
22 Polite address for a man (3)
23 Deactivate an explosive device (6)

Down

2 Critiques (7)
3 State capital of South Carolina (8)
4 Bird of the rail family (4)
5 Rider (7)
6 A contest (7)
7 Modifies (5)
11 Body of an aeroplane (8)
12 Edible marine molluscs (7)
13 Item used by asthma sufferers (7)
15 Returns to a former state (7)
16 Enlighten; educate morally (5)
19 Type of air pollution (4)

Puzzle 105

Across

1 Exuberant merriment (8)
5 Hilltop (4)
9 Looking tired (5)
10 Group of activists (5)
11 Lingering visual impression (10)
14 Dress (6)
15 Go back on (6)
17 Light up (10)
20 Allowed by official rules (5)
21 ___ Lewis: British singer (5)
22 Snag (anag) (4)
23 Recreational area for children (8)

Down

1 Conceal (4)
2 A hole that lets liquid escape (4)
3 Not special (3-2-3-4)
4 Bird eaten at Christmas (6)
6 Blushing with embarrassment (3-5)
7 In any place (8)
8 Not on purpose; inadvertently (12)
12 Greek hero of the Trojan War (8)
13 Young ruffian (8)
16 Cry and sniffle (6)
18 Extinct bird (4)
19 Inner surface of the hand (4)

Crossword

Puzzle 106

Across

1 Favourable aspect of something (6)
5 Father (3)
7 Sandy fawn colour (5)
8 Advocate (7)
9 Inactive (5)
10 Offered (8)
12 State of mental strain (6)
14 Neat and concise; irritable (6)
17 Unit of power (8)
18 Opposite of lows (5)
20 Illegal action in ice hockey (7)
21 Small heron (5)
22 Pub (3)
23 Striped African wild horses (6)

Down

2 Keep safe from harm (7)
3 Spread out (8)
4 Sound system (2-2)
5 Bring to maturity (7)
6 Relating to what you eat (7)
7 Rhythm and ___ : music genre (5)
11 Face-to-face conversation (3-2-3)
12 Japanese dish of raw fish (7)
13 Coarsen (7)
15 Garden flower (7)
16 Correct (5)
19 One of the Channel Islands (4)

Puzzle 107

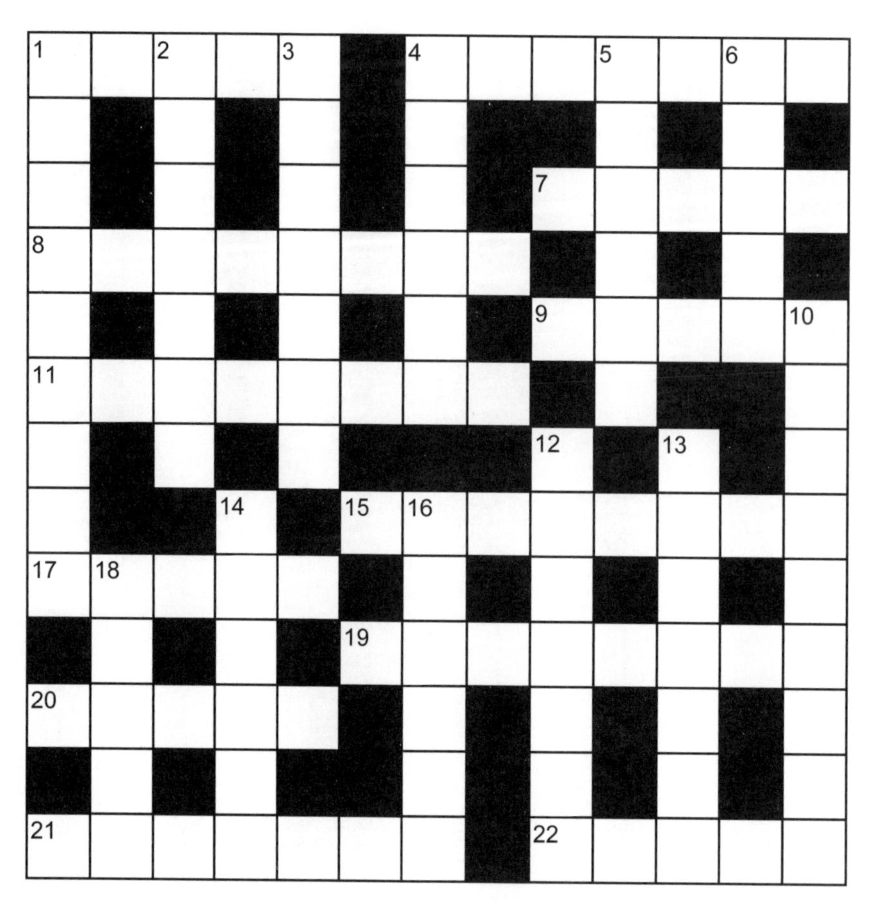

Across

1 The Norwegian language (5)
4 Indulges a desire (7)
7 Humming (5)
8 Set a boat in motion (8)
9 Platforms leading out to sea (5)
11 Lacking intelligence and sense (8)
15 Hard grains left after the milling of flour (8)
17 Mark ___ : US writer (5)
19 Yellowish edible seed (8)
20 Method of colouring textiles (5)
21 Large areas of land (7)
22 Belief in a god or gods (5)

Down

1 Failing to give proper care (9)
2 Need (7)
3 Precisely (7)
4 Fire irons (6)
5 Trash (6)
6 Sharp blade (5)
10 Scheme (9)
12 Agreement (7)
13 Kettledrums (7)
14 Smallest quantities (6)
16 Morals (6)
18 Erodes (5)

Crossword

Puzzle 108

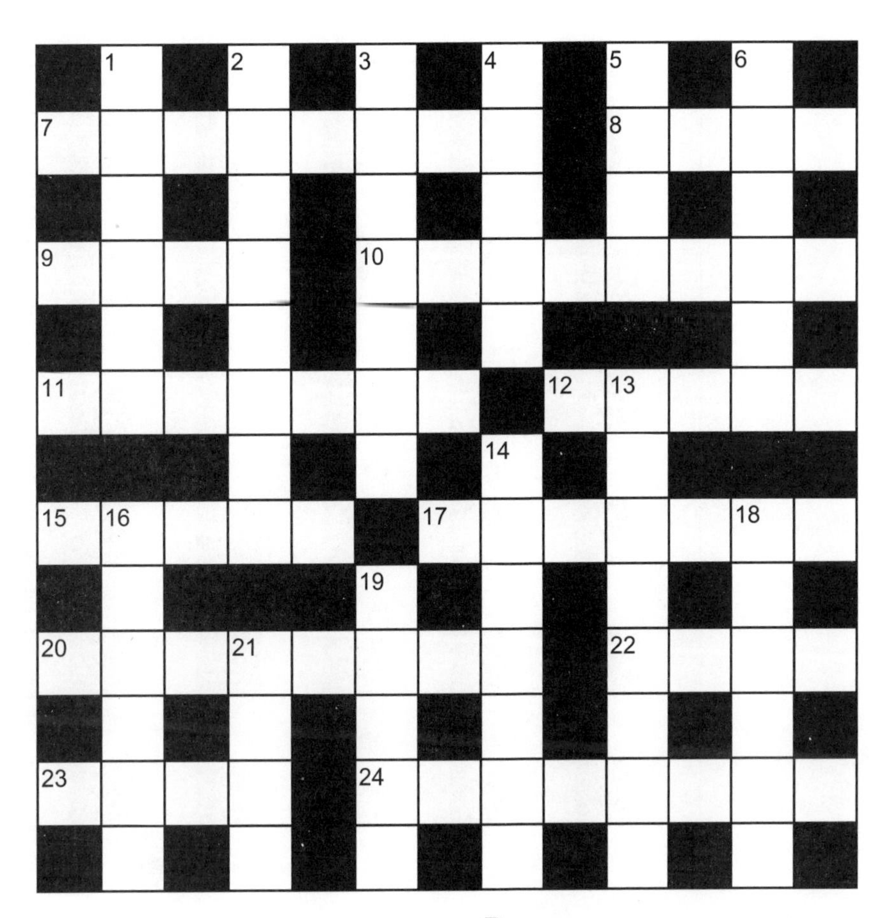

Across

7 Having a pleasing scent (8)
8 Noisy (4)
9 Pretty (4)
10 Last (8)
11 Having great wisdom (7)
12 Reduce the temperature of (5)
15 Eg performs karaoke (5)
17 Decorate food (7)
20 Abode (8)
22 Earth's satellite (4)
23 Type of high-energy radiation (1-3)
24 Royal domains (8)

Down

1 Emotional shock (6)
2 Concurring (8)
3 Rushing (7)
4 Wounded by a wasp (5)
5 Slender (4)
6 Edible bivalve mollusc (6)
13 Individually crafted by a person (8)
14 Drooping (7)
16 Towards the inside (6)
18 Tempestuous (6)
19 Closes and opens an eye (5)
21 Puts down (4)

Puzzle 109

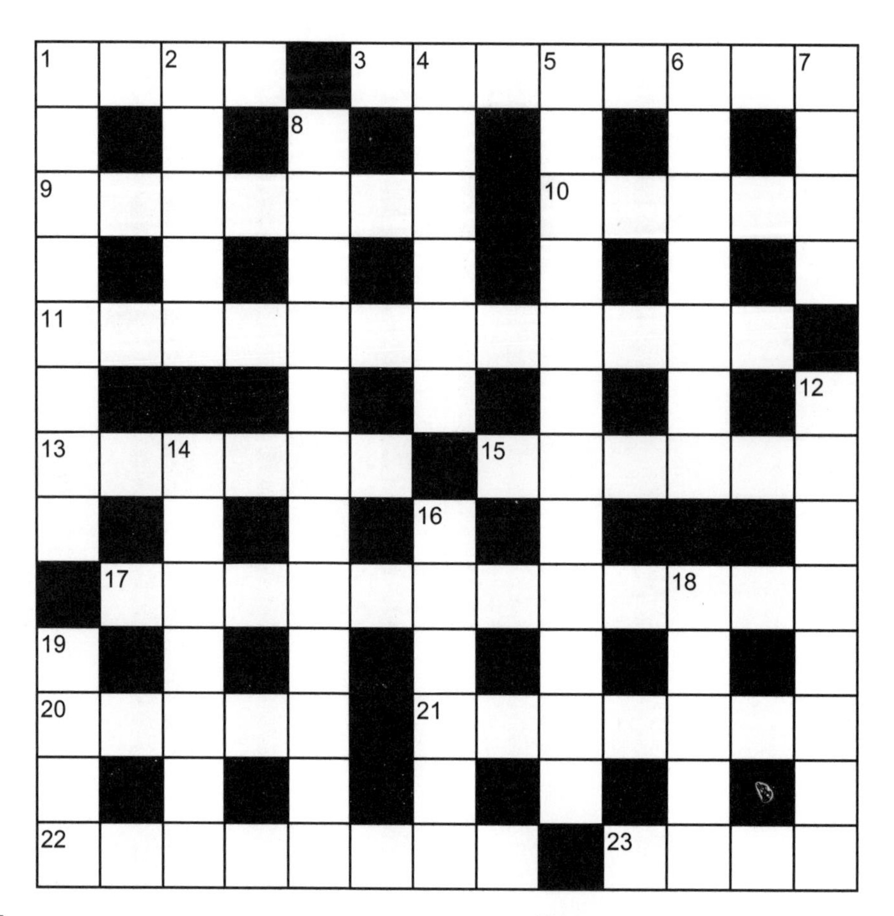

Across

1 Manage (4)
3 Not usual (8)
9 No longer in existence (7)
10 Chris ___ : British radio DJ (5)
11 Accomplishments (12)
13 Symbolic (6)
15 Player (anag) (6)
17 Having a tendency to become liquid (12)
20 Tiny piece of food (5)
21 Tortilla rolled around a filling (7)
22 Component parts (8)
23 US state (4)

Down

1 Ornamental climbing plant (8)
2 Business proposal (5)
4 Giggle (6)
5 Forerunners (12)
6 Talk informally (7)
7 Whip (4)
8 Not capable of being checked (12)
12 A canine (3,5)
14 Exploit to excess (7)
16 European flatfish (6)
18 George ___ : Middlemarch writer (5)
19 Apex (4)

Puzzle 110

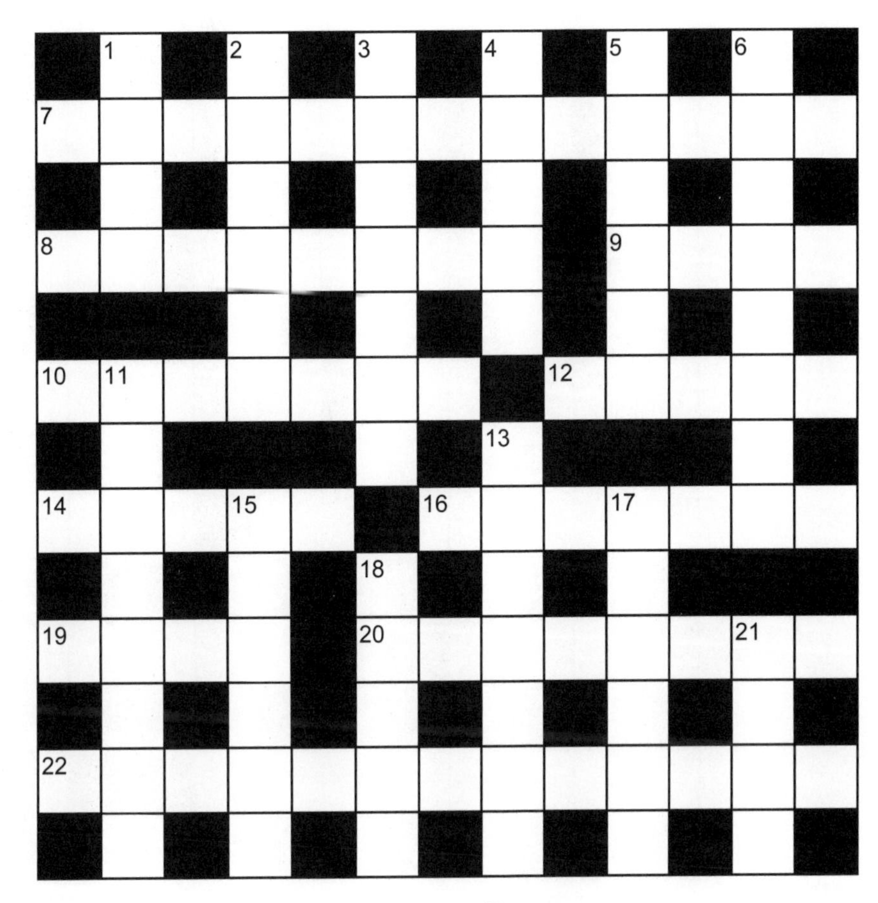

Across

7 As another option (13)
8 Recurrent (8)
9 Feeble (of an excuse) (4)
10 Grew tired (7)
12 Spirit in a bottle (5)
14 Spring flower (5)
16 Encroach (7)
19 Remnant (4)
20 Wanders at random (8)
22 Verified for a second time (6-7)

Down

1 Associate (4)
2 Kitchen tool to remove vegetable skin (6)
3 Played out (7)
4 Avocet-like wader (5)
5 Elegant and slender (6)
6 System of piping that provides water (8)
11 Explosion (8)
13 Understanding of another (7)
15 Drink (6)
17 Bring forth (6)
18 Natural yellow resin (5)
21 Unpleasant smell (4)

Puzzle 111

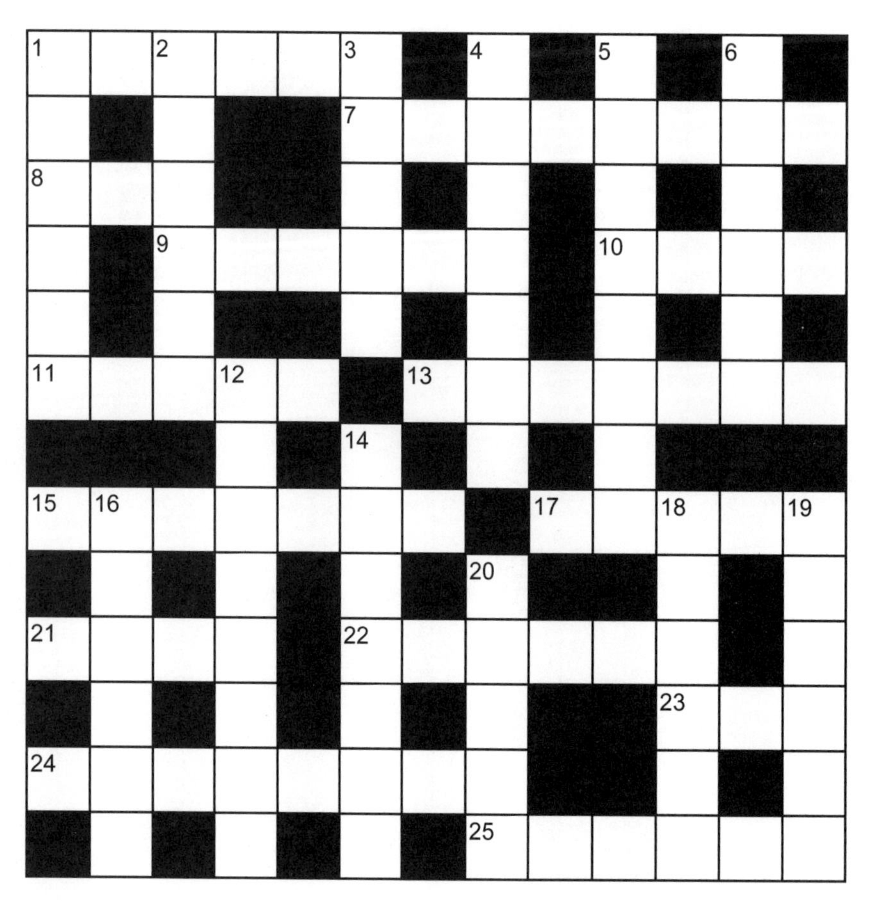

Across

1 Instrumental piece of music (6)
7 Assembles (8)
8 Performed an action (3)
9 Categories; kinds (6)
10 Individual article or unit (4)
11 Gets less difficult (5)
13 Refutes; sends back (7)
15 Tidal mouth of a river (7)
17 Panorama (5)
21 Disgusting (4)
22 No one (6)
23 False statement (3)
24 Places in position (8)
25 Has objective reality (6)

Down

1 Attract powerfully (6)
2 Pokes gently (6)
3 Fruit of the oak (5)
4 Eased in (anag) (7)
5 Disease caused by a lack of thiamine (8)
6 Happen again (6)
12 State of being the same (8)
14 Crossbar set above a window (7)
16 Having pimples (6)
18 Harry ___ : One Direction singer (6)
19 Judge (6)
20 Corpulent (5)

Puzzle 112

Across

7 Far away from home (6)
8 ___ Ryder: US actress (6)
10 Timid (7)
11 Plantain lily (5)
12 Zest; liveliness (4)
13 Brushed clean (5)
17 Love intently (5)
18 Skirt worn by ballerinas (4)
22 Samantha ___ : Irish singer (5)
23 The growth of crystals (7)
24 Where one finds Athens (6)
25 Towards the rear (6)

Down

1 River of East Africa (7)
2 Express disagreement (7)
3 High up (5)
4 Accidents (7)
5 Temporary police force (5)
6 Polite address for a woman (5)
9 Garden plot for plants (6,3)
14 Progress (7)
15 Clergymen (7)
16 Floating; cheerful (7)
19 Adult insect stage (5)
20 Remnant of a dying fire (5)
21 Wash with clean water (5)

Puzzle 113

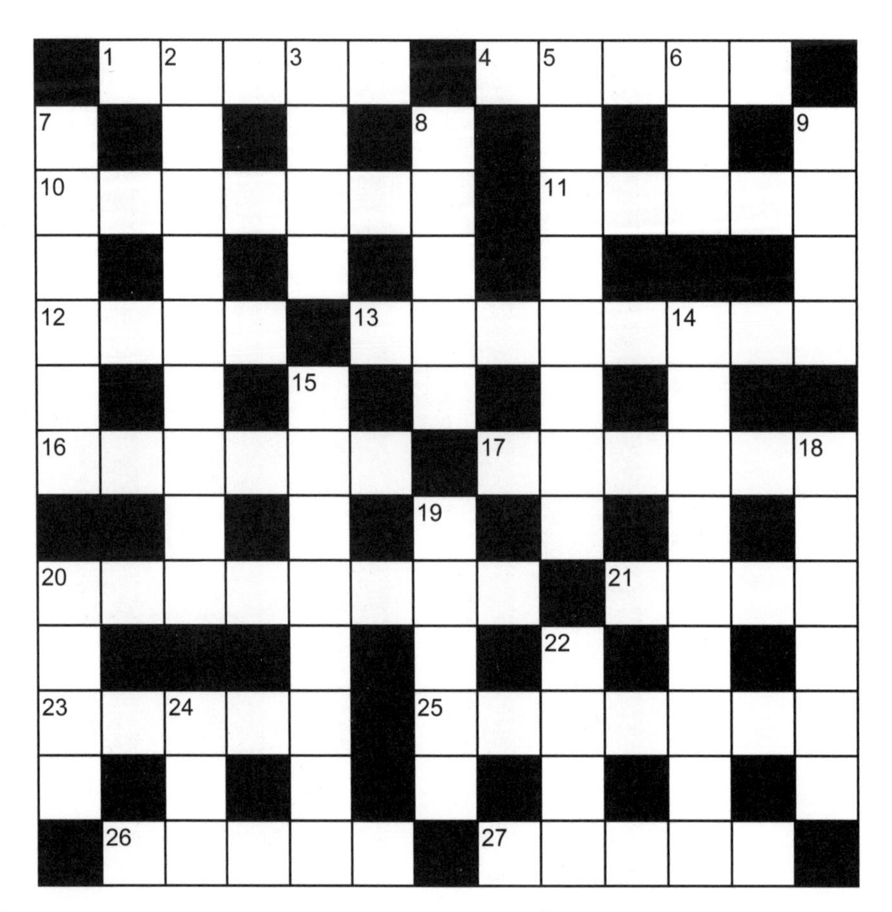

Across

1 Refine metal (5)
4 Steep bank or slope (5)
10 Finery (7)
11 Published false statement (5)
12 Vehicle with four-wheel drive (4)
13 Spread throughout (8)
16 Denial (anag) (6)
17 Archimedes' famous cry (6)
20 Start (8)
21 Near (4)
23 Buyer (5)
25 Ornamental screen (7)
26 Small hill (5)
27 Glasses (abbrev) (5)

Down

2 Natural charm or appealing quality (9)
3 Hang loosely; droop (4)
5 State capital of Ohio (8)
6 Steal (3)
7 Inhabitant of Troy (6)
8 Renowned (5)
9 Primary colour (4)
14 Irregular (9)
15 Postponement (8)
18 Struck by overwhelming shock (6)
19 Skin marks from wounds (5)
20 Domestic felines (4)
22 Enclose a gift in paper (4)
24 Relations (3)

Crossword

Puzzle 114

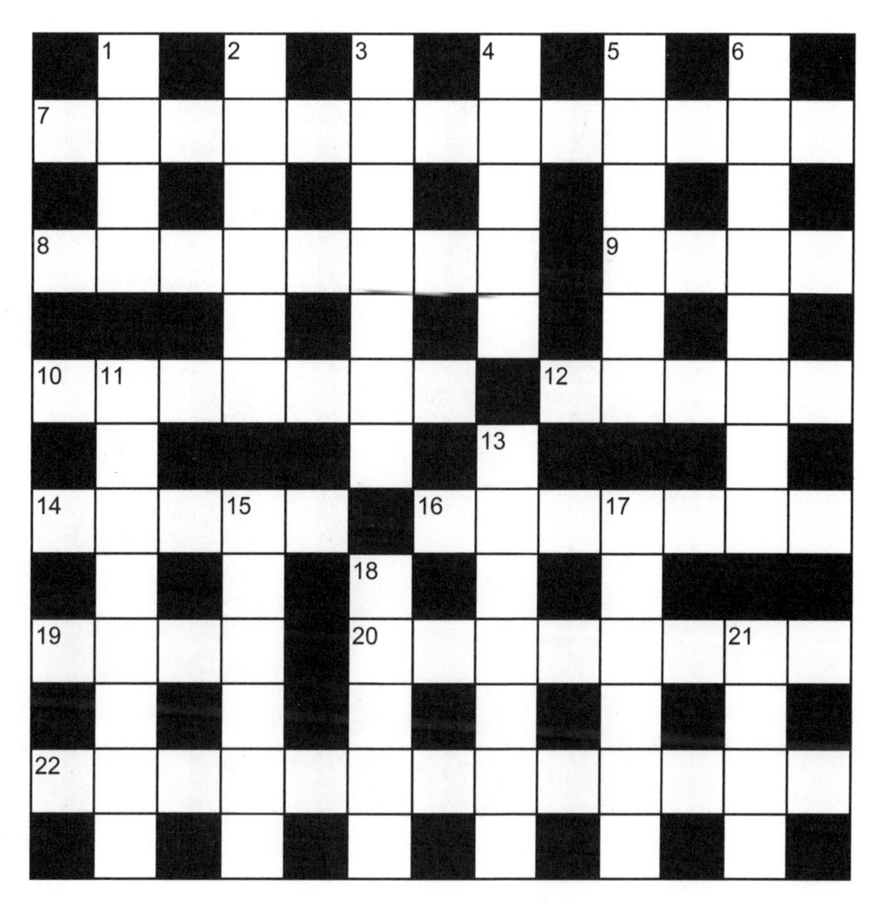

Across

7 Irascible (5-8)
8 Fantastic (8)
9 Opposite of thick (4)
10 Support (7)
12 Fragile (5)
14 Enumerates (5)
16 Touching down (7)
19 Platform leading out to sea (4)
20 Good-looking (8)
22 Manage badly (13)

Down

1 Ancient German letter (4)
2 Frightens (6)
3 Manned (7)
4 Loose overall (5)
5 Zone (6)
6 Ridicule (8)
11 Inventive; creative (8)
13 Meriting (7)
15 Hatred (anag) (6)
17 Discontinuance; neglect (6)
18 Pollex (5)
21 Manner or appearance (4)

Puzzle 115

Across

1 Unrefined (6)
4 Alter or adapt (6)
9 Capital of Kenya (7)
10 Thing causing outrage (7)
11 Kind of wheat (5)
12 Conditions (5)
14 Drives out from a place (5)
15 Feeling of fear (5)
17 Acquires through merit (5)
18 Position in rugby (3,4)
20 Curved upwards (7)
21 Changing the colour of hair (6)
22 Garment part that covers an arm (6)

Down

1 Ottawa is the capital here (6)
2 Corrosive precipitation (4,4)
3 Violent atmospheric disturbance (5)
5 Pours off liquid (7)
6 Second-hand (4)
7 Eg Sir and Dame (6)
8 Unpleasant (11)
13 Fetch (8)
14 Eight-sided polygon (7)
15 Breathless (6)
16 Insect that transmits sleeping sickness (6)
17 Frame for holding an artist's work (5)
19 Ivy League university (4)

Crossword

Puzzle 116

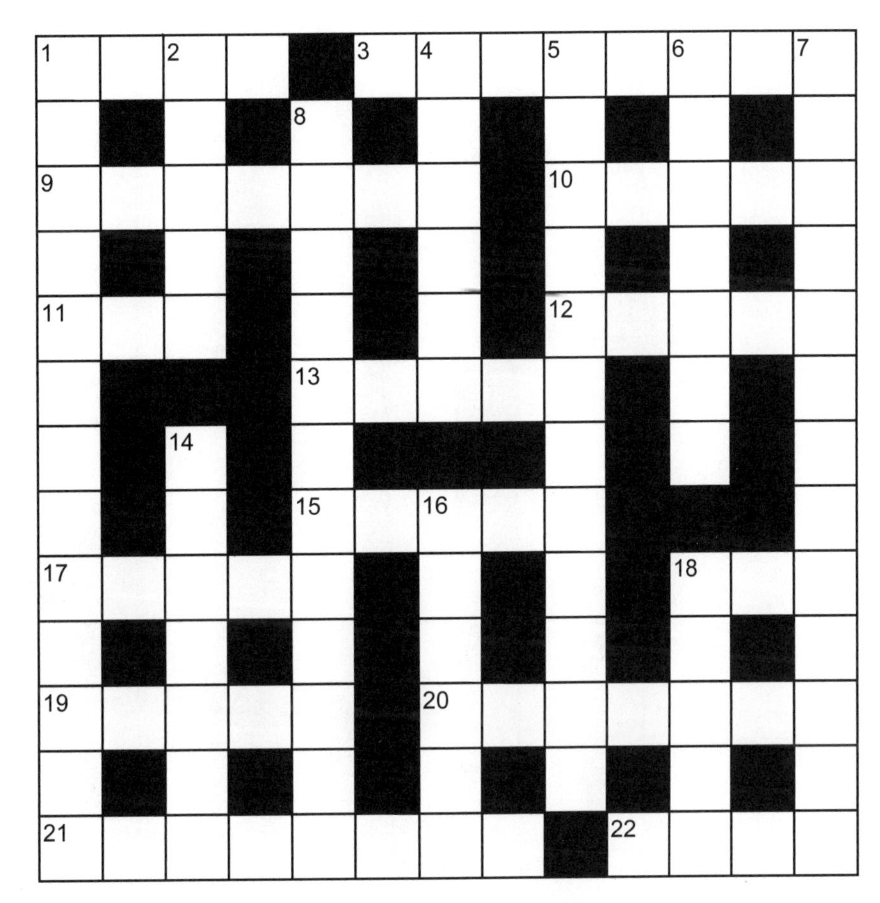

Across

1 Chief magistrate of Venice (4)
3 Against the current (8)
9 Aquatic bird (7)
10 Chopping (5)
11 Make a choice (3)
12 Woollen fabric (5)
13 Unit of heat (5)
15 Religious groups (5)
17 Flowers (5)
18 Male person (3)
19 Moved by air (5)
20 Not as tall (7)
21 Make weak (8)
22 Wire lattice (4)

Down

1 Causing disgrace (13)
2 Allocate money (5)
4 Courteous (6)
5 Act of sending a message (12)
6 Regimes (anag) (7)
7 Direction to which a compass points (8,5)
8 Most perfect example of a quality (12)
14 Free a ship from her moorings (4,3)
16 Long-bladed hand tool (6)
18 Unit of length (5)

Puzzle 117

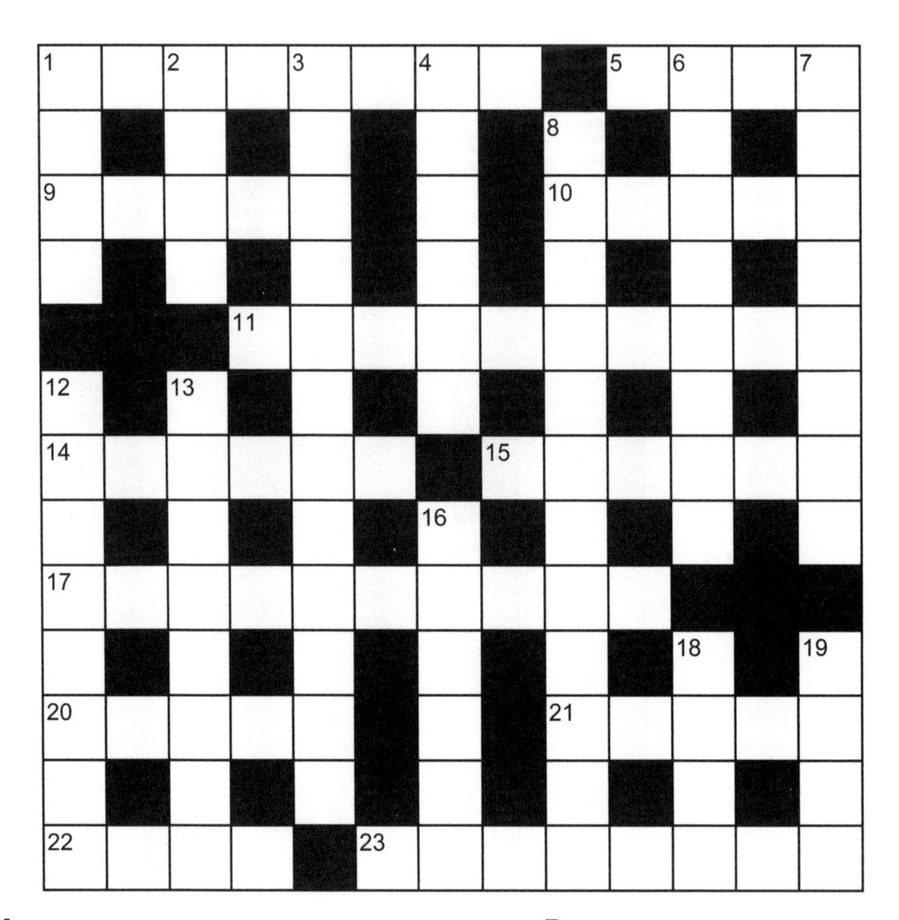

Across

1 Relating to office work (8)
5 Mountain system in Europe (4)
9 Fire a weapon (5)
10 Seeped (5)
11 Skull and ___ : emblem of piracy (10)
14 Starting point (6)
15 Tenant (6)
17 Spoke with a spitting sound (10)
20 Country in NE Africa (5)
21 Tidily kept (5)
22 Turn or slide violently (of a vehicle) (4)
23 Create an account deficit (8)

Down

1 Group of actors in a show (4)
2 Greek god of love (4)
3 Sporadic (12)
4 Superior of a nunnery (6)
6 Sloth (8)
7 Move out the way of (8)
8 Type of bus (6-6)
12 Is composed of (8)
13 Force out of position (8)
16 History play by Shakespeare (5,1)
18 ___ Sharif: Egyptian actor (4)
19 Wets (anag) (4)

Puzzle 118

Across

1 Metallic element (6)
5 Nestle together (6)
8 Beloved; expensive (4)
9 How a crab moves (8)
10 Smooth textile fibre (5)
11 Inflatable rubber bag (7)
14 Act of vanishing (13)
16 People who are in a club (7)
18 Starts to bubble (of liquid) (5)
20 Extension of a debt (8)
22 Grey-haired with age (4)
23 Venomous snakes (6)
24 Grow more ill (6)

Down

2 Having effect (9)
3 No pears (anag) (7)
4 Situation involving danger (4)
5 Refuge (8)
6 Wooden pin used to join surfaces together (5)
7 Put down (3)
12 Vibrate back and forth (9)
13 Authorises (8)
15 One more (7)
17 Nonsense (5)
19 ___ Barrymore: Hollywood actress (4)
21 Not new (3)

Puzzle 119

Across

1 Person who foresees the future (11)
9 Last Greek letter (5)
10 Dr ___ : US record producer (3)
11 Push away (5)
12 Compass point (5)
13 Midday (8)
16 Unusual (8)
18 Egg-shaped solid (5)
21 ___ Nash: writer of light verse (5)
22 Eg pecan (3)
23 Bedfordshire town (5)
24 Defect in the eye (11)

Down

2 Publicly criticise using ridicule (7)
3 Set apart (7)
4 Watched (6)
5 Long for (5)
6 Lowest point (5)
7 Fortified defensive position (11)
8 Holland (11)
14 Small crown (7)
15 Wolfgang ___ Mozart: composer (7)
17 Opposite of top (6)
19 Solemn promises (5)
20 New ___ : Indian capital (5)

Crossword

Puzzle 120

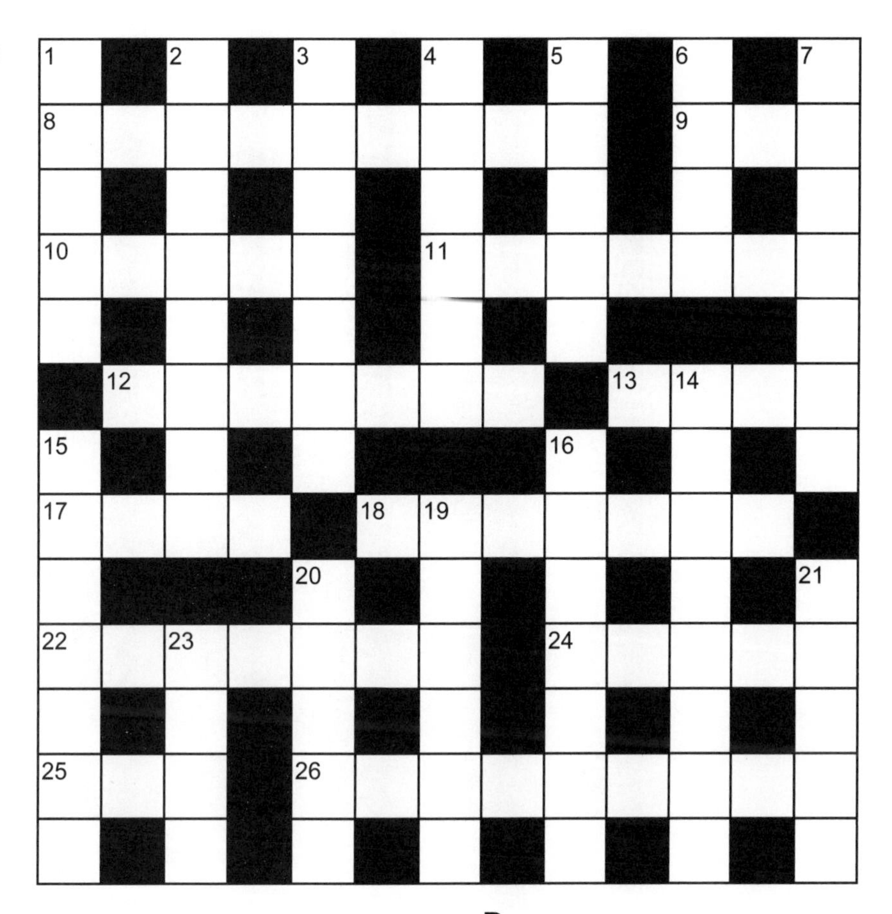

Across

- **8** Unprecedented (7-2)
- **9** Eek (anag) (3)
- **10** Roadside form of lodging (5)
- **11** Identifying outfit (7)
- **12** Left out (7)
- **13** Young deer (4)
- **17** Haystack (4)
- **18** Moderately slow tempo (music) (7)
- **22** Alfresco (4-3)
- **24** Intuitive feeling (5)
- **25** Food item from a hen (3)
- **26** Ongoing television serial (4,5)

Down

- **1** Mock-up (5)
- **2** Occurring regularly (8)
- **3** Money holders (7)
- **4** Request earnestly (6)
- **5** Attach (5)
- **6** Block a decision (4)
- **7** Radiant (7)
- **14** Participant in a meeting (8)
- **15** Singer (7)
- **16** Mode (7)
- **19** Standard; usual (6)
- **20** Impudent; full of spirit (5)
- **21** Bottle (5)
- **23** Therefore (Latin) (4)

Puzzle 121

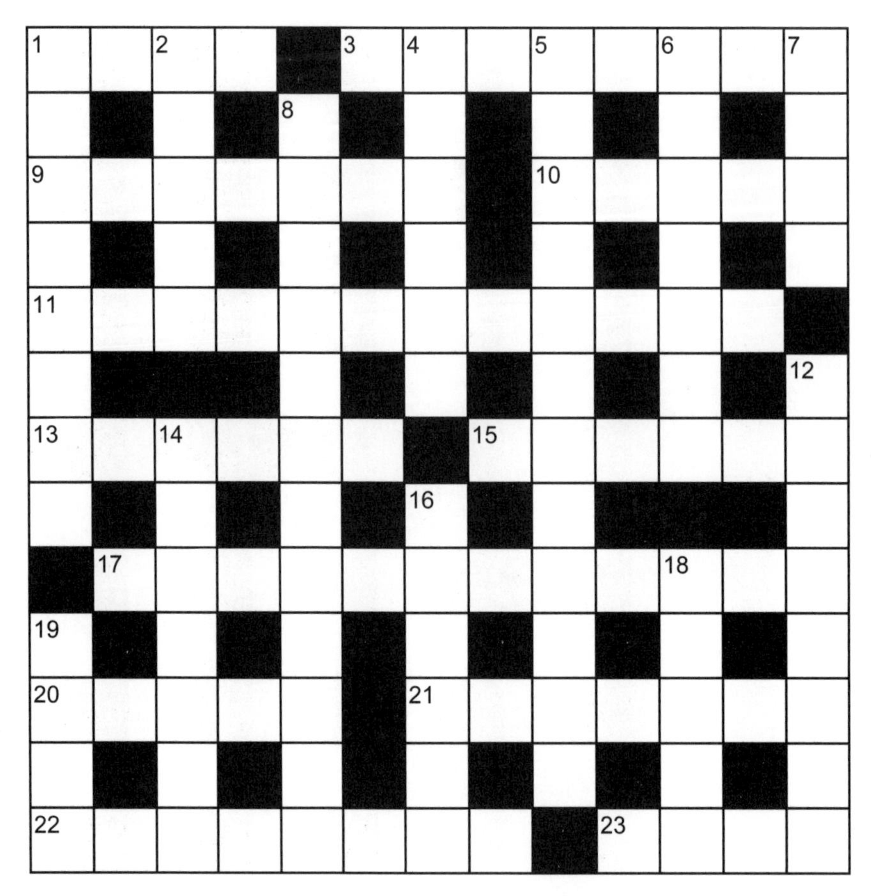

Across

1 Second Greek letter (4)
3 Sweet food courses (8)
9 Side by side (7)
10 Maurice ___ : French composer (5)
11 Clearly evident (12)
13 Bandage (6)
15 Revoke (6)
17 Mentally acute (5-7)
20 Crave; desire (5)
21 List one by one (7)
22 Finely chopped (8)
23 English public school (4)

Down

1 Wave or flourish a weapon (8)
2 Monotonous hum (5)
4 Distinct being (6)
5 Stretched out completely (12)
6 Reassess financial worth (7)
7 Marine flatfish (4)
8 Lacking courage (5-7)
12 Short heavy club (8)
14 Finished (3,4)
16 Seek ambitiously (6)
18 Impair (5)
19 Decorates a cake (4)

Crossword

Puzzle 122

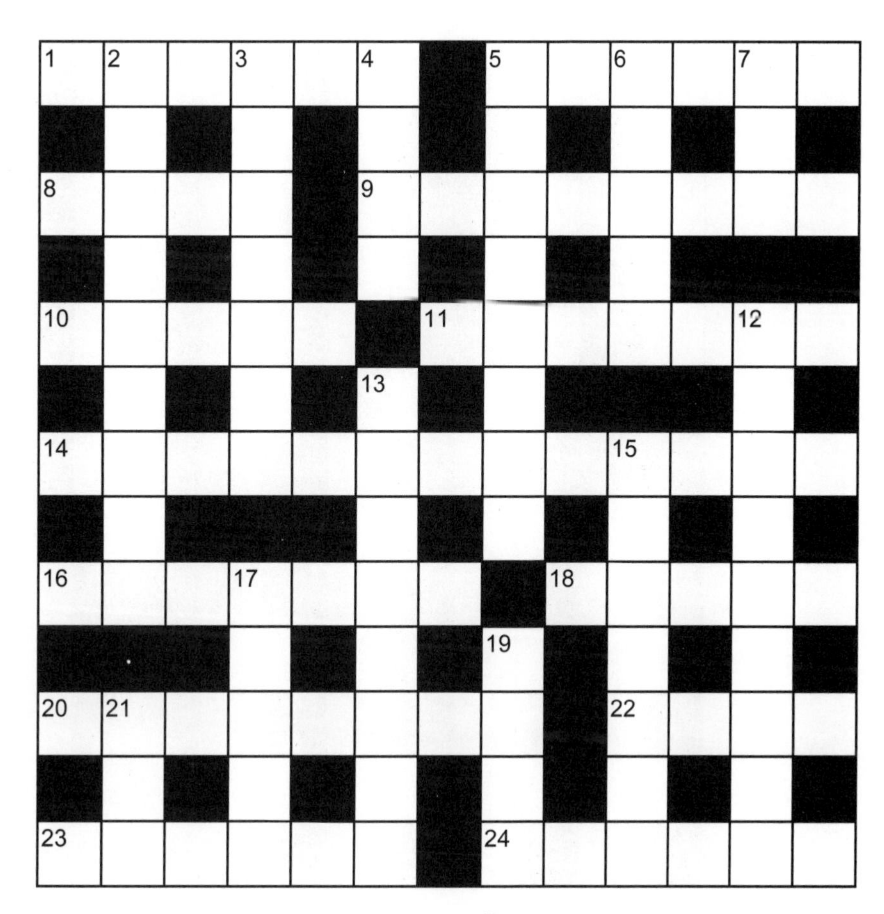

Across

1 Protects from direct sunlight (6)
5 Most secure (6)
8 Rebuff (4)
9 Artificial water channel (8)
10 Thigh bone (5)
11 Burnt fragments of wood (7)
14 Virtuousness (13)
16 Nimbleness (7)
18 Reddish (5)
20 Substantial (8)
22 Pointer on a clock (4)
23 Compensate for (6)
24 Failed to hit the target (6)

Down

2 Longing (9)
3 Corrupt (7)
4 Shut with force (4)
5 Scholarly (8)
6 Grew fainter (5)
7 Pouch; enclosed space (3)
12 Home (9)
13 Able to feel things (8)
15 Zeroes (7)
17 Passes the tongue over (5)
19 Curl one's hair (4)
21 Clumsy person (3)

Puzzle 123

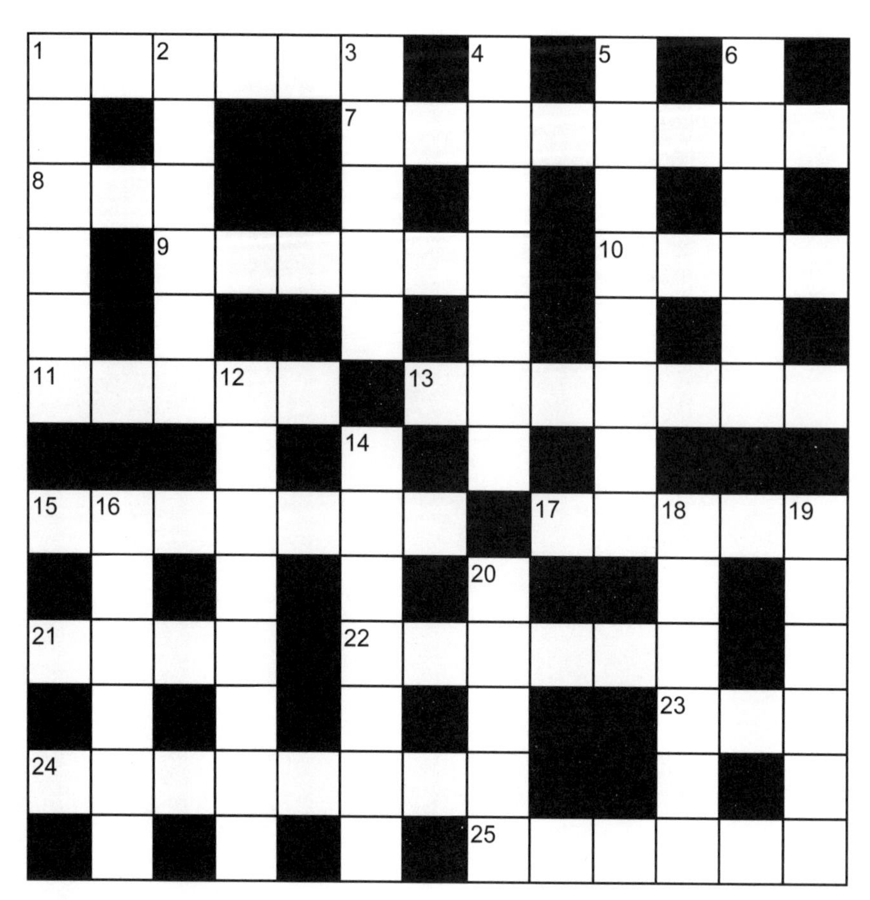

Across

1 Having colourless skin (6)
7 Excessive eating (8)
8 Organ of hearing (3)
9 Be aggrieved by (6)
10 Playing cards (4)
11 Stitched (5)
13 Grandeur (7)
15 Lack of success (7)
17 Insect larva (5)
21 Swinging barrier (4)
22 Fanatic (6)
23 Long period of time (3)
24 Form the base for (8)
25 Decide with authority (6)

Down

1 Wards off (6)
2 Dig a hole (6)
3 Unpleasant giants (5)
4 Standup (anag) (7)
5 Plan of action (8)
6 Put inside another object (6)
12 Expanded (8)
14 Very light rain (7)
16 Apply ointment for religious reasons (6)
18 ___ shower: eg the Perseids (6)
19 Merciful (6)
20 Became less severe (5)

Puzzle 124

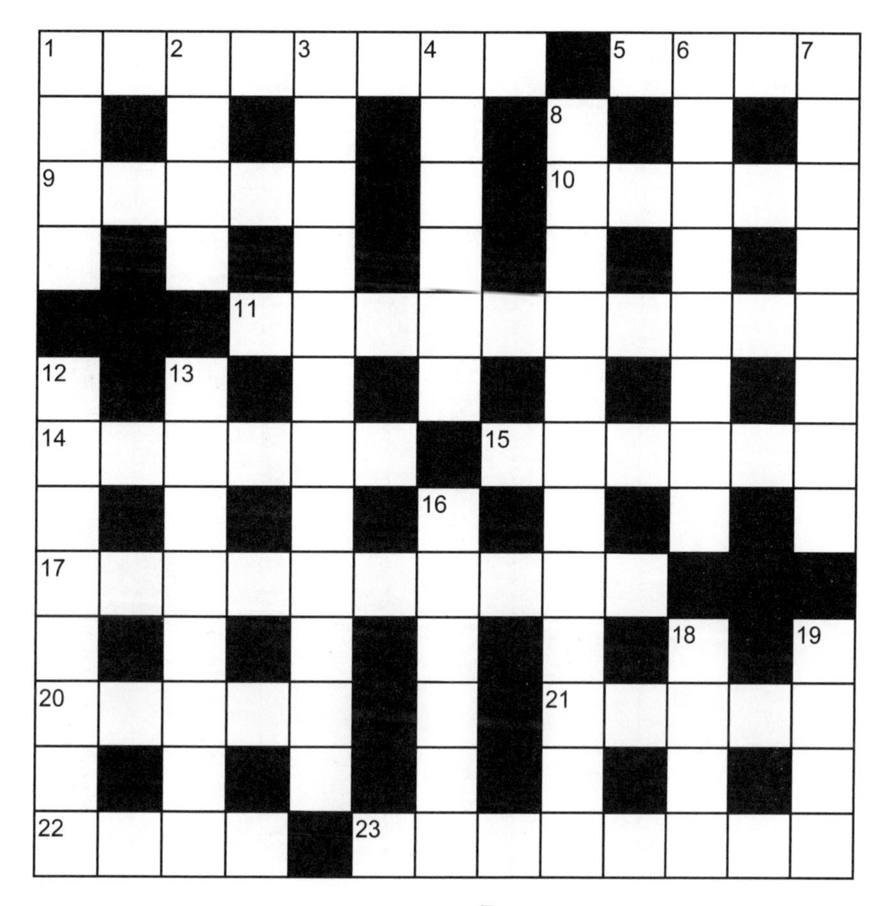

Across

1 Of a court of law (8)
5 Literary composition (4)
9 Plant flower (5)
10 Ceases (5)
11 Suppression of objectionable material (10)
14 Fibre from the angora goat (6)
15 Widespread (6)
17 Parts that are left over (10)
20 Open disrespect (5)
21 Put in position (5)
22 Too; in addition (4)
23 Dark colour that is virtually black (4,4)

Down

1 Occupations (4)
2 Pairs of people (4)
3 Contests (12)
4 Evoke a feeling (6)
6 US state (8)
7 Squander money (8)
8 Art of planning a dance (12)
12 Food of the gods (8)
13 Hair-cleansing preparations (8)
16 ___ Currie: former politician (6)
18 Small metal spike (4)
19 Small pond (4)

Puzzle 125

Across

1 Small branches (5)
4 Glisten (5)
10 Having an obscure meaning (7)
11 Eg copper or calcium (5)
12 Less than average tide (4)
13 Intentionally hidden (8)
16 Brushes (6)
17 Stopped (6)
20 Unchangeable; certain (4,4)
21 Prod (anag) (4)
23 Short bolt or pin (5)
25 Data input device (7)
26 Work of fiction (5)
27 Effluent system (5)

Down

2 Travellers (9)
3 Movable barrier (4)
5 Battered (8)
6 Louse egg (3)
7 Perfumes (6)
8 Skin on top of the head (5)
9 Smudge (4)
14 Indemnity (9)
15 Sliver of wood (8)
18 Leave (6)
19 ___ Way: famous Roman road (5)
20 Suppress (4)
22 Pottery (4)
24 Vessel (3)

Puzzle 126

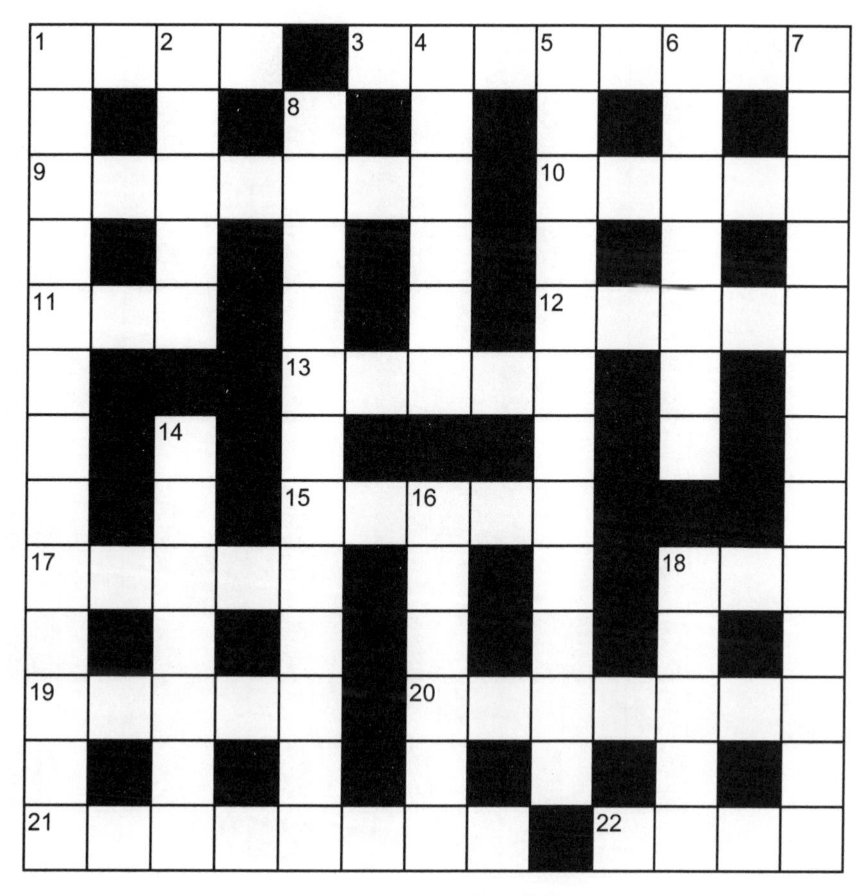

Across

1 Alcoholic drink (4)
3 Sues arms (anag) (8)
9 Rise into the air (of an aircraft) (4,3)
10 Coral reef (5)
11 Mountain pass (3)
12 Open up (5)
13 Titles (5)
15 Enthusiasm (5)
17 Small room used as a steam bath (5)
18 Insect that can sting (3)
19 Implant (5)
20 Mountain in the Himalayas (7)
21 Tubes for ejecting liquids (8)
22 Dairy product (4)

Down

1 Spite (13)
2 Dreadful (5)
4 State publicly (6)
5 Marksman (12)
6 Idealistic (7)
7 Obviously (4-9)
8 Popular district in London (6,6)
14 Sleep (7)
16 Ball-shaped object (6)
18 Large tree (5)

Puzzle 127

Across

1 Equine sounds (6)
5 Treelike grass (6)
8 Pose (anag) (4)
9 Unbarred (8)
10 Deliberate; cogitate (5)
11 Addresses boldly (7)
14 Not fully valued (13)
16 Assign (7)
18 Stage items (5)
20 Dawn (8)
22 Hoodwink (4)
23 Glasses contain these (6)
24 Freshest (6)

Down

2 Massive land mammals (9)
3 Adult (5-2)
4 Poor city district (4)
5 Device that regulates water flow (8)
6 Piece of code to automate a task (5)
7 Single in number (3)
12 Actors (9)
13 Difficulties (8)
15 Farnborough ___ : famous flying display (7)
17 Loose outer garments (5)
19 Of similar character (4)
21 Wonder (3)

Crossword

Puzzle 128

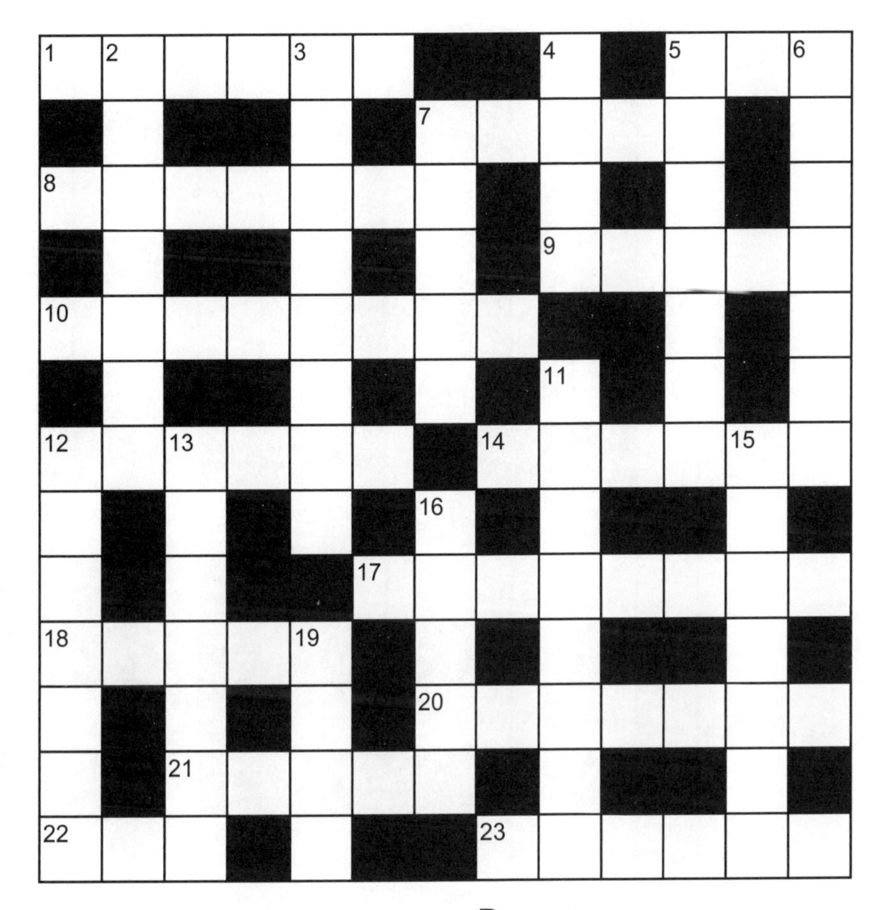

Across

1 Half-conscious state (6)
5 Water barrier (3)
7 A pair of something (5)
8 Type of conference (7)
9 Expansive (5)
10 Cheapest berth on a ship (8)
12 Being with organic and cybernetic parts (6)
14 Address a person boldly (6)
17 Make more attractive (8)
18 Meal (5)
20 Pledged to marry (7)
21 Opposite of lower (5)
22 Acquire (3)
23 Strange thing (6)

Down

2 Act of going back in (2-5)
3 Opposite in meaning (8)
4 Mob (4)
5 Actually; in reality (2,5)
6 Biting (7)
7 Melvyn ___ : British broadcaster (5)
11 Whipped (8)
12 Travelling by bike (7)
13 Mental collapse (7)
15 Least hard (7)
16 Not at all (5)
19 Wish for (4)

Puzzle 129

Across

1 Goes before (8)
5 Endure; animal (4)
8 Attractively stylish (5)
9 Stuffing (7)
10 Reconstruct (7)
12 Eg kings and queens (7)
14 Fulfil a desire (7)
16 Decipher (7)
18 Bring a law into effect again (2-5)
19 Celestial body (5)
20 Go out with (4)
21 Able to adjust (8)

Down

1 Nips (anag) (4)
2 Representation of a person (6)
3 The origin of a word (9)
4 End of the period when something is valid (6)
6 Magical potion (6)
7 Lack of flexibility (8)
11 Yellow flower (9)
12 Provided a service (8)
13 Consent to receive (6)
14 Specified (6)
15 Norway lobsters (6)
17 Inflammation of an eyelid (4)

Puzzle 130

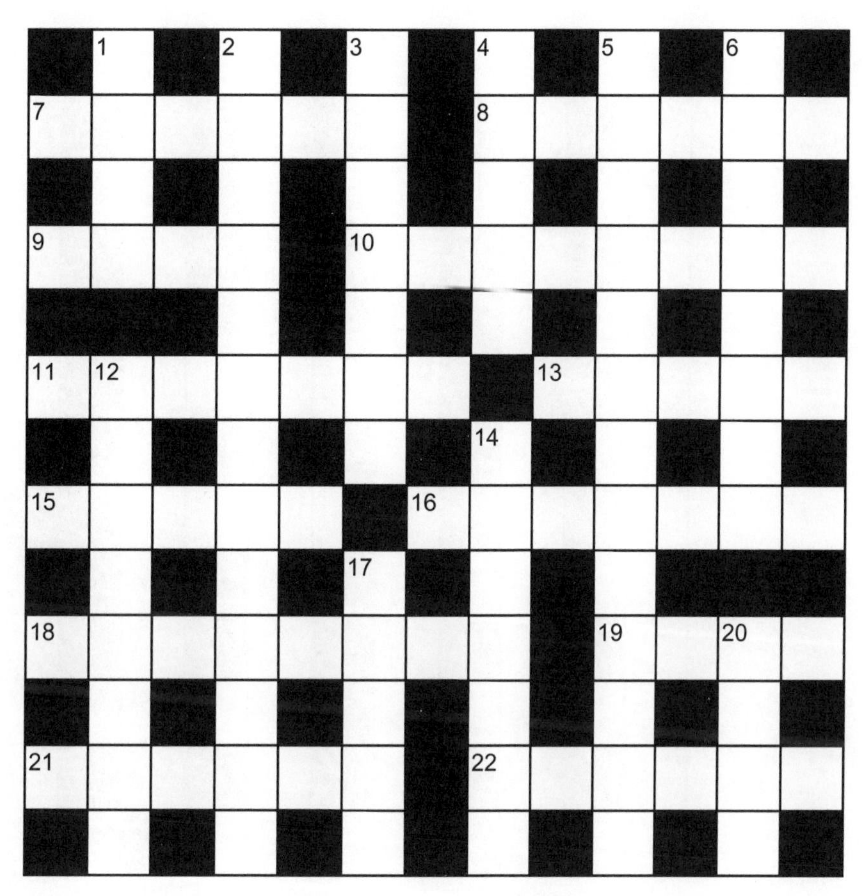

Across

7 Plump (6)
8 Soup flavour (6)
9 Bond movie (2,2)
10 Precedence in rank (8)
11 Reduce the price of (7)
13 Element with atomic number 5 (5)
15 Small particle (5)
16 Man-made fibre (7)
18 Leonardo ___ : US actor (8)
19 Wild mountain goat (4)
21 Chap (6)
22 Absence of passion or interest (6)

Down

1 Male hog (4)
2 In a reflex manner (13)
3 Modified (7)
4 Invigorating medicine (5)
5 Lacking originality (13)
6 Brilliant performers (8)
12 Women noted for great courage (8)
14 Learned person (7)
17 Headdress of a monarch (5)
20 Sound reflection (4)

Puzzle 131

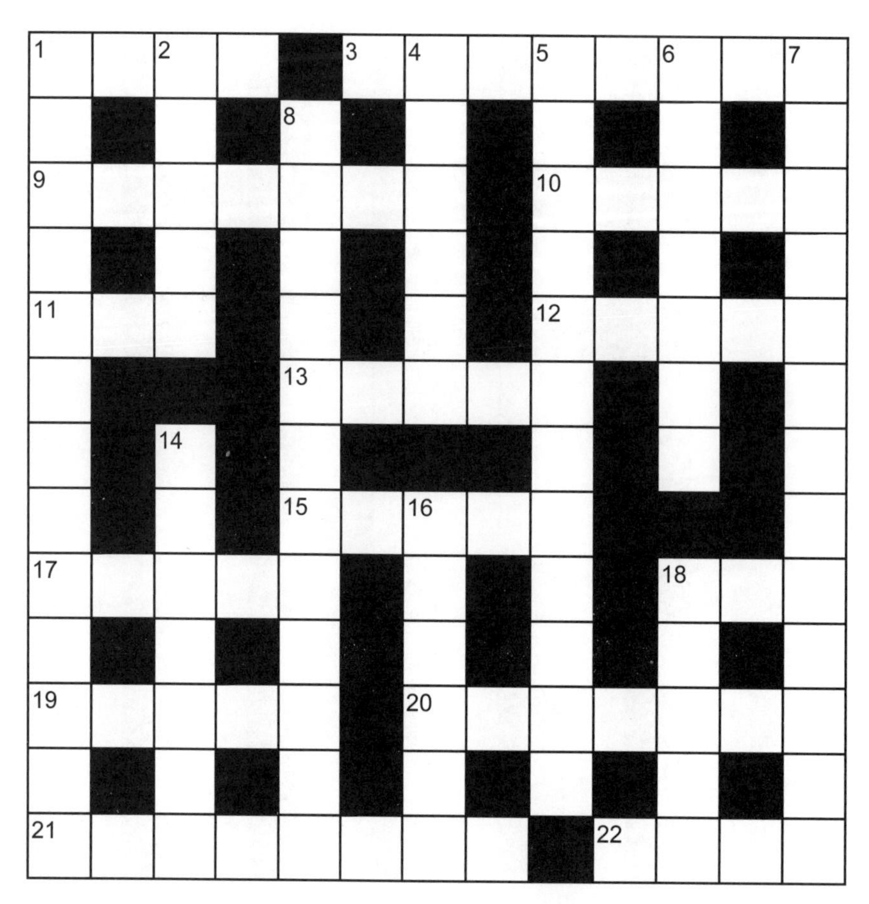

Across

1 Snooker players use these (4)
3 Excited or annoyed (8)
9 Remove an obstruction (7)
10 Explosive devices (5)
11 Pull a vehicle (3)
12 Edward ___ : composer (5)
13 External (5)
15 Part of the human body (5)
17 Conical tent (5)
18 21st Greek letter (3)
19 Pertaining to the ear (5)
20 Nightdress (7)
21 Square scarf worn over the head (8)
22 Repudiate (4)

Down

1 Respond aggressively to military action (7-6)
2 Arm joint (5)
4 Racing vehicle (2-4)
5 Erase trumpet (anag) (12)
6 This evening (7)
7 Devastatingly (13)
8 A grouping of states (12)
14 Tallest species of penguin (7)
16 Frozen water spear (6)
18 Cost (5)

Crossword

Puzzle 132

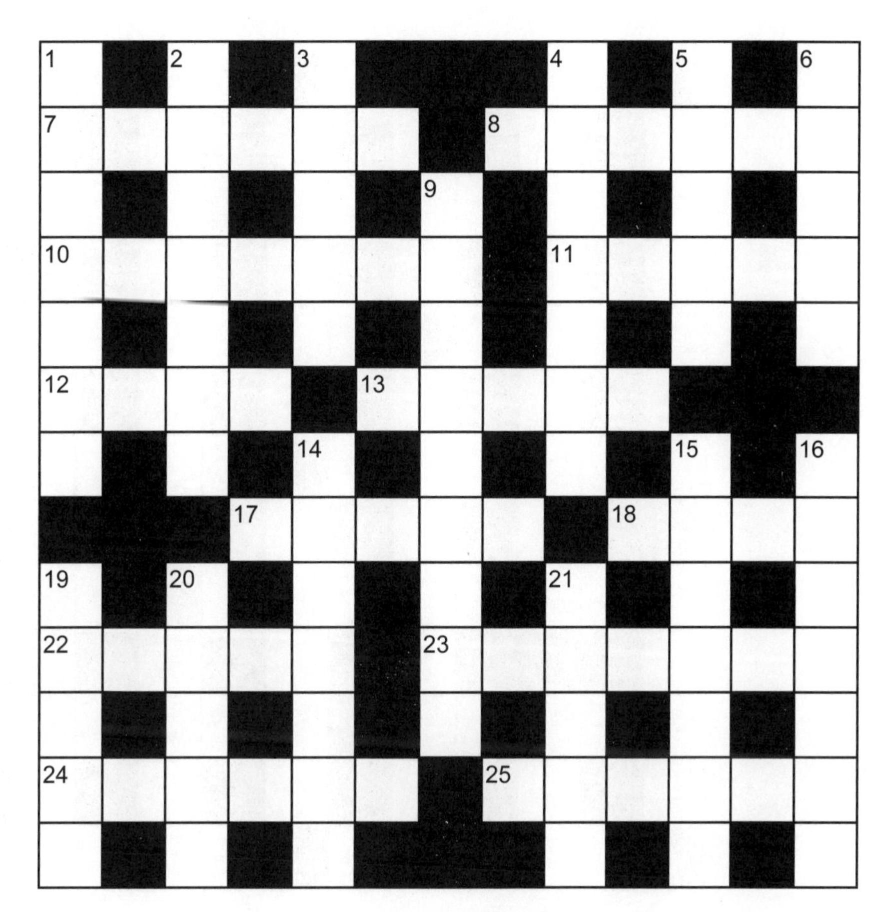

Across

7 Child of your aunt or uncle (6)
8 ___ Williams: tennis star (6)
10 Water container (7)
11 Bird sound (5)
12 Repeat an action (4)
13 Aromatic spice (5)
17 Makes a garment from wool (5)
18 ___ Moore: Hollywood actress (4)
22 ___ Dushku: actress (5)
23 Reverberating (7)
24 Deep pit (6)
25 Synopsis; diagram (6)

Down

1 ___ lettuce: salad vegetable (7)
2 Imprisonment (7)
3 Reverence for God (5)
4 Jovially celebratory (7)
5 Beets (anag) (5)
6 Type of coffee (5)
9 Talents (9)
14 Early childhood (7)
15 Lives in (7)
16 Fabric (7)
19 SI unit of frequency (5)
20 Less narrow (5)
21 Verify (5)

Puzzle 133

Across

1 Small rounded cake (5)
4 Juicy fruit (5)
10 African country (7)
11 Simpleton (5)
12 Eurasian crow (4)
13 Discard; abandon (8)
16 Obtain by coercion (6)
17 Increased rapidly (6)
20 People who shape horseshoes (8)
21 Loot (4)
23 Small woodland (5)
25 Apprehensive (7)
26 Copper and zinc alloy (5)
27 Grin (5)

Down

2 Baby's dummy (9)
3 Pen points (4)
5 Arithmetic operation (8)
6 Trap; ensnare (3)
7 False (6)
8 Oscillations in water (5)
9 Plant with fronds (4)
14 Casual survey of opinion (5,4)
15 Coaches (8)
18 Process food (6)
19 Guttural sound made by a pig (5)
20 True information (4)
22 Harsh and miserable (4)
24 For each (3)

Puzzle 134

Across

1 Put an end to (6)
5 Reason for doing something (6)
8 Fish (4)
9 Channels of the nose (8)
10 Rigid (5)
11 Speak very quietly (7)
14 Warily; cautiously (13)
16 Into parts (7)
18 Lump or bump (5)
20 Fighter in close combat (8)
22 Oodles (4)
23 Moved back and forth (6)
24 Working steadily with a tool (6)

Down

2 Eg India and Spain (9)
3 Movement of vehicles en masse (7)
4 Suggestion or tip (4)
5 Emphasis (anag) (8)
6 Small lakes (5)
7 ___ Kilmer: famous actor (3)
12 Illuminate (9)
13 Driven to action (8)
15 Brutality (7)
17 Beastly (5)
19 Support (4)
21 Uncooked (of meat) (3)

Puzzle 135

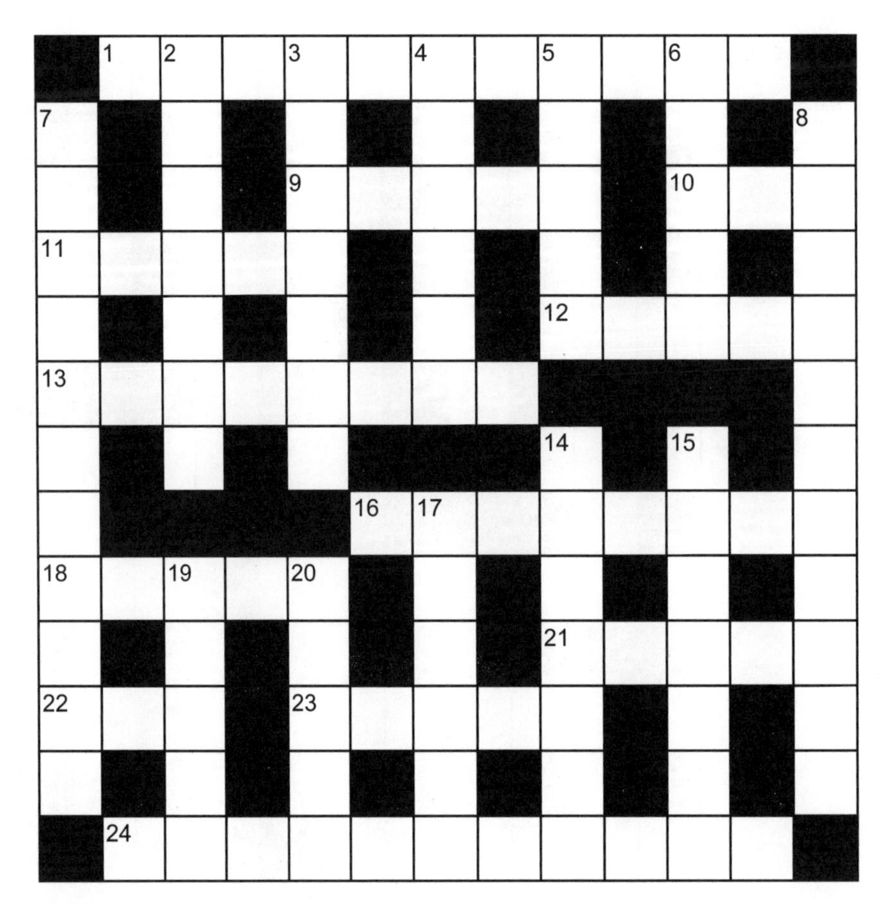

Across

1 Byword for the British Press (5,6)
9 Paula ___ : US singer (5)
10 Asp (anag) (3)
11 Raised areas of land (5)
12 Vault under a church (5)
13 Person who sees something (8)
16 Small pieces of coloured paper (8)
18 Neck warmer (5)
21 Assumed proposition (5)
22 Muhammad ___ : boxer (3)
23 Spore-producing organisms (5)
24 Official bodies (11)

Down

2 Anarchic (7)
3 These remove pencil marks (7)
4 Seat on the back of a horse (6)
5 Ancient object (5)
6 Try (5)
7 Substance that arouses desire (11)
8 Take part in (11)
14 Upset; affect (7)
15 Walk unsteadily (7)
17 Batsman who starts an innings (6)
19 Word of farewell (5)
20 ___ Avenue: NY shopping thoroughfare (5)

Crossword

Puzzle 136

Across

1 Defer (8)
5 Volcano in Sicily (4)
8 Whim or caprice; find attractive (5)
9 Meddles with (7)
10 Boats (7)
12 Stiff and formal (7)
14 Ionised gases (7)
16 Predatory fish (7)
18 Japanese flower arranging (7)
19 Old-fashioned (5)
20 The Orient (4)
21 Nobel ___ : winner of a Nobel Prize (8)

Down

1 Light blast of wind (4)
2 Spanish title for a married woman (6)
3 Medical practitioner (9)
4 Inform (6)
6 Long essay (6)
7 Judges (8)
11 Quantity that is left over (9)
12 Blue precious stone (8)
13 Putting lawns in golf (6)
14 Country in Central America (6)
15 Sacred phrase (6)
17 Axelike tool (4)

Puzzle 137

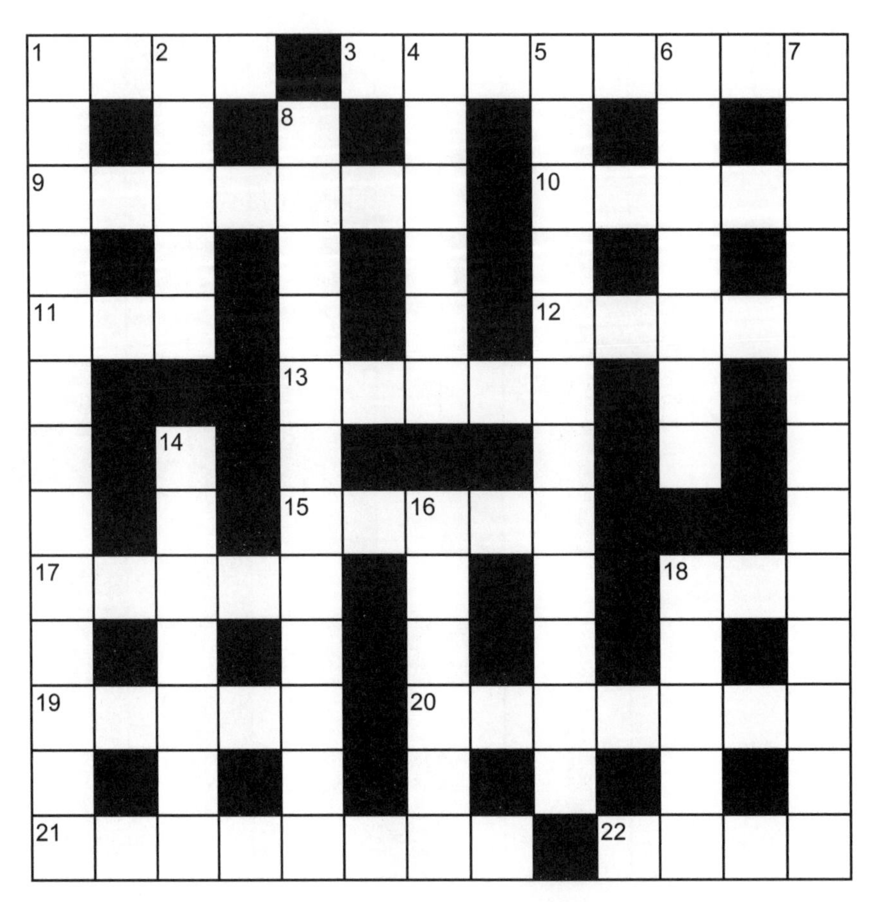

Across

1 River sediment (4)
3 Search for minerals (8)
9 Responses (7)
10 Insect grub (5)
11 Magic spell (3)
12 Parts of the cerebrum (5)
13 Speed (5)
15 Sprites (5)
17 The entire scale (5)
18 Small numbered cube (3)
19 Indifferent to emotions (5)
20 Pompous person (7)
21 Extreme form of scepticism (8)
22 Disgust with an excess of sweetness (4)

Down

1 The Duchess of York (5,8)
2 Milky fluid found in some plants (5)
4 Hurries (6)
5 Altruism (12)
6 Dressed in a vestment (7)
7 Party lanterns (anag) (13)
8 Relating to numeric calculations (12)
14 Large extinct elephant (7)
16 Principles (6)
18 Speak in a slow manner (5)

Crossword

Puzzle 138

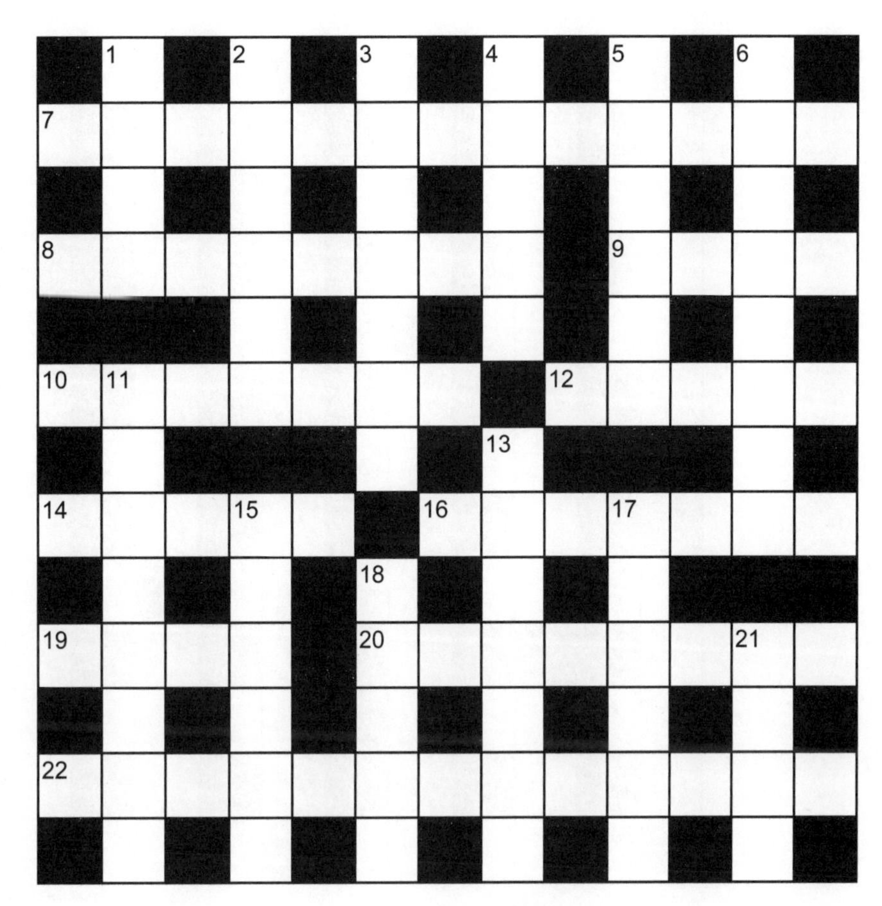

Across

7 Unfeasible (13)
8 Mentally sharp (8)
9 ___ Friel: English actress (4)
10 Mislead on purpose (7)
12 Take part in combat (5)
14 Garden buildings (5)
16 Confirms a decision; supports (7)
19 Stone block (4)
20 Restrict to a particular place (8)
22 Assemblage (13)

Down

1 Supermodel married to David Bowie (4)
2 Bearlike (6)
3 Accomplish (7)
4 Totally erases (5)
5 US state of islands (6)
6 Drained the colour from (8)
11 Study of animal behaviour (8)
13 Carpets (anag) (7)
15 Make a hole (6)
17 Flattened at the poles (6)
18 Ascend (5)
21 Black powdery substance (4)

Puzzle 139

Across

1 Long-necked birds (5)
4 Bodies of water (5)
10 Customs of a society (7)
11 Alcoholic beverage (5)
12 Engrossed (4)
13 Walks unsteadily (8)
16 Wood cutter (6)
17 ___ mundum: defying everyone (6)
20 Cross-bred dogs (8)
21 Central (4)
23 From the capital of Italy (5)
25 Scrawny (7)
26 Pile (5)
27 Empty area; gap (5)

Down

2 Self-control (9)
3 Common sense (4)
5 Rare (8)
6 Nourished (3)
7 Multiples of twenty (6)
8 Nuisances (5)
9 Undergarments (4)
14 Lacking energy (9)
15 Person who repairs cars (8)
18 Grates on (6)
19 Very unpleasant (5)
20 Old Italian currency (pl) (4)
22 Journey (4)
24 Floor covering (3)

Crossword

Puzzle 140

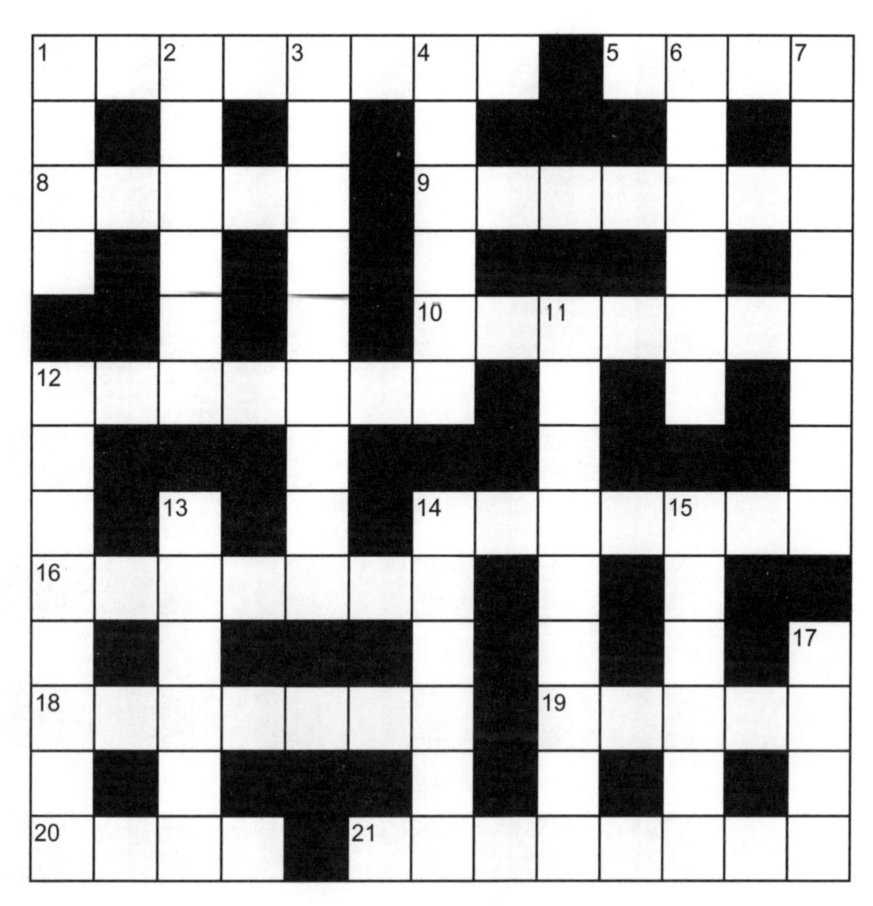

Across

1 Covering in paper (8)
5 Loop of cloth worn around the waist (4)
8 Stylish (5)
9 Drinking glass (7)
10 Small community (7)
12 A dancer or singer (7)
14 Harden (7)
16 Preventing success; unfavourable (7)
18 Non-specific (7)
19 With speed (5)
20 Rode (anag) (4)
21 Magnificent (8)

Down

1 One's customary behaviour (4)
2 Bear witness (6)
3 Person who distributes wages (9)
4 Indigenous (6)
6 Not sinking (6)
7 Male riders (8)
11 Convert into cash (of assets) (9)
12 Put in order (8)
13 ___ Q: musical (6)
14 Drinking vessel (6)
15 Something causing peril (6)
17 Unwanted wild plant (4)

Puzzle 141

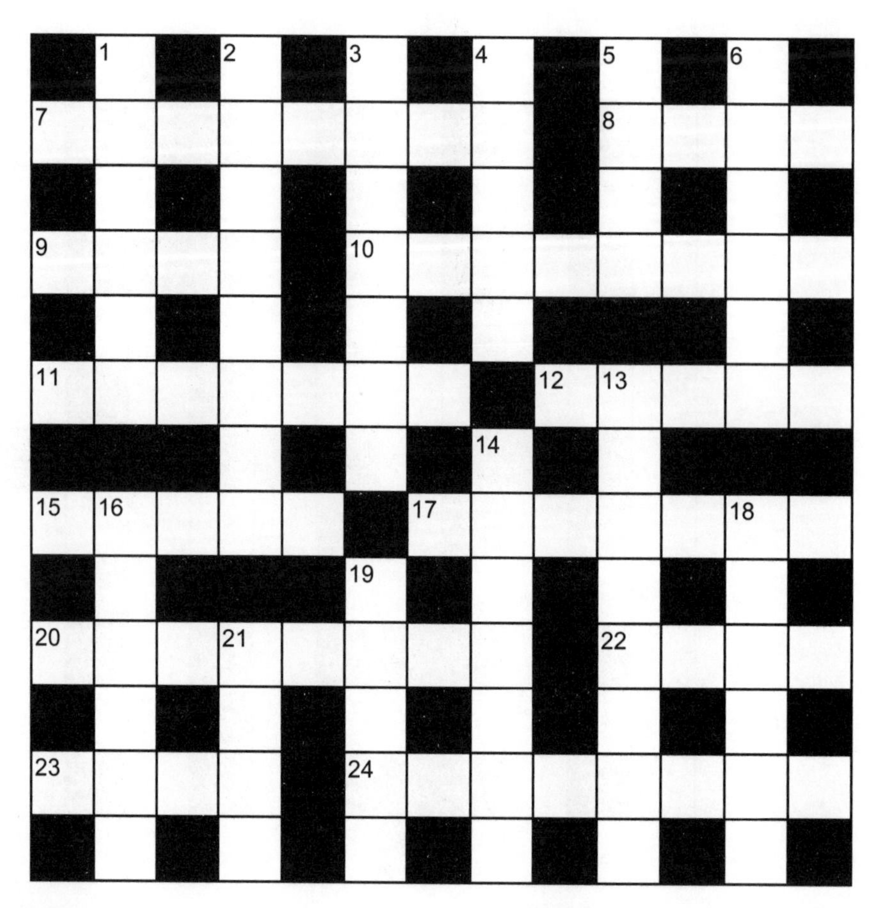

Across

7 Elastic (8)
8 Greasy (4)
9 Sheet of floating ice (4)
10 Hating (8)
11 Confusing (7)
12 Isle of ___ : island near Southampton (5)
15 Frumpy (5)
17 Distribute illicitly (7)
20 Filled with air (8)
22 True and actual (4)
23 Percussion instrument (4)
24 Changeable (8)

Down

1 Unemotional (6)
2 Made uniform (8)
3 Triangle with three unequal sides (7)
4 Bob ___ : US singer (5)
5 Tease (4)
6 Close tightly (6)
13 Break in activity (8)
14 Very fine substances (7)
16 Possessors (6)
18 Make possible (6)
19 Kitchen appliance (5)
21 Type of light (4)

Puzzle 142

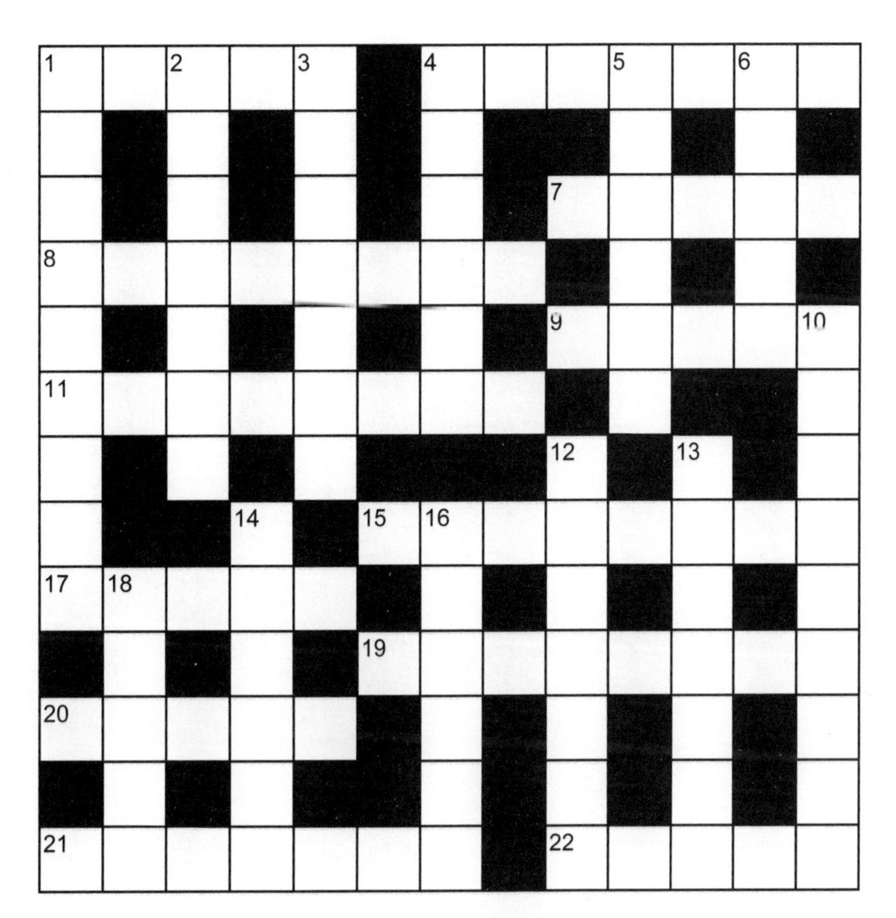

Across

1 ___ Witherspoon: actress (5)
4 Avoidance (7)
7 Knocks loudly (5)
8 Loan against a house (8)
9 Converses casually (5)
11 Without warning (8)
15 Universal in extent (8)
17 Run away with a lover (5)
19 Greek dish (8)
20 Climbing shrubs (5)
21 Smiled broadly (7)
22 Hank of wool (5)

Down

1 Refund (9)
2 Endless (7)
3 Mournful (7)
4 Regime (anag) (6)
5 Attack with severe criticism (6)
6 Should (5)
10 Artificial sweetener (9)
12 Science of matter and energy (7)
13 Rid of something unpleasant (7)
14 Abdominal organ (6)
16 On a ship or train (6)
18 Crowbar (5)

Puzzle 143

Across

1 Capture a piece in chess (4)
3 Pertaining to the body (8)
9 Root vegetable (7)
10 ___ Willis: daughter of Demi Moore (5)
11 Careful management of the environment (12)
14 Lay seed in the ground (3)
16 Holding or grasping device (5)
17 19th Greek letter (3)
18 Reckless; ready to react violently (7-5)
21 Big (5)
22 Sad and abandoned (7)
23 Preserve or hold sacred (8)
24 Ruse (4)

Down

1 Always in a similar role (of an actor) (8)
2 Donna ___ New York: clothing label (5)
4 Leap on one foot (3)
5 Atmospheric layer (12)
6 Behave well (7)
7 Edible fat (4)
8 Detective (12)
12 ___ Cable: Liberal Democrat politician (5)
13 Ability to float (8)
15 Labourers (7)
19 Go about stealthily (5)
20 Look at amorously (4)
22 Enjoyable (3)

Crossword

Puzzle 144

Across

1 Disturb (8)
5 Spread clumsily on a surface (4)
8 Less moist (5)
9 Cherubic (7)
10 Extensive domains (7)
12 Repositories of antiques (7)
14 Person who keeps watch (7)
16 Friendly understanding (7)
18 Conquer by force (7)
19 Coldly (5)
20 ___ Turner: US singer (4)
21 Extremely compatible partner (8)

Down

1 Unravel (4)
2 Sets of rooms (6)
3 Heavy-duty waterproof cloth (9)
4 Departs (6)
6 Entice or attract (6)
7 Chair at the rear of a vehicle (4,4)
11 Narrow-minded (9)
12 Distance marker in a race (8)
13 Scattered about (6)
14 Rough shelter (4-2)
15 Top aim (anag) (6)
17 Sort (4)

Puzzle 145

Across

1 Stare with an open mouth (4)
3 Bridge above another road (8)
9 Swells (7)
10 Wrong (5)
11 Discourage (5)
12 Give reasons for (7)
13 Naive and superficial (6)
15 Mineral of lead sulphide (6)
17 Type of scientist (7)
18 Main artery (5)
20 Derogatory in an indirect way (5)
21 Eg shrimp or crab (7)
22 Denial of something (8)
23 ___ Giggs: football star (4)

Down

1 British actress who became an MP (6,7)
2 Songbird (5)
4 ___ Lynd: character in Casino Royale (6)
5 Re-emergence (12)
6 Bring to life (7)
7 Thelma & Louise actress (5,8)
8 Inflexible (12)
14 Taunting; mocking (7)
16 Workroom of a painter (6)
19 Make good on a debt (5)

Crossword

Puzzle 146

Across
- **1** Emerge from an egg (5)
- **4** Snug and nice to wear (5)
- **10** Eyelash cosmetic (7)
- **11** Smooth cream of vegetables (5)
- **12** Roald ___ : author (4)
- **13** Ate (8)
- **16** Irritable (6)
- **17** Large pebbles (6)
- **20** Seemly (8)
- **21** Head of a university faculty (4)
- **23** Narrow roads (5)
- **25** Prospered (7)
- **26** Small marine fish (5)
- **27** Thick woollen fabric (5)

Down
- **2** Concerned with beauty (9)
- **3** Persuade gently (4)
- **5** Facing (8)
- **6** Soft animal hair (3)
- **7** Among (6)
- **8** Army rank (5)
- **9** Curve in a road (4)
- **14** Movement requiring skill and care (9)
- **15** Personal magnetism (8)
- **18** Church councils (6)
- **19** Tarnished (of a metal object) (5)
- **20** Valley (4)
- **22** Ward (anag) (4)
- **24** Quick sleep (3)

Puzzle 147

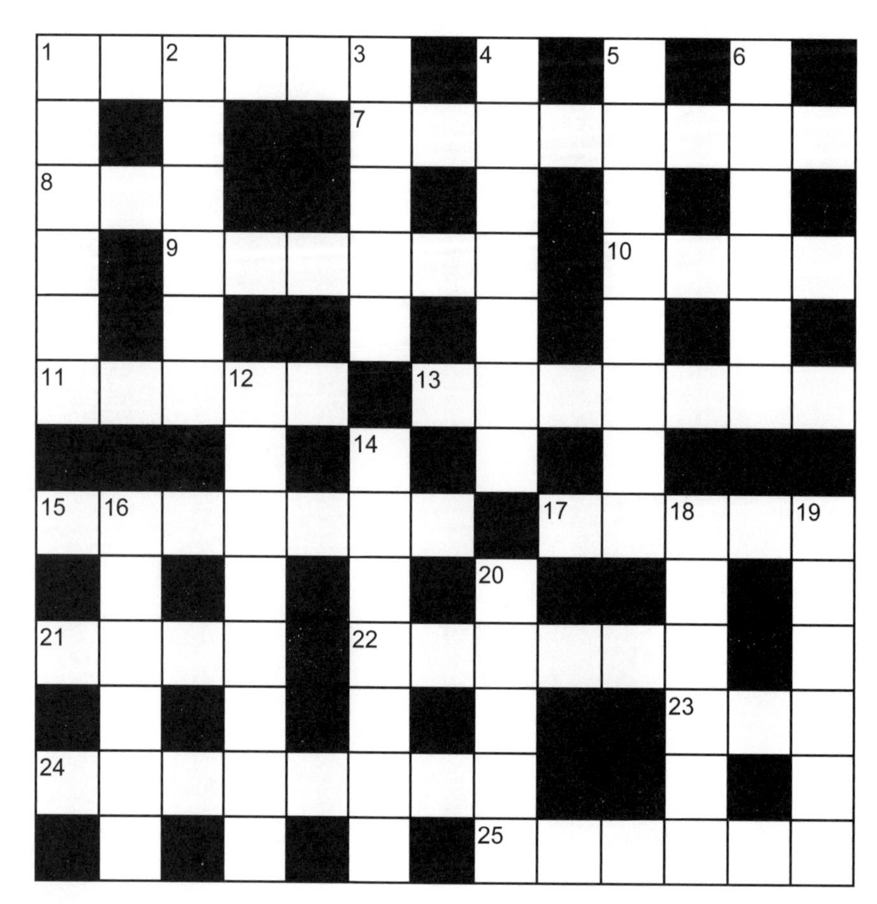

Across

1 Composite of different species (6)
7 Accepted (8)
8 Lubricate (3)
9 Cosmetic cream (6)
10 Elephant tooth (4)
11 Iffy (5)
13 Unaccompanied musician (7)
15 Practising self-denial (7)
17 Male aristocrat (5)
21 Public transport vehicle (4)
22 Horn (6)
23 Perceive (3)
24 Final performance (8)
25 Consuming food (6)

Down

1 Aquiline (6)
2 Simple song (6)
3 Celtic priest (5)
4 John ___ : former US tennis star (7)
5 Person highly skilled in music (8)
6 Wild animals (6)
12 Shining (8)
14 Coward (7)
16 Small fasteners (6)
18 Dwarfed tree (6)
19 Stefan ___ : Swedish tennis player (6)
20 Huge (5)

Crossword

Puzzle 148

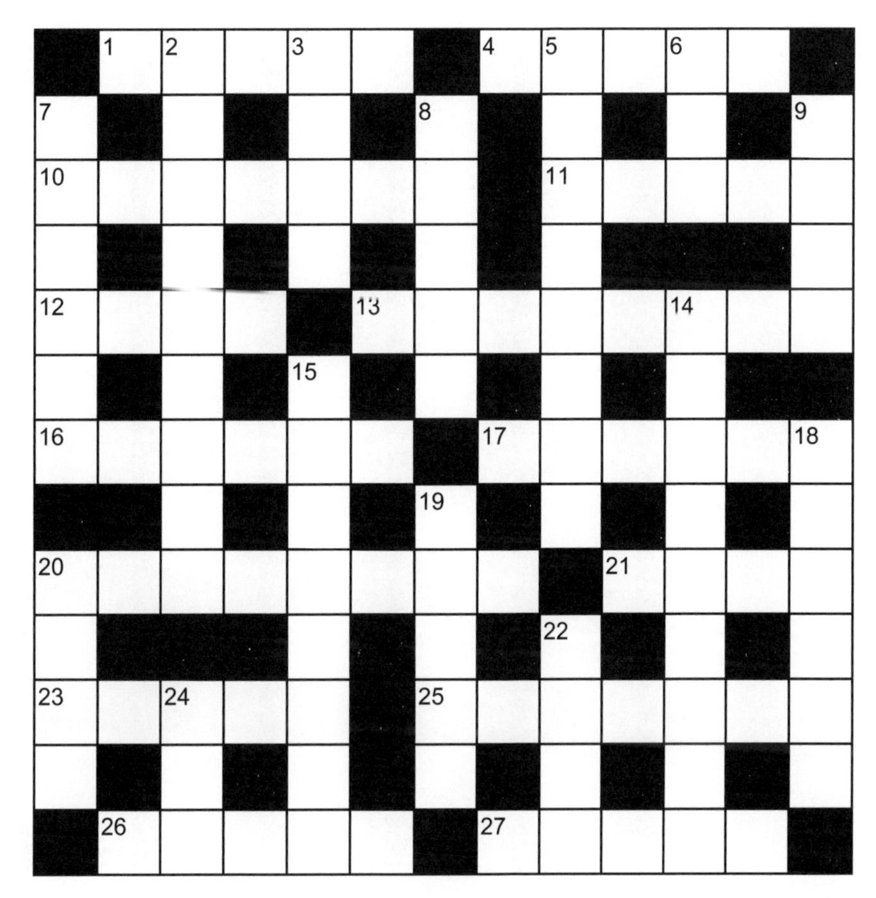

Across

1 Giddy (5)
4 Keep (5)
10 Thoroughly (2,5)
11 ___ Federer: tennis star (5)
12 Willing to do something (4)
13 Lowered one's body (8)
16 This Is ___ Tap: film (6)
17 Chase (6)
20 Forceful blow (8)
21 Secure a boat (4)
23 Unsteady (5)
25 Travelling very quickly (7)
26 Clean with a brush (5)
27 Silly trick (5)

Down

2 Security against a loss (9)
3 Coat fastening devices (4)
5 Full of twists and turns (8)
6 Floor mat (3)
7 Military blockades (6)
8 Horse (anag) (5)
9 Walked or stepped (4)
14 Person who studies the past (9)
15 Accelerate a reaction (8)
18 Infuriate (6)
19 Take hold of (5)
20 Solid (4)
22 Decant (4)
24 Domestic bovine animal (3)

Puzzle 149

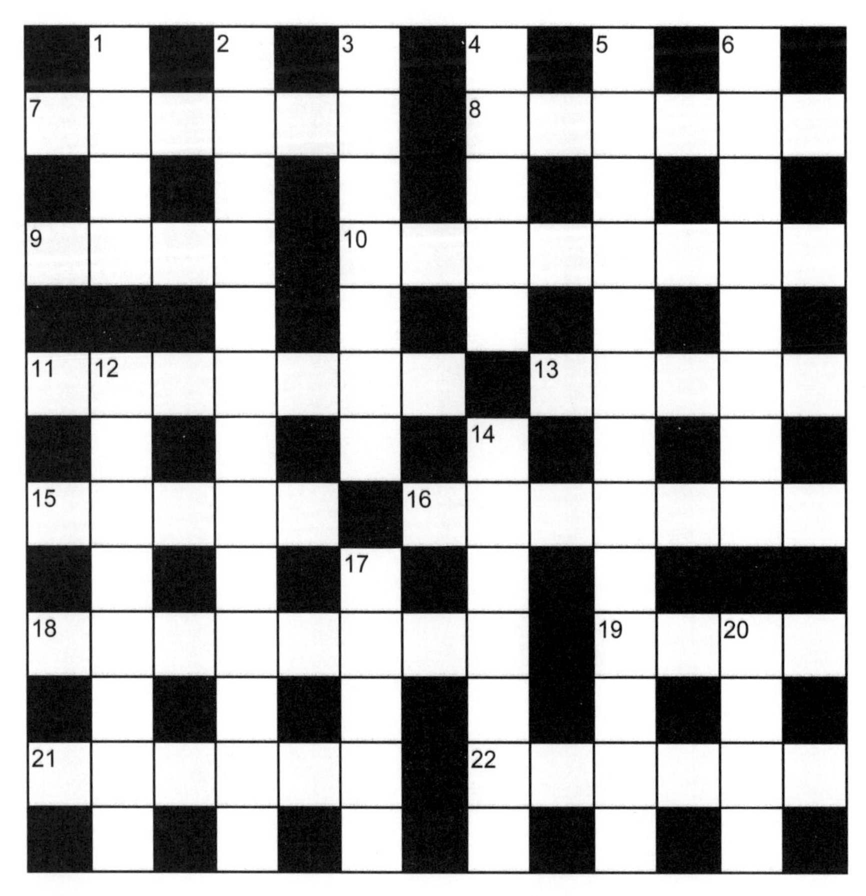

Across

7 Living things (6)
8 Underling of a powerful person (6)
9 ___ Amos: US singer-songwriter (4)
10 Graceful (of movement) (8)
11 Agrees (7)
13 Epsom horse race (5)
15 Halts (5)
16 Move like a snake (7)
18 Husband of one's daughter (3-2-3)
19 Require (4)
21 Return to a former condition (6)
22 Experience again (6)

Down

1 Nothing (4)
2 Lacking in control (13)
3 Lines of equal pressure on maps (7)
4 State indirectly (5)
5 Fascinatingly (13)
6 Companionable (8)
12 Antique; obsolete (8)
14 Scowls (7)
17 Polish monetary unit (5)
20 Feeling of resentment or jealousy (4)

Crossword

Puzzle 150

Across

1 Pierre-Auguste ___ : French artist (6)
4 Limp (6)
9 Type of porch (7)
10 Unfurls (7)
11 Kingdom (5)
12 Programmer (5)
14 Muscular tissue (5)
15 About (5)
17 Not tight (5)
18 Slips something inside (7)
20 Molecules that bind to others (7)
21 Cease (6)
22 Greatly respect (6)

Down

1 Written document (6)
2 One who tells a story (8)
3 Phrase that is not taken literally (5)
5 Large flightless bird (7)
6 Ian ___ : England cricketer (4)
7 Pencil rubber (6)
8 Politely (11)
13 Condemn publicly (8)
14 Small imaginary beings (7)
15 Curled or wound (6)
16 Wreckage washed ashore (6)
17 Company emblems (5)
19 Drains of energy (4)

Puzzle 151

Across

1 Person who goes on long walks (5)
4 Moves at great speed (7)
7 Misty (5)
8 Merciless (8)
9 Thorax (5)
11 Grow longer (8)
15 Tonic (4-2-2)
17 Urges on (5)
19 Loyal and hard-working (8)
20 Draws into the mouth (5)
21 Unintelligent (7)
22 Avoid (5)

Down

1 Timing device (9)
2 Young cats (7)
3 The world as it is (7)
4 Notable inconvenience (6)
5 Award (6)
6 Borders (5)
10 Wicked behaviour (9)
12 Visible horizon (7)
13 Porch (7)
14 Mythical sea monster (6)
16 Chant; speak solemnly (6)
18 Purple fruits (5)

Crossword

Puzzle 152

Across

7 Joke-telling entertainer (8)
8 Greek god of war (4)
9 Unorthodox religion or sect (4)
10 Intrusive (8)
11 One of the archangels (7)
12 Damien ___ : modern English artist (5)
15 Climb (5)
17 Novelty (7)
20 Lasting longer than required (5-3)
22 Pleasant (4)
23 Dam (4)
24 Predict the future (8)

Down

1 Czech monetary unit (6)
2 Pertaining to the chest (8)
3 Separates into parts (7)
4 Rogue; scoundrel (5)
5 Soak (anag) (4)
6 Gives out food (6)
13 Exemption (8)
14 Giggles (7)
16 Part of a flower (6)
18 Laugh in a harsh way (6)
19 Foolish (5)
21 Watchful (4)

Puzzle 153

Across

1 In a lazy way (4)
3 Unequal; biased (3-5)
9 Numbs (7)
10 Underside of a projecting roof (5)
11 Area of open land (5)
12 Having sharp corners (7)
13 Calamitous (6)
15 Imminent danger (6)
17 Welcomed (7)
18 Saying (5)
20 ___ Midler: American comedienne (5)
21 Resistance to change (7)
22 Letting off (8)
23 Depend on (4)

Down

1 Untiring (13)
2 Let (5)
4 Capital of the Bahamas (6)
5 Heavy long-handled tool (12)
6 Share information (7)
7 Carry editions (anag) (13)
8 Presiding female officer of a school (12)
14 Sterile (7)
16 ___ Brody: actor in The Pianist (6)
19 Levy (5)

Crossword

Puzzle 154

Across

1 Opposite of least (4)
3 ___ Islands: country in the NW Pacific (8)
9 Least fresh (of food) (7)
10 Prevent (5)
11 Difficulty (12)
14 Mock (3)
16 Germaine ___ : Australian author (5)
17 Bruce ___ : martial artist (3)
18 Type of cloud (12)
21 Language of the Romans (5)
22 Correctional institutions (7)
23 Omens (8)
24 Comes together; coheres (4)

Down

1 Eg a trumpeter or pianist (8)
2 Large group of insects (5)
4 Statute (3)
5 Disorganised person (12)
6 Newtlike salamander (7)
7 Covers; tops (4)
8 Hostile aggressiveness (12)
12 Cooks (5)
13 Continues obstinately (8)
15 Termite (anag) (7)
19 Ironic metaphor (5)
20 A brief piece of film (4)
22 Place (3)

Puzzle 155

Across

1 Large farming implement (6)
5 Degenerate (3)
7 Move effortlessly through air (5)
8 Medicated tablet (7)
9 Pools (anag) (5)
10 Capital of Syria (8)
12 Worshipper (6)
14 Abilities (6)
17 Paper printout of data (4,4)
18 Take the place of (5)
20 Skeleton of a motor vehicle (7)
21 Petulant (5)
22 Possesses (3)
23 Amended (6)

Down

2 Large spotted cat (7)
3 Mobster (8)
4 Bird beak (4)
5 Decide firmly (7)
6 Scuffles (7)
7 Biological taxonomic grouping (5)
11 Forest (8)
12 Great suffering (7)
13 Conceals something from view (7)
15 Cold-blooded vertebrate like a crocodile (7)
16 Impertinent; cheeky (5)
19 Position adopted for a photo (4)

Crossword

Puzzle 156

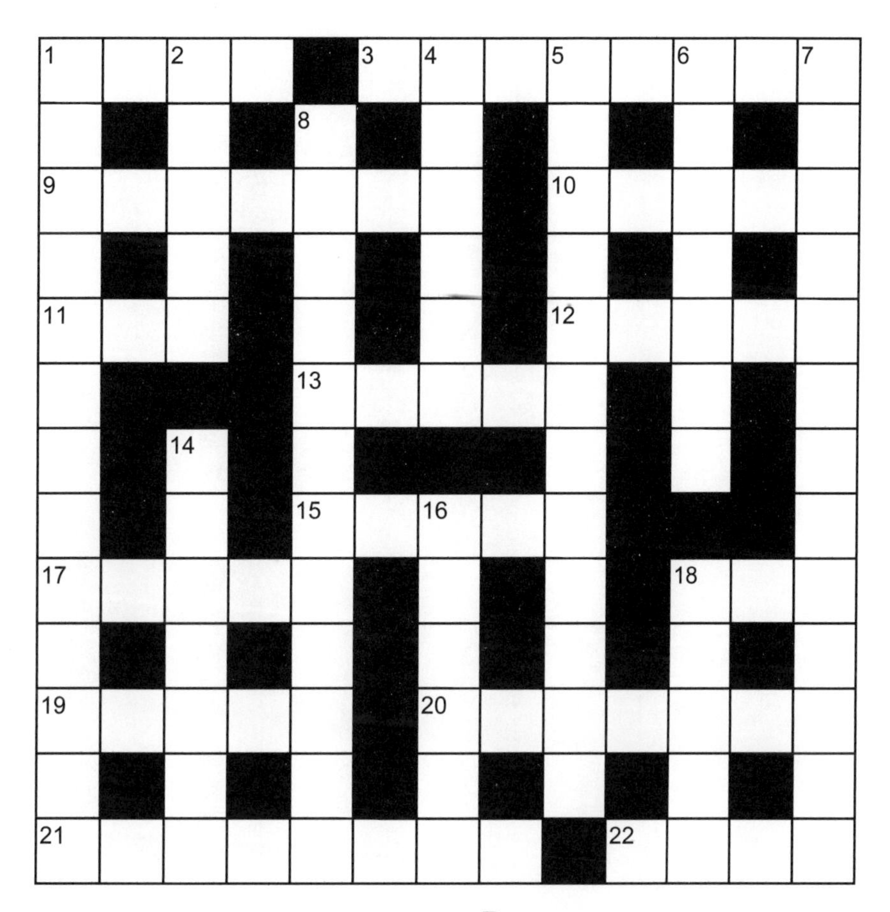

Across

1 Seed containers (4)
3 Creative (8)
9 Refiles (anag) (7)
10 Radio receiver (5)
11 Layer of a folded material (3)
12 Awake (5)
13 Device used to connect to the internet (5)
15 Unbuttoned (5)
17 A central point (5)
18 Disallow (3)
19 Not heavy (5)
20 Framework (7)
21 Co-opted council member (8)
22 Payment to a landlord (4)

Down

1 Miscellaneous equipment (13)
2 Interruption (5)
4 Dared; exposed to danger (6)
5 Coming between two things (12)
6 Shaving of the crown of head (7)
7 Person who writes letters regularly (13)
8 Pram (12)
14 Severely damaged (7)
16 Flowering plant (6)
18 Seawater (5)

Puzzle 157

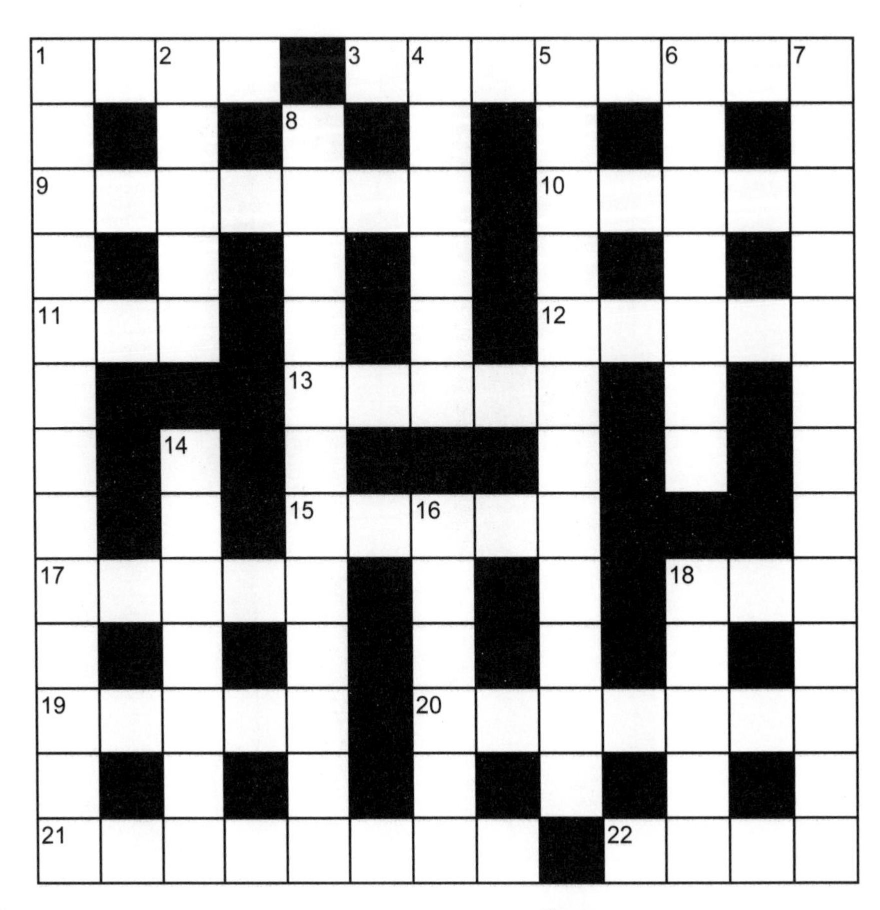

Across

1 Curved (4)
3 Uncertain if God exists (8)
9 A number defining position (7)
10 Cloth woven from flax (5)
11 Former measure of length (3)
12 Outdo (5)
13 Male relation (5)
15 Eyelashes (5)
17 ___ Cooper: US rocker (5)
18 Half of four (3)
19 Sheet (anag) (5)
20 Light periods of rainfall (7)
21 Sketching out (8)
22 Wet with condensation (4)

Down

1 Overwhelmed with sorrow (6-7)
2 Rafael ___ : Spanish tennis star (5)
4 Characteristically French (6)
5 Destruction (12)
6 Particular languages (7)
7 Prominently (13)
8 Formal notice (12)
14 Grotesque monster (7)
16 Make less tight (6)
18 Recurrent topic (5)

Puzzle 158

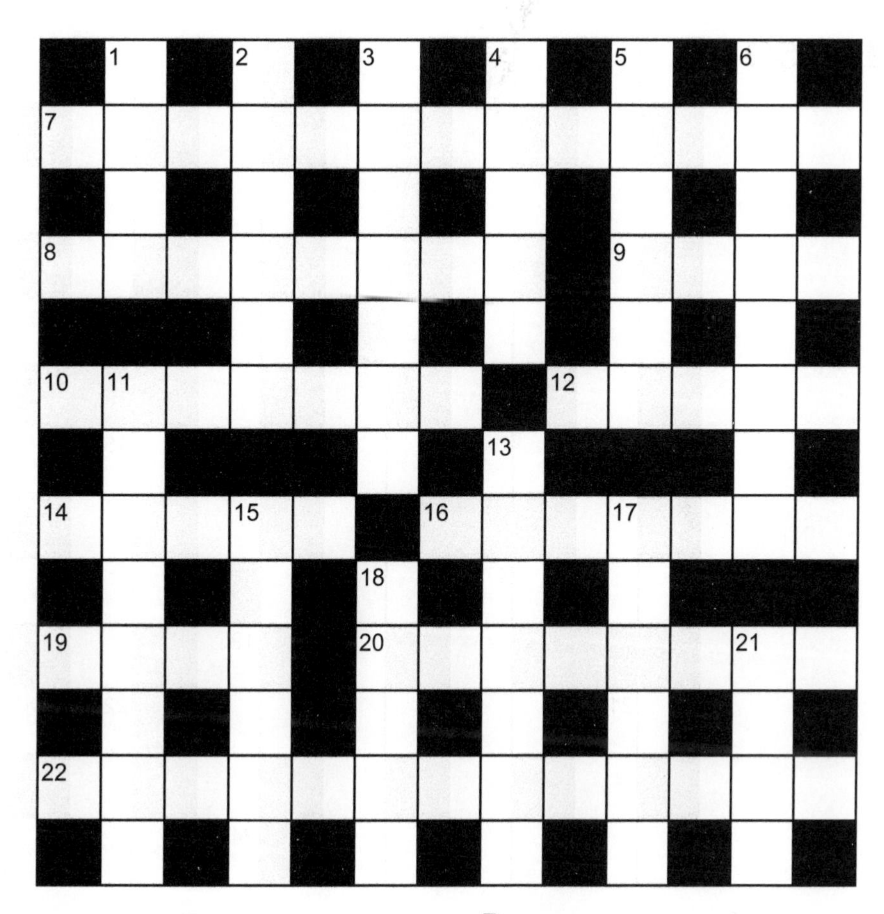

Across

7 An event with good and bad implications (5,8)
8 Large fish (8)
9 Official language of Pakistan (4)
10 Make by mixing ingredients (7)
12 Aromatic plants (5)
14 Muscular (5)
16 Nevertheless (7)
19 Bonus; positive (4)
20 An indirect implication (8)
22 Film (6,7)

Down

1 Core meaning (4)
2 A system of measurement (6)
3 Lack of (7)
4 Blood vessels (5)
5 Take as being true (6)
6 Unfit for consumption (of food) (8)
11 Fail to notice (8)
13 A governing body in a county (7)
15 Remains preserved in rock (6)
17 Votes into office (6)
18 Evil spirit (5)
21 Mend with rows of stitches (4)

Puzzle 159

Across

1 Speaker (6)
5 Film that makes one laugh (6)
8 Acquire (4)
9 Implicated in (8)
10 Ceases trading (5)
11 Engraving (7)
14 Measurable by a common standard (13)
16 Equality of political rights (7)
18 Sully or blemish (5)
20 Unmarried woman (8)
22 Cease (4)
23 Engaged in games (6)
24 Patterns (6)

Down

2 Comparable in some respects (9)
3 Domain (7)
4 Restrain (4)
5 Desirous (8)
6 Mixture that insulates soil (5)
7 Female deer (3)
12 Invalidated (9)
13 Excited; lively (8)
15 Not modern (7)
17 Character in the musical Oliver! (5)
19 A Crown document (4)
21 Friend (3)

Puzzle 160

Across

1 Historical records (6)
5 Sharp chopping implement (3)
7 Elongated cephalopod (5)
8 Got too big for something (7)
9 Reject with disdain (5)
10 Determination; doggedness (8)
12 Coercion (6)
14 Slumbers (6)
17 ___ rose: climbing Chinese rose (8)
18 Republic in the Middle East (5)
20 Enunciate (7)
21 Synthetic fibre (5)
22 Pop music performance (3)
23 Old Portuguese currency (6)

Down

2 Modern; up to date (7)
3 Writer of the words to a song (8)
4 Small shelters (4)
5 Declare to be the case (7)
6 People who make money (7)
7 Hits swiftly (5)
11 Having a striking beauty (8)
12 Declaring to be untrue (7)
13 Wandering (7)
15 Penetrated (7)
16 Shine (5)
19 Invalid; void (4)

Puzzle 161

Across

- **1** Black ___: Colombian bird (4)
- **3** Strong type of coffee (8)
- **9** Fishing boat (7)
- **10** Main (5)
- **11** The protection of a particular person (5)
- **12** In addition to (7)
- **13** Passionate (6)
- **15** Taxonomic groupings (6)
- **17** Small grain (7)
- **18** Lure (5)
- **20** Indentation (5)
- **21** Flog; whip (7)
- **22** Encrypting (8)
- **23** Small ink stain (4)

Down

- **1** Inflexibility (13)
- **2** ___ Bellamy: Welsh footballer (5)
- **4** Person who copies out documents (6)
- **5** Act of reclamation (12)
- **6** Pin in a spinning wheel (7)
- **7** Exaggeration (13)
- **8** Reticent; secretive (12)
- **14** Flexible (7)
- **16** Period of instruction (6)
- **19** Fourth month (5)

Crossword

Puzzle 162

Across

1 11th Greek letter (6)
7 Relating to weather (8)
8 Cup (3)
9 That is to say (6)
10 Small children (4)
11 Ditches (5)
13 Making a loud sound (7)
15 Tenth month (7)
17 ___ Allan Poe: American writer (5)
21 Legendary creature (4)
22 Lump or blob (6)
23 Opposite of cold (3)
24 Pithy saying (8)
25 Penetrate (6)

Down

1 Walked awkwardly (6)
2 Large wine bottle (6)
3 Performed on stage (5)
4 Two-wheeled vehicle (7)
5 Started to lose strength (8)
6 Give one's attention to a sound (6)
12 Qualifications (8)
14 Let in again (7)
16 Weird (6)
18 Burrowing rodent (6)
19 Child's toy (6)
20 Decline sharply (5)

Puzzle 163

Across

1 Assisted (5)
4 Betrays (slang) (7)
7 Music with a recurrent theme (5)
8 Official list of names (8)
9 Furnish with new weapons (5)
11 Rebellious (8)
15 Lays in wait for (8)
17 Lock of hair (5)
19 Comfy seat (8)
20 Mingle with something else (5)
21 Entrap (7)
22 Living thing (5)

Down

1 Flat (9)
2 Brave and persistent (7)
3 Act of finding water (7)
4 Rich cake (6)
5 Taken illegally (6)
6 Senior figure in a tribe (5)
10 Calculating a dimension (9)
12 Give in to temptation (7)
13 Italian red wine (7)
14 Mete out (6)
16 Form of limestone (6)
18 Noble gas (5)

Crossword

Puzzle 164

Across

1 Forever (6)
4 Of the universe (6)
9 Accept to be true (7)
10 Aptitude (7)
11 Judged; ranked (5)
12 ___ MacArthur: sailor (5)
14 Injures (5)
15 Camera image (abbrev) (5)
17 Attractive flower (5)
18 Repeat performances (7)
20 Absolutely incredible (7)
21 Cord (6)
22 Steers (anag) (6)

Down

1 Reddish-brown hair colour (6)
2 Moderately rich (4-2-2)
3 Give up (5)
5 Business establishments (7)
6 The south of France (4)
7 Stick of coloured wax (6)
8 Re-evaluation (11)
13 Legal ambiguity (8)
14 Become husky (7)
15 Small folds in clothing (6)
16 Smiles contemptuously (6)
17 City in West Yorkshire (5)
19 US actress and singer (4)

Puzzle 165

Across

1 Money that is owed (4)
3 Complying with orders (8)
9 Admit to (7)
10 Gardeners sow these (5)
11 Commensurate (12)
13 Coop up (6)
15 Work hard; toil (6)
17 Scolding (8-4)
20 Porcelain (5)
21 Stinted (anag) (7)
22 Dishes that begin a meal (8)
23 Precious stones (4)

Down

1 Interpret the meaning of (8)
2 Game of chance (5)
4 Attacks on all sides (6)
5 Disheartening (12)
6 Green gemstone (7)
7 Throw a coin in the air (4)
8 Medicine taken when blocked-up (12)
12 Newborn children (8)
14 Birthplace of Napoleon (7)
16 Cover for holding sheets of paper together (6)
18 Expect; think that (5)
19 Performs in a play (4)

Crossword

Puzzle 166

Across

7 Scarcity (6)
8 Woman's garment (6)
10 Impure acetic acid (7)
11 View; picture (5)
12 What you hear with (4)
13 Snow house (5)
17 Variety of chalcedony (5)
18 Sham (anag) (4)
22 Japanese dish (5)
23 Less quiet (7)
24 First born (6)
25 Not written in any key (of music) (6)

Down

1 Trailer (7)
2 Storehouse for grain (7)
3 Bucks (5)
4 Act of avoiding capture (7)
5 Melodies (5)
6 Annoys (5)
9 Scares (9)
14 Least attractive (7)
15 Countries (7)
16 Acutely (7)
19 Valuable thing or person (5)
20 Apart from (5)
21 Merriment (5)

Puzzle 167

Across

1 Tangible (8)
5 Portent (4)
9 In the middle of (5)
10 Stringed instruments (5)
11 Act of putting right (10)
14 Male pub worker (6)
15 You may have these while asleep (6)
17 Up for debate (10)
20 Loft (5)
21 Add coal to a fire (5)
22 Look after (4)
23 Minced meat products (8)

Down

1 Splendid display (4)
2 Outdoor swimming pool (4)
3 Science of space travel (12)
4 French museum (6)
6 Fictitious (8)
7 Curiosity (8)
8 Decomposition by a current (12)
12 Abounding (8)
13 Scare (8)
16 Country in central Africa (6)
18 Unpleasant smell (4)
19 Alicia ___ : US singer (4)

Crossword

Puzzle 168

Across

1 Curved shape (4)
3 Definite and clear (8)
9 Warm-blooded vertebrates (7)
10 Flour dough used in cooking (5)
11 Shallow recess (5)
12 Seedless raisin (7)
13 Walked quickly (6)
15 Characteristic (6)
17 Huge coniferous tree (7)
18 More recent (5)
20 Walk heavily and firmly (5)
21 Vague and uncertain (7)
22 Shy; bashful (8)
23 Sums together (4)

Down

1 Person who manages the affairs of an insolvent company (13)
2 Funny person (5)
4 Misapply (6)
5 Despair (12)
6 Having a valid will (7)
7 Bland and dull (13)
8 Person who listens into conversations (12)
14 Write again (7)
16 Border (6)
19 Injure (5)

Puzzle 169

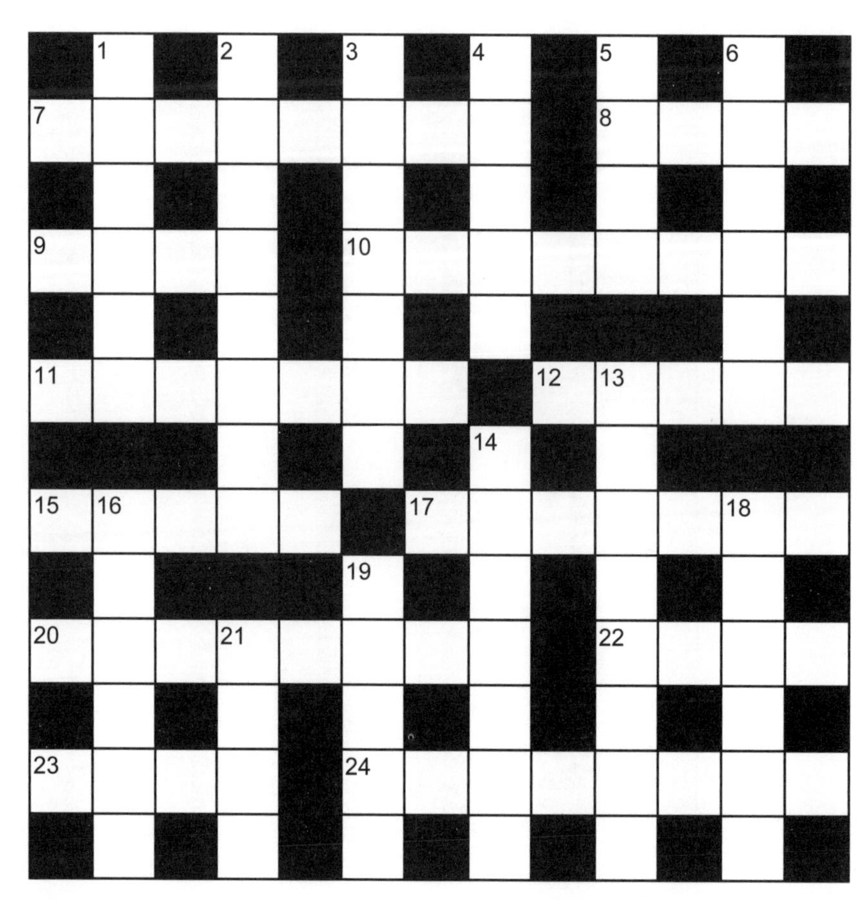

Across

7 Clip to keep something in place (8)
8 Listen to (4)
9 Look slyly (4)
10 Daring feats (8)
11 Narrow strip of land (7)
12 Small decorative balls (5)
15 Stinging insects (5)
17 Devise beforehand (7)
20 Children who are beginning to walk (8)
22 Greases (4)
23 Skilfully (4)
24 Gathers together (8)

Down

1 A spell (anag) (6)
2 Spacecraft (8)
3 A Roman Catholic devotion (7)
4 Chart (5)
5 Drive away (4)
6 Separated (6)
13 In work (8)
14 Table support (7)
16 Single-celled organism (6)
18 Doles out (6)
19 Compassion (5)
21 24 hour periods (4)

Crossword

Puzzle 170

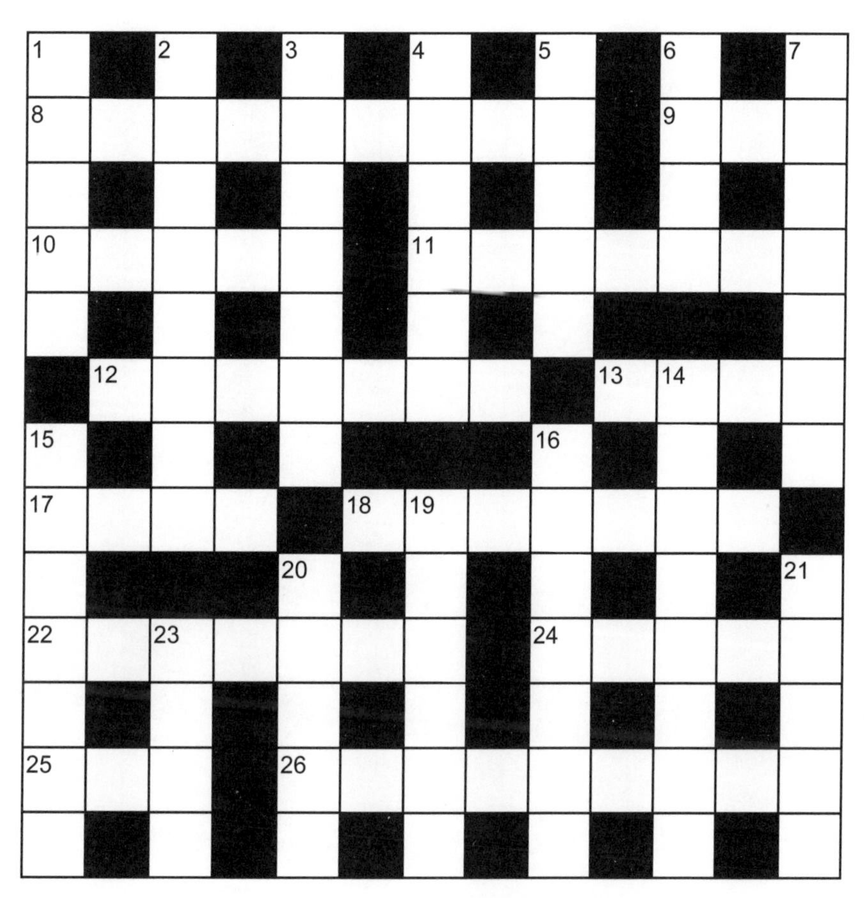

Across

8 Very basic (9)
9 ___ Tyler: US actress (3)
10 Hidden storage space (5)
11 Sharp painful blow (7)
12 One event in a sequence (7)
13 Self-satisfied (4)
17 Comply (4)
18 Wife of a duke (7)
22 Bathing tub with bubbles (7)
24 Arrive at (5)
25 Frozen water (3)
26 Kit; gear (9)

Down

1 Aromatic flavouring (5)
2 Follower (8)
3 Authorise the use of (7)
4 Not impartial (6)
5 A sum owed (5)
6 Golf (anag) (4)
7 Surplus or excess (7)
14 Incorrect (8)
15 Unite together (7)
16 Type of treatment for a disorder (7)
19 One of a kind (6)
20 ___ Camera: band (5)
21 Waterslide (5)
23 City in NW France (4)

Puzzle 171

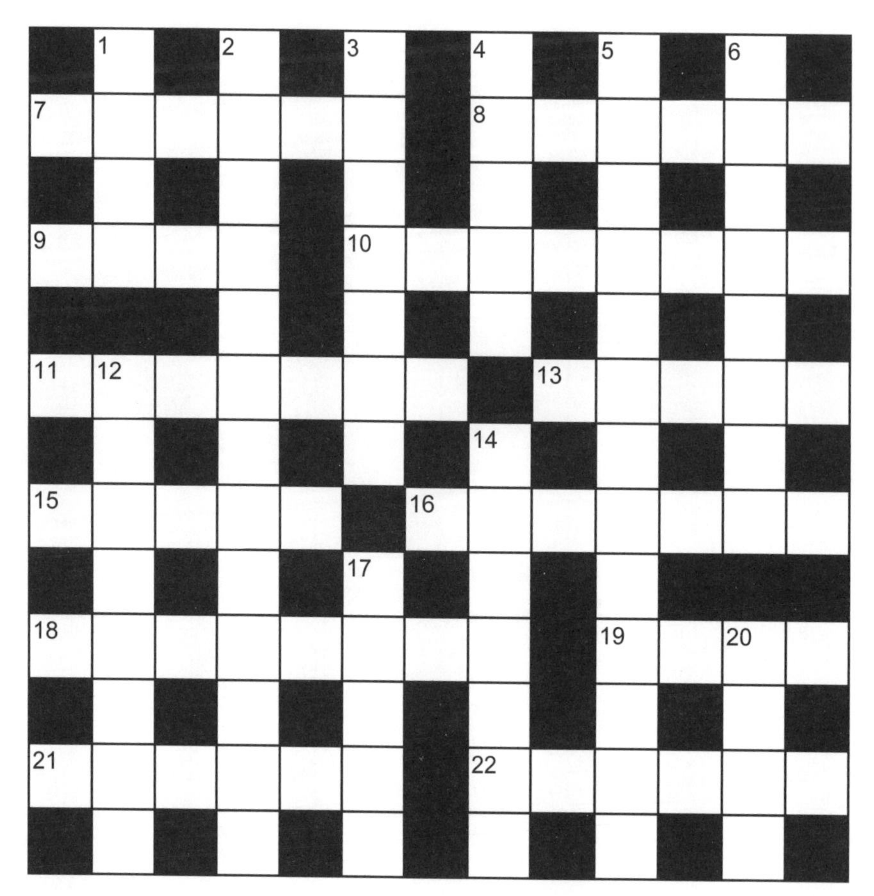

Across

7 Conduct reconnaissance (6)
8 Not allowing light to pass through (6)
9 Cereal plant (4)
10 Paucity (8)
11 Treachery (7)
13 Severe (5)
15 Permit (5)
16 Subdues (7)
18 Light brown cane sugar (8)
19 Appendage (4)
21 Tensed (anag) (6)
22 Coronets (6)

Down

1 Burkina ___ : African country (4)
2 German film actress (6,7)
3 Omission of a sound when speaking (7)
4 Move as fast as possible (5)
5 Involvement (13)
6 Metallic element used in light bulbs (8)
12 Assuages (8)
14 Emotional stability (7)
17 Useful (5)
20 Pubs (4)

Crossword

Puzzle 172

Across

- **1** Famous street in Manhattan (8)
- **5** Complain unreasonably (4)
- **9** Narrow valleys (5)
- **10** Satisfied a desire (5)
- **11** Done in return (10)
- **14** Sharp reply (6)
- **15** Not noticed (6)
- **17** Oppressively heavy (10)
- **20** Inducement (5)
- **21** Coarse twilled cotton fabric (5)
- **22** Spool-like toy (2-2)
- **23** Fanaticism (8)

Down

- **1** Listening devices (4)
- **2** Opposite of shut (4)
- **3** Dispirited (12)
- **4** East ___ : where one finds Norfolk (6)
- **6** Recitals (anag) (8)
- **7** Trifling (8)
- **8** Extremely large (12)
- **12** Very likely (8)
- **13** Infinite time (8)
- **16** Get away from (6)
- **18** Hoist (4)
- **19** Emaciated (4)

Puzzle 173

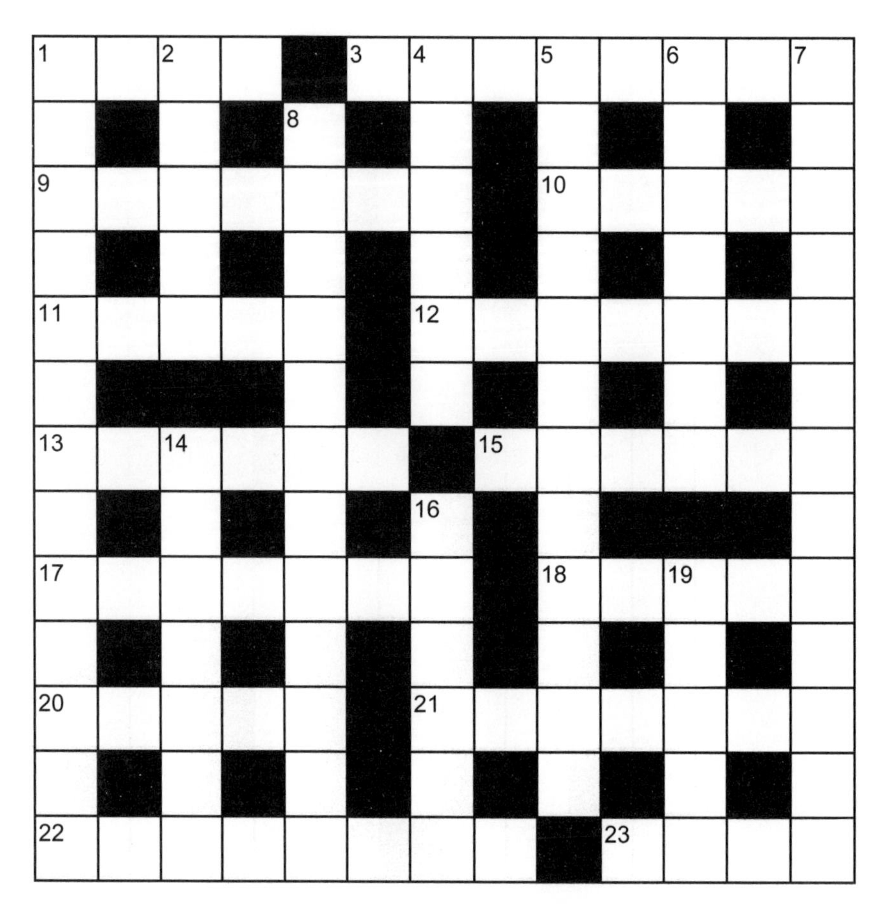

Across

1 Closed hand (4)
3 Baptise (8)
9 Hopes to achieve (7)
10 Evil spirit (5)
11 Detected a sound (5)
12 Least difficult (7)
13 Establish by calculation (6)
15 Walk very quietly (6)
17 Something showing a general rule (7)
18 Enclosed (of animals) (5)
20 Third Greek letter (5)
21 Brighten up (7)
22 Streams of rain (8)
23 Arthur ___ : former US tennis player (4)

Down

1 Boxing class division (13)
2 Dark brown colour (5)
4 Move or travel hurriedly (6)
5 Dimly; not clearly (12)
6 Storm (7)
7 Failure to be present at (13)
8 Most prominent position (5,2,5)
14 Charismatic person (7)
16 Discover (6)
19 Donates (5)

Puzzle 174

Across

- **1** God (5)
- **4** Content (5)
- **10** Learned (7)
- **11** Lumberjack (5)
- **12** Ring (4)
- **13** In a fair manner (8)
- **16** Garment maker (6)
- **17** Comfort (6)
- **20** Thought curiously (8)
- **21** Crustacean (4)
- **23** Weatherproof coat (5)
- **25** Road pen (anag) (7)
- **26** Pay out money (5)
- **27** Grasp tightly (5)

Down

- **2** Process of learning (9)
- **3** Link a town with another (4)
- **5** Mike ___ : former England cricket captain (8)
- **6** Animal foot (3)
- **7** Tyrant (6)
- **8** Supports (5)
- **9** Tailless amphibian (4)
- **14** Breaks in activities (9)
- **15** Alert in advance (8)
- **18** Symbolise (6)
- **19** Yellow citrus fruit (5)
- **20** Erase (4)
- **22** Examine by touch (4)
- **24** Tear (3)

Puzzle 175

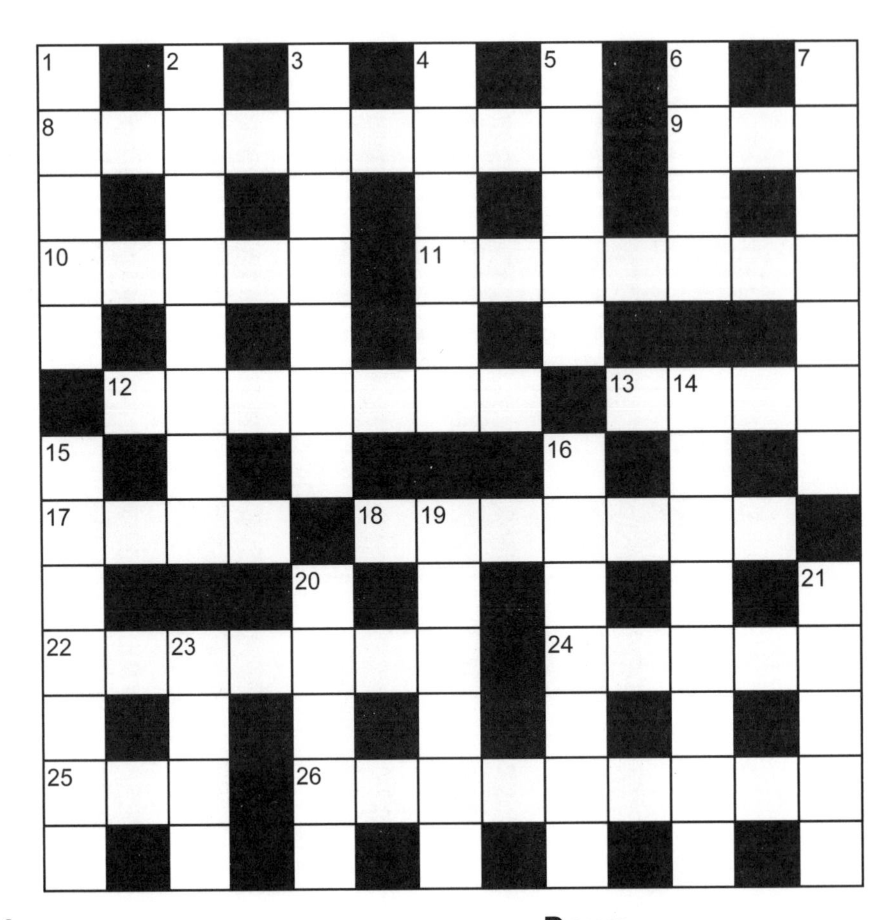

Across

8 Tailless Australian marsupial (5,4)
9 Place where one sees animals (3)
10 Confound (5)
11 Far away (7)
12 An unknown person (7)
13 Exposes to natural light (4)
17 Ask questions (4)
18 Intimidate (7)
22 Fifth Greek letter (7)
24 Hurled away (5)
25 Metal container; is able to (3)
26 Loyally (9)

Down

1 Seabirds (5)
2 Type of pasta (8)
3 Skipped about (7)
4 Involving direct confrontation (4-2)
5 Put clothes on (5)
6 ___ Pound: US poet (4)
7 Boorish (7)
14 Undeserving (8)
15 Make a sucking sound (7)
16 Noting down (7)
19 Criminal (6)
20 Lavish (5)
21 Moves in the wind (5)
23 Musical composition (4)

Crossword

Puzzle 176

Across

1 Hinder today (anag) (11)
9 Pick out; choose (5)
10 Metal container; element (3)
11 Path to follow (5)
12 More pleasant (5)
13 Common insect (8)
16 Dregs (8)
18 Chefs (5)
21 Skewered meat (5)
22 Source of a metal (3)
23 Small antelope (5)
24 Property professional (6,5)

Down

2 Error in printing or writing (7)
3 Gave way to pressure (7)
4 Expressing regret (6)
5 Largest moon of Saturn (5)
6 Relating to vision (5)
7 Shaman (5,6)
8 Stubborn (11)
14 Choosing (7)
15 Very young infant (7)
17 Machine that creates motion (6)
19 Baking appliances (5)
20 Minute pore in a leaf (5)

Puzzle 177

Across

1 Vein of metal ore (4)
3 Head of a government department (8)
9 Unfasten (7)
10 Naves (anag) (5)
11 Restrict within limits (12)
14 Unit of energy (3)
16 Arose from slumber (5)
17 Female sheep (3)
18 Absolute authority in any sphere (12)
21 Change (5)
22 Round building (7)
23 Domains (8)
24 Give up one's rights (4)

Down

1 Propels with force (8)
2 The furnishings in a room (5)
4 Mischievous sprite (3)
5 Lacking a backbone (12)
6 Plausible; defensible (7)
7 Corrode (4)
8 Made (12)
12 Part of a teapot (5)
13 Partner (8)
15 Tough animal tissue (7)
19 Door hanger (5)
20 Young cow (4)
22 Edge of a cup (3)

Crossword

Puzzle 178

Across

1 Grinned (6)
5 Seabird (6)
8 Frozen precipitation (4)
9 Reaching a destination (8)
10 Polite and courteous (5)
11 Decorated (7)
14 Act of questioning (13)
16 Proportionately (3,4)
18 Cards used for fortune-telling (5)
20 Spherical (8)
22 Turn over (4)
23 Business organisation (6)
24 Sailing vessels (6)

Down

2 Prelate (9)
3 Despicable person (7)
4 Haul (4)
5 Representative example (8)
6 State of nervous excitement (5)
7 Particle that is electrically charged (3)
12 Emoticons (anag) (9)
13 Viciously (8)
15 Movement of vehicles en masse (7)
17 Bird with a red breast (5)
19 Address a deity (4)
21 Fall behind (3)

Puzzle 179

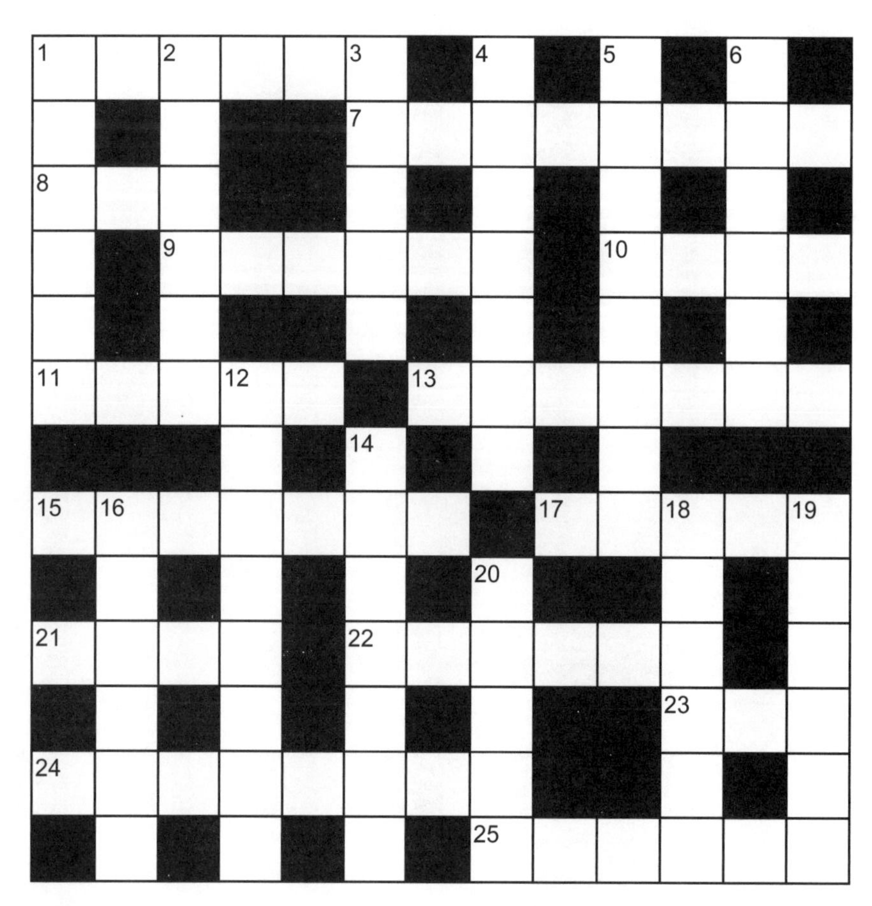

Across

1 Dark blue dye (6)
7 Hated (8)
8 State of matter (3)
9 Make receptive or aware (6)
10 Arduous journey (4)
11 Thick slice of meat (5)
13 Coolness (7)
15 Distinct sort or kind (7)
17 Sacred song (5)
21 Nourishment (4)
22 Meaning; purpose (6)
23 ___ Titmuss: TV personality (3)
24 Constant movement backwards and forwards (2,3,3)
25 Slender; thin (6)

Down

1 Blocks of metal (6)
2 Quantity of medicine to take (6)
3 Scent (5)
4 Intrinsic nature (7)
5 Fixtures (8)
6 Alludes to (6)
12 Mishap (8)
14 Firm opinions (7)
16 Positively charged atomic particle (6)
18 Reach a specified level (6)
19 Insurrection (6)
20 The spirit of a people (5)

Crossword

Puzzle 180

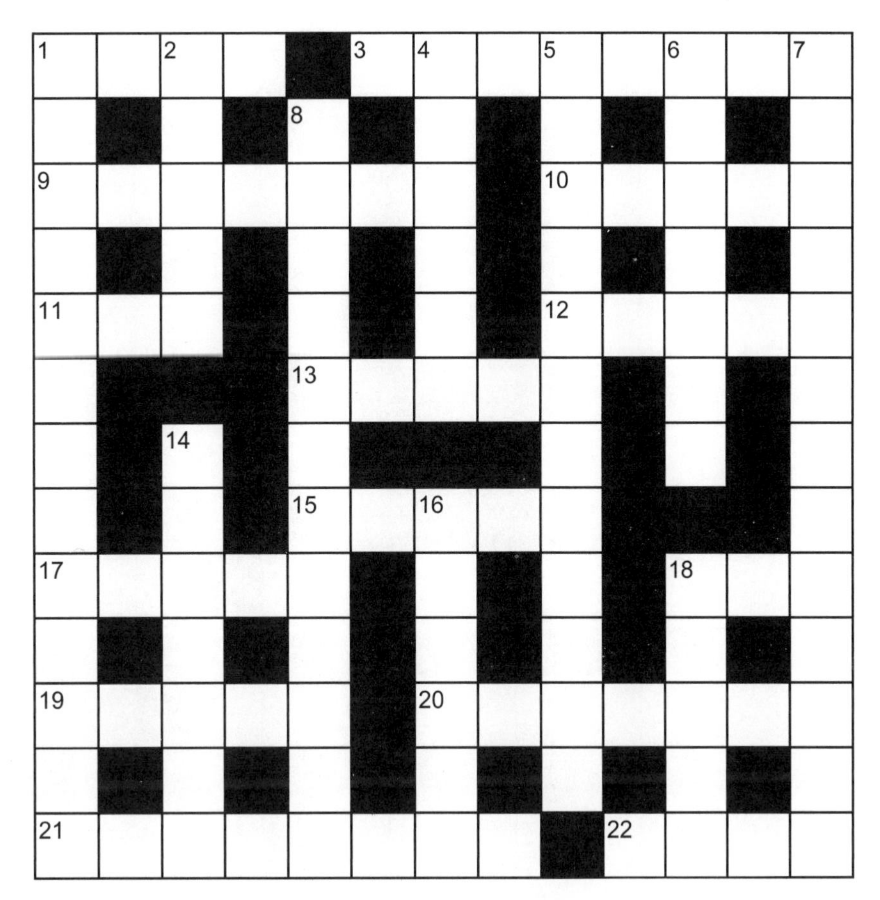

Across

1 Of like kind (4)
3 Opposition to war (8)
9 Person proposed for office (7)
10 Ice cream is often served in these (5)
11 Unwell (3)
12 Wading bird (5)
13 Female relation (5)
15 Composition for a solo instrument (5)
17 Instruct; teach (5)
18 Form of public transport (3)
19 Exit (5)
20 ___ Bloom: English actor (7)
21 Christmas season (8)
22 Low dull sound (4)

Down

1 Mawkishly (13)
2 Humped ruminant (5)
4 Strongly opposed (6)
5 Incomprehensibly (12)
6 Paid no attention to (7)
7 Misinterpreted (13)
8 Awkward; untimely (12)
14 Burdensome work (7)
16 Maintain a decision (6)
18 Long wooden seat (5)

Puzzle 181

Across

1 Sumptuous and large (of a meal) (4-2)
5 Hay-cutting tool (6)
8 Board game (4)
9 Defeat (8)
10 Eateries (5)
11 To what place (7)
14 Betrayer (6-7)
16 Cause to absorb water (7)
18 Mournful song (5)
20 Traveller (8)
22 Cooking pots (4)
23 Hired out (6)
24 Heavy load (6)

Down

2 Expressing praise (9)
3 Popular saying (7)
4 Short hollow thud (4)
5 Give guidance to (8)
6 Sailing vessel (5)
7 Sewn edge (3)
12 Act of becoming apparent (9)
13 Gave prominence to (8)
15 Light indoor shoe (7)
17 Wading birds (5)
19 Thrash (4)
21 Beer (3)

Crossword

Puzzle 182

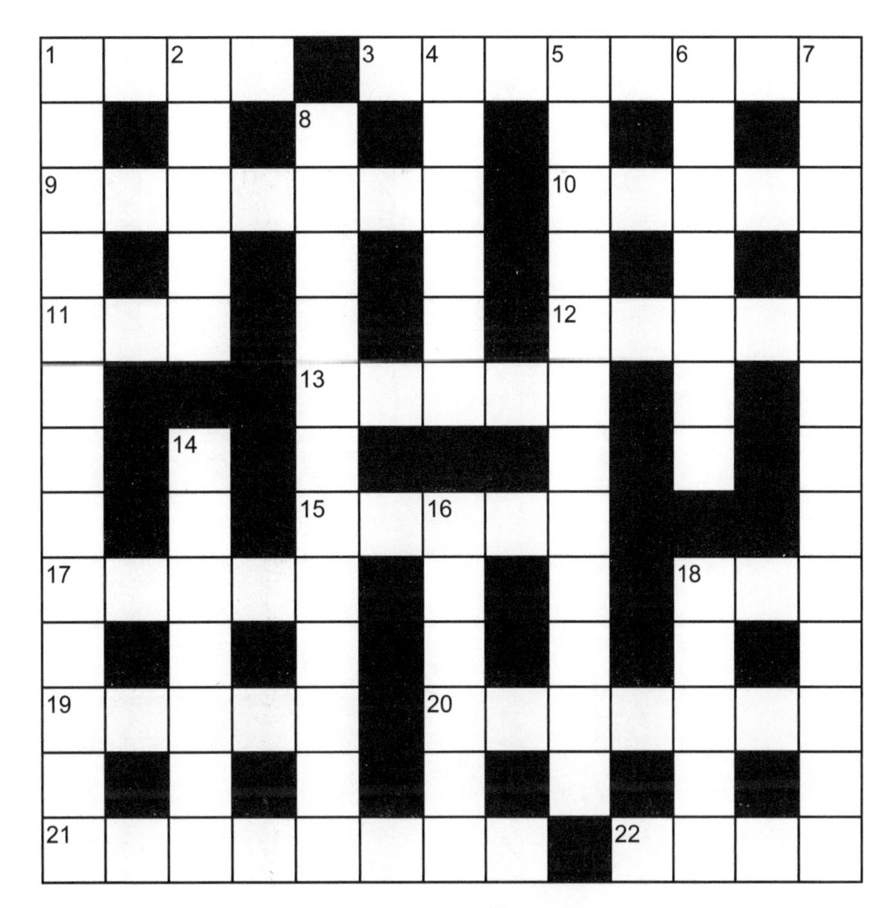

Across

1 Sink (anag) (4)
3 A reduction in price (8)
9 Has an impact on (7)
10 Floor of a building (5)
11 Legume (3)
12 US state (5)
13 Exposed (5)
15 Narrow pieces of land (5)
17 Refute by evidence (5)
18 Our star (3)
19 ___ du Beke: ballroom dancer (5)
20 Cut of beef (7)
21 Establish firmly (8)
22 Tiny parasite (4)

Down

1 Not suitable (13)
2 Franz ___ : novelist (5)
4 Reply (6)
5 Children's toy (12)
6 Remove a difficulty (7)
7 Former President of South Africa (6,7)
8 Person one knows (12)
14 Natural environment (7)
16 Reviewer (6)
18 Rinse out with water (5)

Puzzle 183

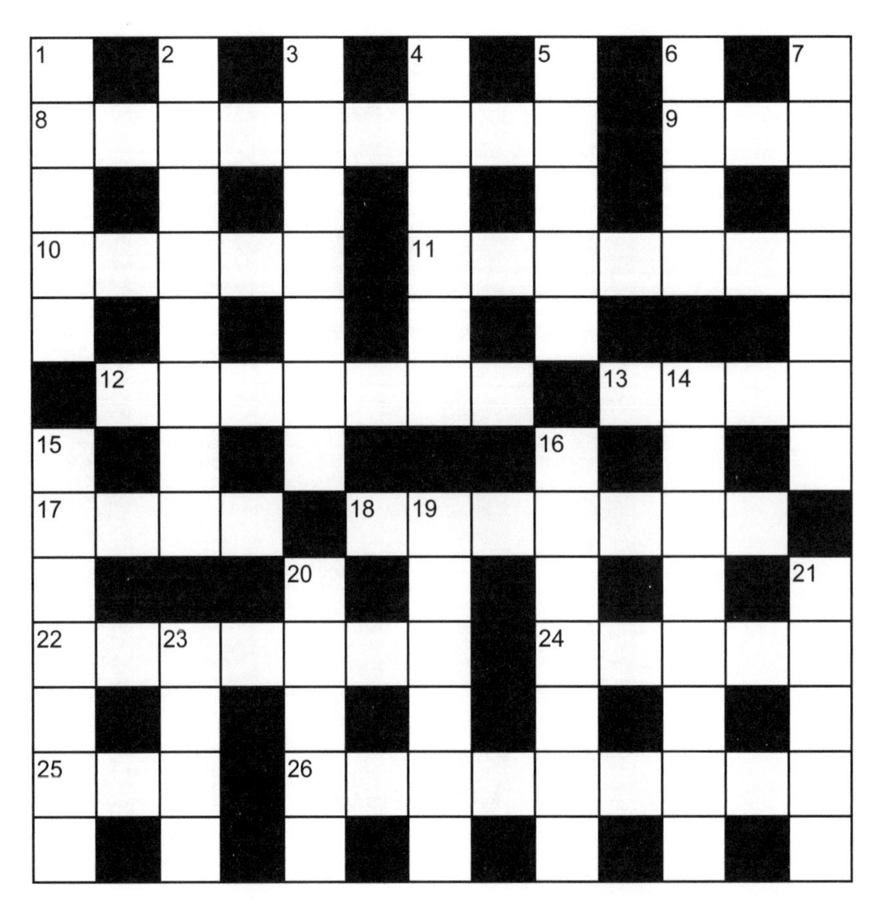

Across

8 Establish (9)
9 In favour of (3)
10 Snow and rain mix (5)
11 Arm exercise (5-2)
12 Companion (7)
13 Slide (4)
17 Fathers (4)
18 Flowing bodies of water (7)
22 Dark pigment in skin (7)
24 One who makes bread (5)
25 Annoy constantly (3)
26 Very small (4-5)

Down

1 ___ Elliott: US singer (5)
2 Space rock (8)
3 Extreme nervousness (7)
4 Swallowed quickly (6)
5 Take delight in (5)
6 Mocks (4)
7 Underwater projectile (7)
14 Potentially self-destructive (8)
15 Remnant (7)
16 Wordy (7)
19 Occupant (6)
20 Shoot with great precision (5)
21 Networks of lines (5)
23 Light toboggan (4)

Crossword

Puzzle 184

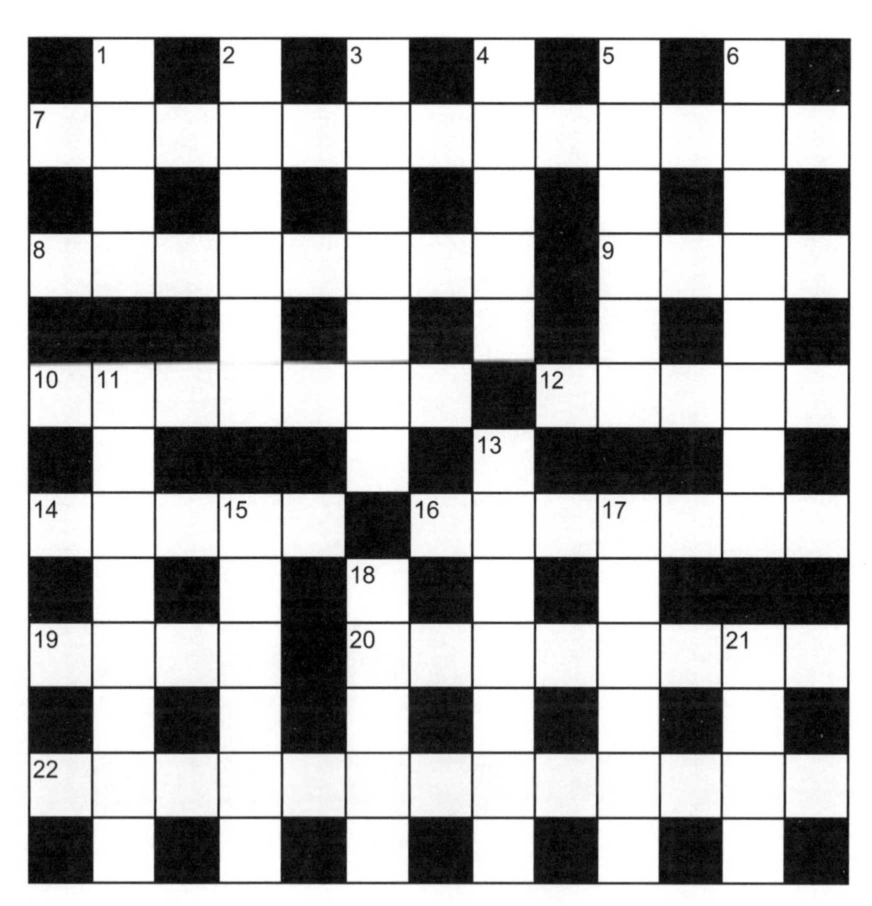

Across

7 Magnificently (13)
8 Eg Baz Luhrmann (8)
9 Intense anger (4)
10 Explanations (7)
12 Type of chemical bond (5)
14 Currently in progress (5)
16 Trace of something (7)
19 Backbone; fortitude (4)
20 Unjustly (8)
22 Serving to show (13)

Down

1 German car manufacturer (4)
2 Precious stones (6)
3 Brazenly obvious (7)
4 Grim (5)
5 Exaggerate (6)
6 Filling in a hole (8)
11 Confrere (anag) (8)
13 Carry out an action (7)
15 Choice (6)
17 Distorts (6)
18 Courageous (5)
21 Molten rock (4)

Puzzle 185

Across

1 Believes tentatively (8)
5 Mineral powder (4)
8 Skilled job (5)
9 Friendly (7)
10 Fusion chamber (7)
12 Gives satisfaction (7)
14 Feeling of great happiness (7)
16 Gambling houses (7)
18 Small shark (7)
19 ___ Simpson: cartoon character (5)
20 Circular storage medium (4)
21 Sparkled (8)

Down

1 Eg use a straw (4)
2 Rarely encountered (6)
3 Addition to a building (9)
4 Browns bread (6)
6 Collections of photos (6)
7 Impertinently (8)
11 Female relative (9)
12 Went before (8)
13 Customary practices (6)
14 Shun (6)
15 Without ethics (6)
17 Clutched (4)

Puzzle 186

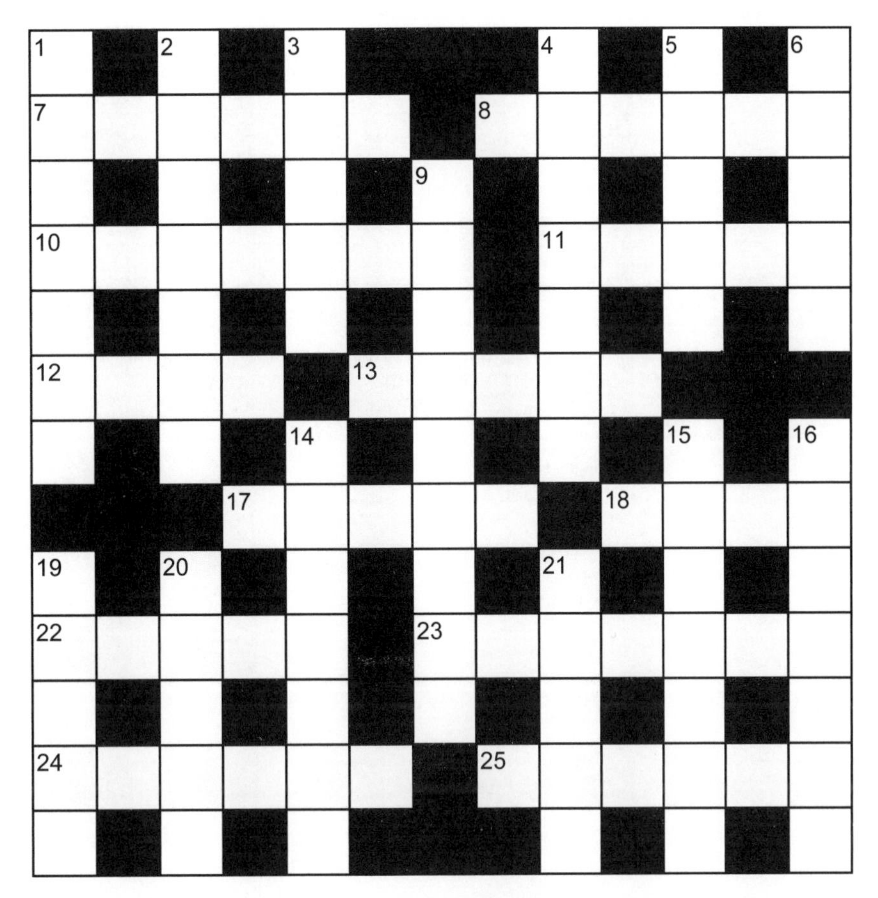

Across

7 Take out (6)
8 Incidental activity (6)
10 Country house (7)
11 Foreign language (informal) (5)
12 Subsequently (4)
13 Select; formally approve (5)
17 Broadcast again (5)
18 Place where a wild animal lives (4)
22 Forelock of hair (5)
23 Inclination (7)
24 Geneva (anag) (6)
25 Make changes to improve something (6)

Down

1 Teach (7)
2 Having folds (of a garment) (7)
3 Engross oneself in (5)
4 One-eyed giant (7)
5 Hold on to tightly (5)
6 ___ Fury: British boxer (5)
9 Fourfold (9)
14 Foliage (7)
15 Seat of the US Congress (7)
16 Art of paper-folding (7)
19 Be the same as (5)
20 Smarter (5)
21 Consumed (of food) (5)

Puzzle 187

Across

1 Banner or flag (6)
4 Administrative body (6)
9 Things that evoke reactions (7)
10 Casual shoes (7)
11 Completely correct (5)
12 Long-___ owl: bird (5)
14 Unit of capacitance (5)
15 Bird droppings used as fertiliser (5)
17 Give a solemn oath (5)
18 More jolly (7)
20 Folds in a material (7)
21 Substance added to make dough rise (6)
22 Dry and brittle (of food) (6)

Down

1 Christian festival (6)
2 Formerly Ceylon (3,5)
3 Haggard (5)
5 Modernised (7)
6 ___ Macpherson: model (4)
7 In mint condition (6)
8 Tree with distinctive bark (6,5)
13 Goes backwards (8)
14 Decorated with leaves (7)
15 Frolic (6)
16 Playful; energetic (6)
17 Guide a vehicle (5)
19 Ostrich-like bird (4)

Crossword

Puzzle 188

Across

1 Leave a ship (6)
5 Tavern (3)
7 Leg bone (5)
8 Large German city (7)
9 Divide by cutting (5)
10 Humorous verse (8)
12 Wesley ___ : US actor (6)
14 Admit openly (6)
17 Business organisations (8)
18 Very bad (5)
20 Ugly building (7)
21 Titled (5)
22 Used to be (3)
23 Agreement (6)

Down

2 Eg anger or love (7)
3 Took into account (8)
4 Large wading bird (4)
5 Upstart; one who has recently gained wealth (7)
6 Ill-mannered (7)
7 Instruct (5)
11 Fairness (8)
12 Lacking depth (7)
13 Challenges the truth of (7)
15 V-shaped mark (7)
16 ___ on : encouraged (5)
19 Sweet potatoes (4)

Puzzle 189

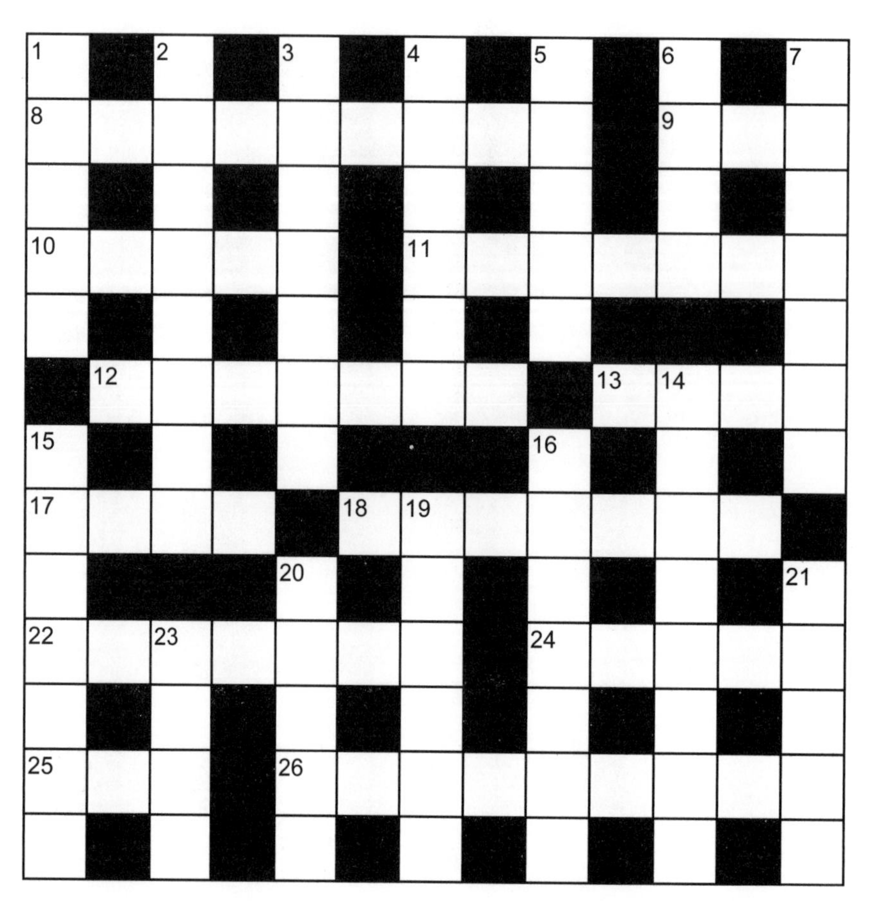

Across

8 Happen as a result (9)
9 Male sheep (3)
10 Plants of a region (5)
11 ___ Crowe: Gladiator actor (7)
12 Urging to be true (7)
13 Move from side to side (4)
17 Small circular band (4)
18 Vehicle equipped for living in (7)
22 Pierre ___ : French mathematician (7)
24 Beer (5)
25 State (3)
26 Heaped ice (anag) (9)

Down

1 Glazed earthenware (5)
2 Total commitment; loyalty (8)
3 ___ case: item for carrying documents (7)
4 Financier (6)
5 Stanza of a poem (5)
6 At liberty (4)
7 Utilises (7)
14 Person engaging in a complicated dispute (8)
15 Precondition (7)
16 Rides at speed (7)
19 Safety device in a car (6)
20 Dubious (5)
21 Eg from Athens (5)
23 Light beams (4)

Puzzle 190

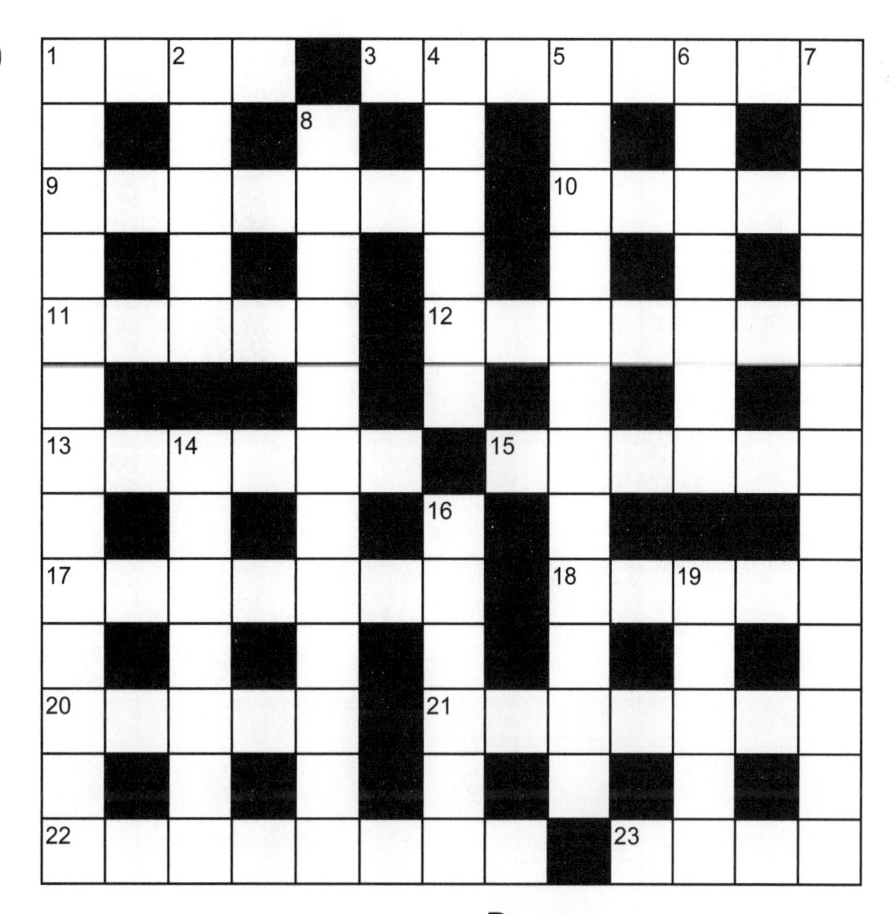

Across

1 Leap (4)
3 Imitates (8)
9 Decreased (7)
10 Short high-pitched tone (5)
11 Latin American dance (5)
12 Expressive (of music) (7)
13 World's largest country (6)
15 Body of running water (6)
17 Removed the contents of (7)
18 Siren (anag) (5)
20 Maritime (5)
21 United States (7)
22 Writer of literary works (8)
23 Extremely (4)

Down

1 Philosophy of law (13)
2 Scale representation (5)
4 Military decorations (6)
5 Scientific research rooms (12)
6 Molasses (7)
7 Additional (13)
8 Now and then (12)
14 Neck-warming garments (7)
16 Standards to be aimed at (6)
19 ___ flu: form of influenza (5)

Puzzle 191

Across

1 Unique (3-3)
4 Snow sport (6)
9 French city (7)
10 Flat slabs (7)
11 Seven (anag) (5)
12 Person who always puts in a lot of effort (5)
14 Administrative capital of Bolivia (2,3)
15 Eighth Greek letter (5)
17 A sense (5)
18 ___ Bedingfield: musician (7)
20 Move slowly (7)
21 Waste matter (6)
22 Crazily (6)

Down

1 Speaks publicly (6)
2 Distinction; high status (8)
3 Discovers (5)
5 Communal settlement in Israel (7)
6 ___ of Wight: English island (4)
7 Hot spring (6)
8 Immoderate (11)
13 Planned (8)
14 Backsliding (7)
15 Colours slightly (6)
16 Drowsy (6)
17 ___ Arabia: country in the Middle East (5)
19 Melt (4)

Puzzle 192

Across

7 Fixed periods of work (6)
8 Event which precedes another (6)
10 Cyclone (7)
11 Short notes (5)
12 Tray (anag) (4)
13 Sheep's sound (5)
17 Frown (5)
18 Garden outbuilding (4)
22 Purchaser (5)
23 Becomes less wide (7)
24 Short trip to perform a task (6)
25 Sheepskin (6)

Down

1 Receptacle for cigarette residue (7)
2 Oscillate (7)
3 Member of the weasel family (5)
4 Public transport vehicle (7)
5 Bivalve marine molluscs (5)
6 Tennis stroke (5)
9 Pursuing (9)
14 Arranging a piece of music (7)
15 Yelled with excitement (7)
16 Epic poem (7)
19 Double-reed instruments (5)
20 Monster with nine heads (5)
21 Adornment (5)

Puzzle 193

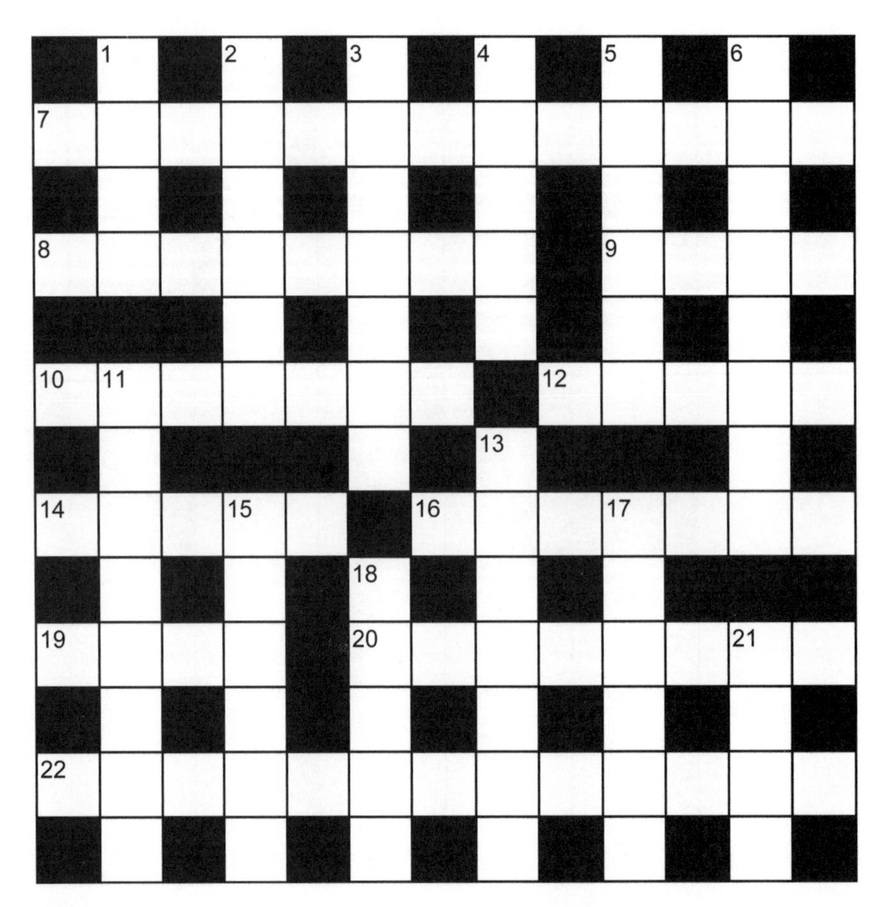

Across

7 Ineptitude in running a business (13)
8 Cowboy (8)
9 Traditional knowledge (4)
10 Be composed of (7)
12 Very skilled at something (5)
14 Danger (5)
16 A person in general (7)
19 Scarpered (4)
20 Extremely lovable (8)
22 Presupposition (13)

Down

1 In ___ : in place of (4)
2 Cooks in wood chippings (6)
3 Coat; decorate lavishly (7)
4 Softly radiant (5)
5 Moved at an easy pace (6)
6 Fearless and brave (8)
11 Ruler (8)
13 Impassive (7)
15 Admit to a post (6)
17 Strong gusts of wind (6)
18 Animal life of a region (5)
21 Plunder; take illegally (4)

Crossword

Puzzle 194

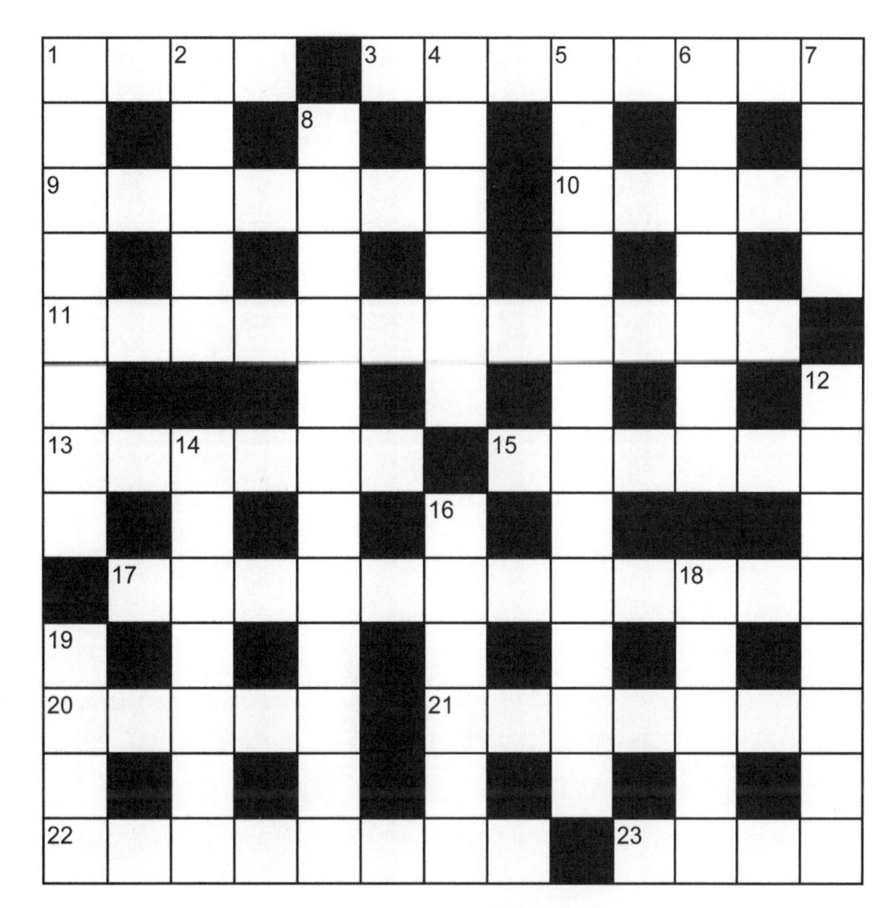

Across

1 Large group of people (4)
3 Harmful in effect (8)
9 Derived from living matter (7)
10 Areas; sectors (5)
11 In accordance with general custom (12)
13 Plant with oil rich seeds (6)
15 Next after third (6)
17 Decide in advance (12)
20 Doglike mammal (5)
21 Segmented worm (7)
22 Term for a pet feline (8)
23 Slender woody shoot (4)

Down

1 Piece of furniture (8)
2 One who avoids animal products (5)
4 Subtle detail (6)
5 Female singing voice (5-7)
6 Mythical being (7)
7 Girl or young woman (4)
8 Middleman (12)
12 Canine that herds animals (8)
14 Thoroughfares (7)
16 Capital of Canada (6)
18 Relative by marriage (2-3)
19 Counter used in poker (4)

Puzzle 195

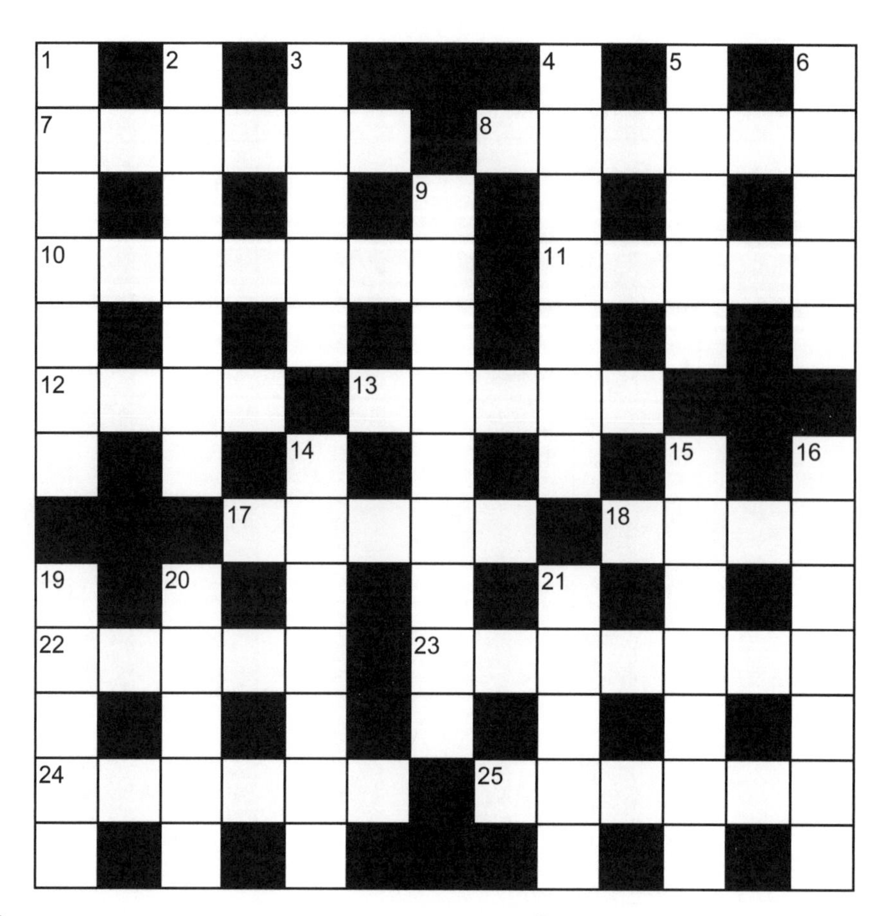

Across

- **7** Thomas Alva ___ : US inventor (6)
- **8** Japanese dress (6)
- **10** Arched structure in a garden (7)
- **11** Packs tightly (5)
- **12** Uncommon (4)
- **13** Pale brownish-yellow colour (5)
- **17** Shed (5)
- **18** Product made from soya beans (4)
- **22** Public meeting for open discussion (5)
- **23** Provoked or teased (7)
- **24** Rinses (anag) (6)
- **25** Examine again (6)

Down

- **1** Aides (7)
- **2** Reflects (7)
- **3** Armature of an electric motor (5)
- **4** Lobster claws (7)
- **5** ___ bear: powerful mammal (5)
- **6** Damp (5)
- **9** Young bird (9)
- **14** French territorial division (7)
- **15** Box of useful equipment (7)
- **16** Summary of results (7)
- **19** Burning (5)
- **20** Recently made (5)
- **21** Asian pepper plant (5)

Puzzle 196

Across

1 Mocking (8)
5 Metal fastener (4)
8 Leader or ruler (5)
9 Trucks (7)
10 Stinging plants (7)
12 Making an offer at auction (7)
14 Device that measures electric current (7)
16 Edible parts of nuts (7)
18 Voter (7)
19 Tremulous sound (5)
20 ___ Daly: TV presenter (4)
21 Lightest chemical element (8)

Down

1 Large bag (4)
2 Controlled; restrained (6)
3 Perform a religious ceremony (9)
4 Doing nothing (6)
6 Multiply by three (6)
7 Catastrophe (8)
11 Period of three months (9)
12 Support you can lean against (8)
13 Welcomes (6)
14 Far from the target (6)
15 Capturing (6)
17 Close-knit group of families (4)

Puzzle 197

Across

1 Hogs (4)
3 Legal soundness (8)
9 Selfishness (7)
10 Creator (5)
11 Showing little judgement (6-6)
14 Piece of cloth (3)
16 Turns (anag) (5)
17 Was in first place (3)
18 Unkind; unsympathetic (12)
21 Ring solemnly (5)
22 Treated unjustly (7)
23 Appraiser; valuer (8)
24 Appear to be (4)

Down

1 Coerce into doing something (8)
2 Marrying man (5)
4 Goal (3)
5 Vaccination (12)
6 Writing fluid holder (7)
7 Of long ago (literary) (4)
8 Orcas (6,6)
12 Lesser (5)
13 Additional book matter (8)
15 Eg male and female (7)
19 Brass instrument (5)
20 Gull-like bird (4)
22 Doctor ___ : TV show (3)

Crossword

Puzzle 198

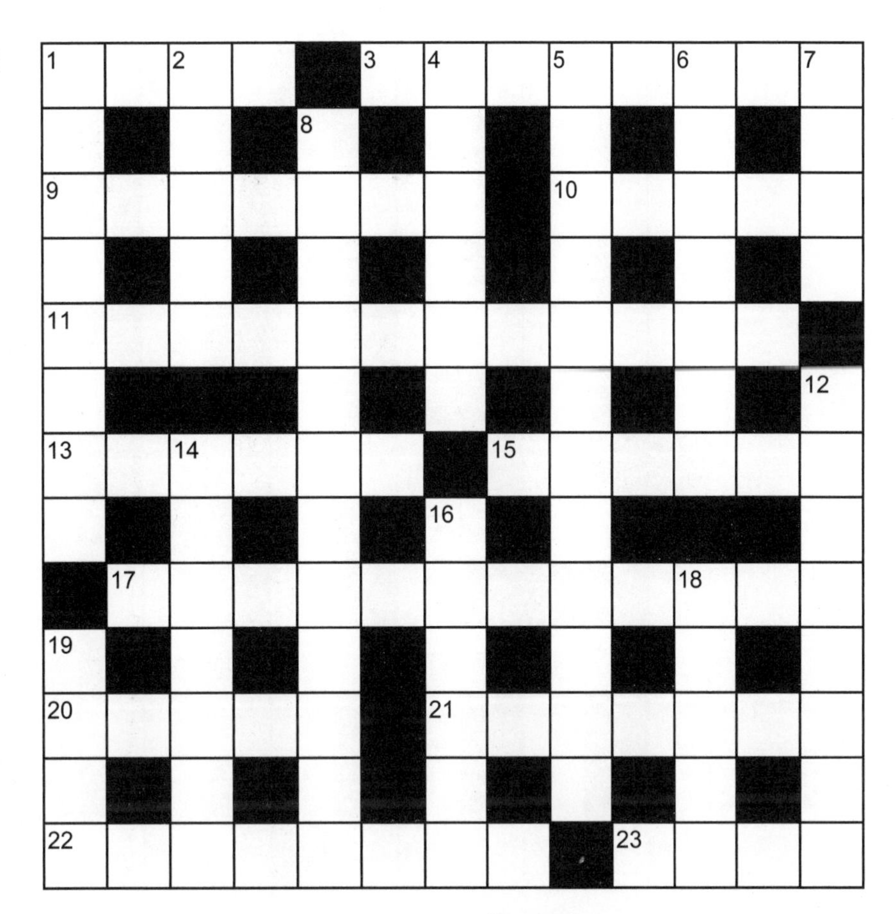

Across

1 Spheres (4)
3 People who act pretentiously (4-4)
9 Mental strain (7)
10 Not straight (of hair) (5)
11 Agreed upon by several parties (12)
13 Turn down (6)
15 With hands on the hips (6)
17 Unhappy (12)
20 City in Tuscany (5)
21 Wavering effect in a musical tone (7)
22 Best (8)
23 Plant stalk (4)

Down

1 Get the better of through being clever (8)
2 Hackneyed (5)
4 Aircraft housing (6)
5 Specialist cricketing position (12)
6 Gun (7)
7 Leguminous plant (4)
8 Germicide (12)
12 Beetle larva that bores into timber (8)
14 Rich sweet roll (7)
16 Gets together (6)
18 Game fish (5)
19 Long and laborious work (4)

Puzzle 199

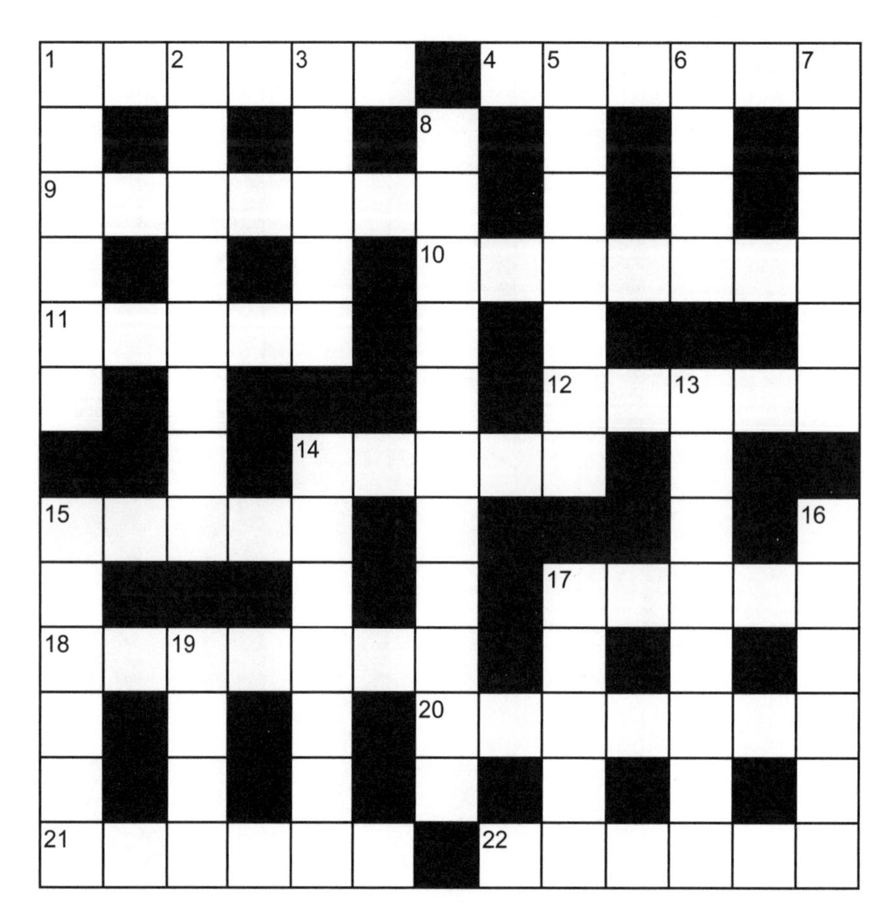

Across

1 Cleaned up (6)
4 Charge with a crime (6)
9 Sheer dress fabric (7)
10 Hears (7)
11 Birds lay their eggs in these (5)
12 Take place (5)
14 Sing like a bird (5)
15 Type of shelf (5)
17 Man (informal) (5)
18 Italian sports car (7)
20 Heavy cotton cloth (7)
21 Work out logically (6)
22 Sprightliness (6)

Down

1 Plant spikes (6)
2 Broke down food (8)
3 Jessica ___-Hill : British heptathlete (5)
5 Without interruption (3-4)
6 Lazy (4)
7 Tricky question (6)
8 Curse (11)
13 Colleague (2-6)
14 Made of clay hardened by heat (7)
15 Elevated off the ground (6)
16 Untape (anag) (6)
17 Spherical objects (5)
19 Peruse (4)

Crossword

Puzzle 200

Across

1 Kind of beet (5)
4 Sturdy motor vehicles (5)
10 Pasta dish (7)
11 Absorbent cloth (5)
12 Fall slowly (of water) (4)
13 Of striking beauty (8)
16 Averts something bad (6)
17 Looked furtively at something (6)
20 Deny (8)
21 Free from doubt (4)
23 Film (5)
25 Female inheritor (7)
26 Fabric with parallel ribs (5)
27 Military constructions (5)

Down

2 Institutions providing healthcare (9)
3 Pieces of cloth (4)
5 Stretched out (8)
6 Long bench (3)
7 Avoids in a skilful way (6)
8 Close-fitting garments (5)
9 Shoe with a wooden sole (4)
14 Rash (9)
15 In a disorderly manner (4-4)
18 Showy (6)
19 Taut (5)
20 Dulls (4)
22 System of credit transfer (4)
24 Solemn promise (3)

Puzzle 201

Across

1 Emit a breath of sadness (4)
3 Hot and humid (8)
9 Blue singer-songwriter (3,4)
10 Grins (anag) (5)
11 Ill-mannered (12)
14 Touch gently (3)
16 Shrub fence (5)
17 Chris ___ : English singer (3)
18 Evening dress for men (6,6)
21 Supply with food (5)
22 Lean back (7)
23 Mythical sea creatures (8)
24 Noble gas (4)

Down

1 Firmness (8)
2 Estimate (5)
4 Sprinted (3)
5 Persistence (12)
6 Vanquish (7)
7 Opposite of won (4)
8 Abnormal anxiety about health (12)
12 Detection technology (5)
13 Temple dedicated to all the gods (8)
15 Artist (7)
19 Cutting instrument (5)
20 Con; swindle (4)
22 Primary colour (3)

Crossword

Puzzle 202

Across

1 Conclude (5)
4 Entangle (7)
7 Colin ___ : English actor in Love Actually (5)
8 Person in second place (6-2)
9 Labour organisation (5)
11 Move to another place (8)
15 Immature (8)
17 Mother-of-pearl (5)
19 Unable to discern musical pitch (4-4)
20 Hurts (5)
21 Sparkle (7)
22 Regal (5)

Down

1 Repetition of a process (9)
2 Decorative altar cloth (7)
3 Let out (7)
4 Make certain of (6)
5 Rules over (6)
6 Prologue (abbrev) (5)
10 Onset of darkness (9)
12 Secret agent (7)
13 Colonial ruler (7)
14 On time (6)
16 Herbert ___ : 31st US President (6)
18 Use to one's advantage (5)

Puzzle 203

Across

- **7** Plaster for coating walls (6)
- **8** Difficult (6)
- **9** Group of three (4)
- **10** Implies (8)
- **11** Growing rapidly; loud (of a voice) (7)
- **13** Alcoholic drinks made from grapes (5)
- **15** Sour substances (5)
- **16** Experienced serviceman (7)
- **18** Totally clean (8)
- **19** Pairs (4)
- **21** Inner part of a seed (6)
- **22** Possessing (6)

Down

- **1** Celestial body (4)
- **2** Easy to deal with (13)
- **3** Stirring (7)
- **4** Raised floor or platform (5)
- **5** Carrying out trials (13)
- **6** Detested thing (8)
- **12** Dweller (8)
- **14** Variant of a thing (7)
- **17** Flat-bottomed vessels (5)
- **20** Pig noise (4)

Crossword

Puzzle 204

1		2		■	3	4		5		6		7
	■		■	8	■		■		■		■	
9							■	10				
	■		■		■		■		■		■	
11			■		■		■	12				
	■	■	■	13					■		■	
	■	14	■		■	■	■		■		■	
	■		■	15		16			■	■	■	
17					■		■		■	18		
	■		■		■		■		■		■	
19					■	20						
	■		■		■		■		■		■	
21								■	22			

Across

1 Domestic cattle (4)
3 Frenzied (8)
9 Newspaper audience (7)
10 Record on tape (5)
11 Not on (3)
12 Upper limits (5)
13 Pop a balloon (5)
15 Stretched tight (of a muscle) (5)
17 Show triumphant joy (5)
18 Smack (3)
19 Loose fibre from old rope (5)
20 Separated; remote (7)
21 Paying out money to buy goods (8)
22 Flat-bottomed boat (4)

Down

1 Period of the Palaeozoic era (13)
2 Fixed platform by water (5)
4 Slice of bacon (6)
5 Notwithstanding (12)
6 Larval frog (7)
7 Dealing with different societies (5-8)
8 Flared (of trousers) (4-8)
14 Laugh (7)
16 Concept (6)
18 Divide in two (5)

Puzzle 205

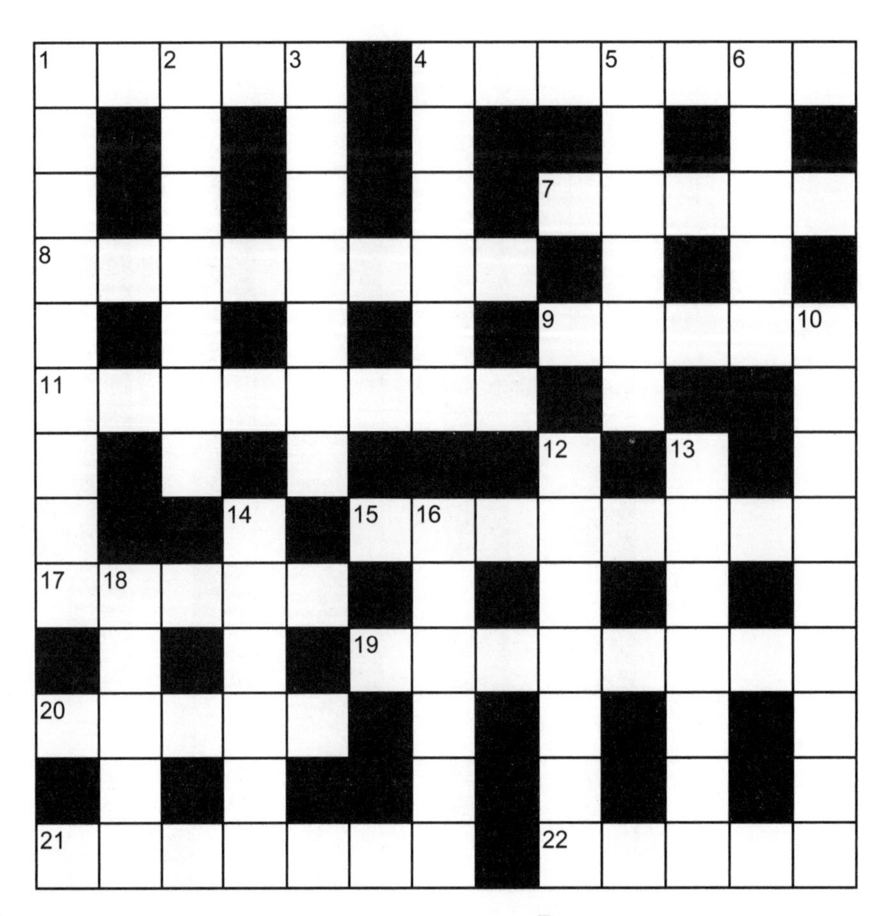

Across

1 ___ Rhymes: rapper (5)
4 Casks (7)
7 Hiding place (5)
8 Flying machine (8)
9 Curt (5)
11 Fleet of ships (8)
15 Sparkles (8)
17 Half of six (5)
19 Using indirect references (8)
20 Holy chalice (5)
21 Road or roofing material (7)
22 Name of a book (5)

Down

1 Morning meal (9)
2 Garden bird (7)
3 Sour in taste (7)
4 Containerful (6)
5 More precisely (6)
6 Endures (5)
10 Being (9)
12 Legal inquiry (7)
13 Cunning (7)
14 Suffer destruction (6)
16 Tree whose wood is used in cabinetmaking (6)
18 Lyres (5)

Crossword

Puzzle 206

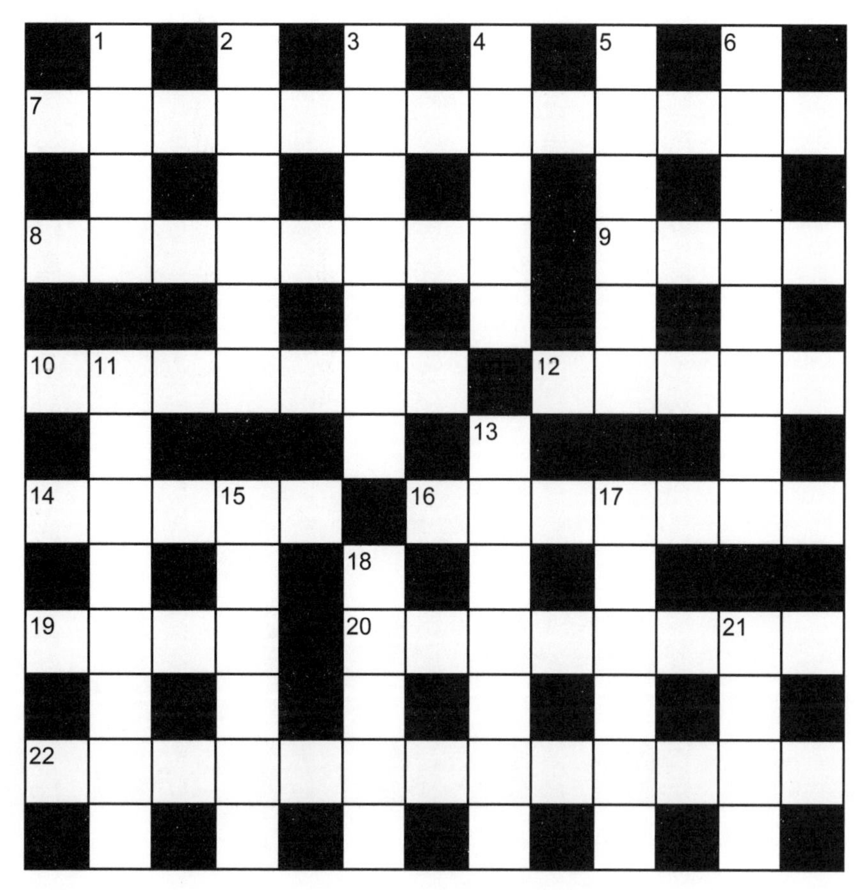

Across

7 Figment of the imagination (13)
8 Cabbage salad (8)
9 Allows to happen (4)
10 Musical composition (7)
12 Saying (5)
14 Deciduous coniferous tree (5)
16 Live longer than (7)
19 Stimulate the appetite (4)
20 Liked sea (anag) (8)
22 Prone to steal (5-8)

Down

1 Type of starch (4)
2 Customer (6)
3 Assistant; follower (7)
4 ___ owl: large white owl (5)
5 Fashioned (6)
6 Semi-rural dwellings (8)
11 Spider (8)
13 Very large; clumsy (7)
15 Easily remembered (6)
17 Diminish (6)
18 Precipice (5)
21 Profound (4)

Puzzle 207

Across

1 Utterly senseless (6)
5 Sagacity (6)
8 Put down gently (4)
9 The training of birds of prey (8)
10 Avoid; garment (5)
11 Chief officer (7)
14 British actress in Goldfinger (5,8)
16 Necessary (7)
18 Play a guitar (5)
20 Sharp heel (8)
22 Incline (4)
23 Fast (6)
24 Took it easy (6)

Down

2 Astronomical phenomenon (5,4)
3 Endure (7)
4 Boiled pudding (4)
5 Highly educated (4-4)
6 Eat quickly (5)
7 Belonging to us (3)
12 Congeal (9)
13 Suddenly (8)
15 Vessels for boiling water (7)
17 Research deeply (5)
19 Number after three (4)
21 Helpful hint (3)

Crossword

Puzzle 208

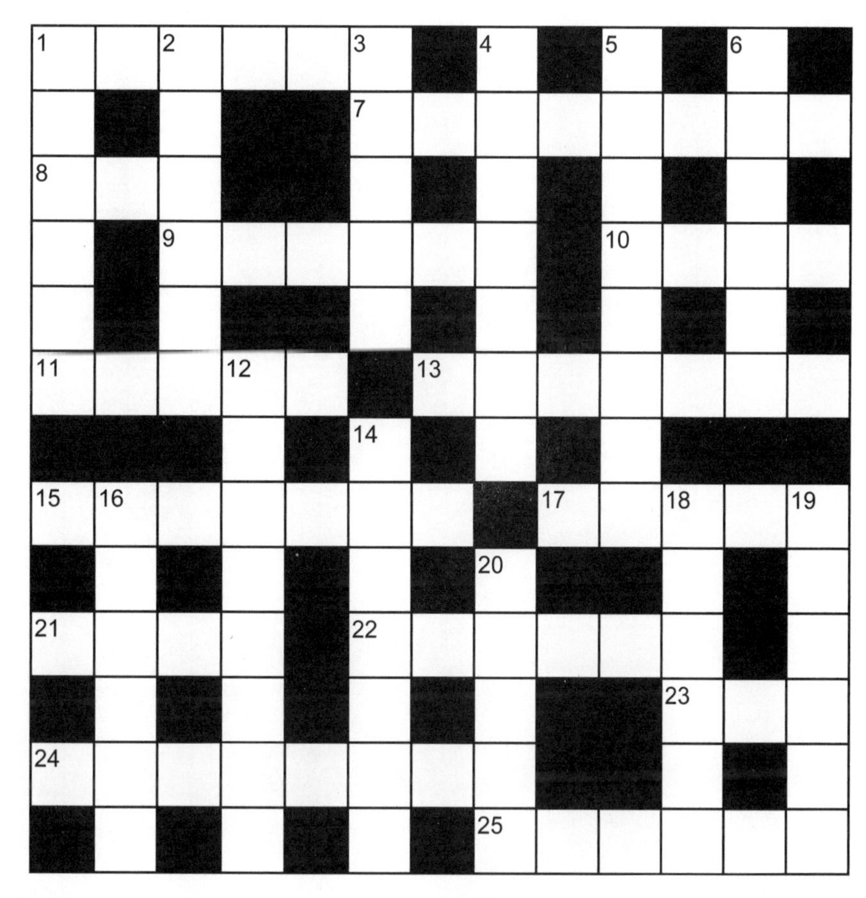

Across

1 Greek goddess (6)
7 Where one finds Glasgow (8)
8 Cut grass (3)
9 Martial art (6)
10 Employs (4)
11 Unfortunately (5)
13 Eg chlorine or bromine (7)
15 Compete (7)
17 Compound tissue in vascular plants (5)
21 Computer memory unit (4)
22 What a spider spins (6)
23 Sense of self-esteem (3)
24 Get ready for a later performance (8)
25 Hospital carers (6)

Down

1 Military forces (6)
2 Offered goods for sale (6)
3 Test or examine (5)
4 At an unspecified future time (7)
5 Deceptive (8)
6 Exist permanently in (6)
12 Formally educated (8)
14 Imaginary creature (7)
16 Gas we breathe (6)
18 Identifying tags (6)
19 Things that impart motion (6)
20 Henrik ___ : Norwegian author (5)

Puzzle 209

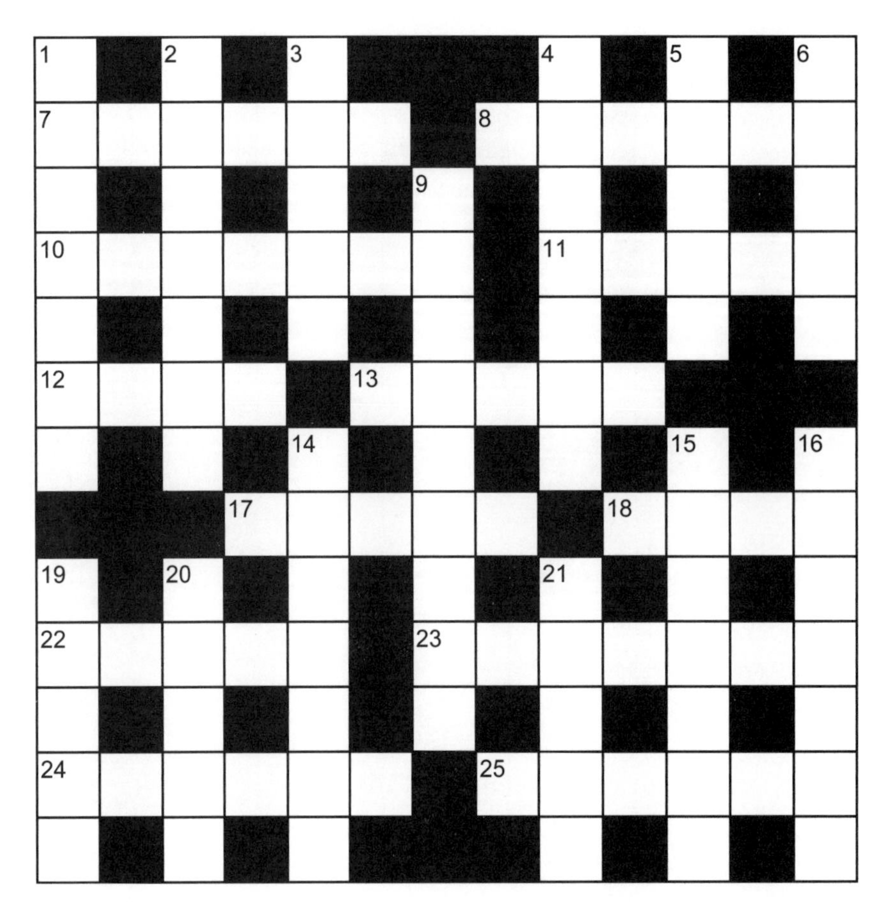

Across

7 Displaying concern for others (6)
8 Pondering (6)
10 Opposite (7)
11 Symbol (5)
12 Ponder or consider (4)
13 Set out (5)
17 Main plant stem (5)
18 Sleeveless cloak; headland (4)
22 Quantitative relation (5)
23 ___ power: source of energy (7)
24 Pertaining to the mind (6)
25 Moderate an impact (6)

Down

1 Divisions of a group (7)
2 Seriously (7)
3 Act of going in (5)
4 College storeroom (7)
5 Cuts slightly (5)
6 Representative (5)
9 Deadly (9)
14 Piece of furniture (7)
15 Become airborne (4,3)
16 Listeners (7)
19 Bend or curl (5)
20 Make amends (5)
21 Search thoroughly for (5)

Puzzle 210

Across

1 Act of harassing someone (11)
9 Sticky substance exuded by trees (5)
10 Marry (3)
11 Island in the Mediterranean Sea (5)
12 Pertaining to sound (5)
13 Secret (4-4)
16 Squid (8)
18 One image within another (5)
21 Condescend (5)
22 Mischievous sprite (3)
23 Roger ___ : English actor (5)
24 Act of checking the accuracy of an instrument (11)

Down

2 Creepiest (7)
3 Aural pain (7)
4 Topics for debate (6)
5 Lists of restaurants dishes (5)
6 Certain to fail (2-3)
7 Unrestrained (11)
8 Serving to enlighten; instructive (11)
14 Most difficult (7)
15 Famous Italian astronomer (7)
17 Burning passion (6)
19 Capital of Bulgaria (5)
20 Musical speeds (5)

Puzzle 211

Across

1 Knocks lightly (4)
3 Scornful negativity (8)
9 Notable feat (7)
10 Deceives or misleads (5)
11 Shrewdness (12)
14 Plant liquid (3)
16 Tool for boring holes (5)
17 Pair of people (3)
18 Untimely (12)
21 Not together (5)
22 Mound made by insects (7)
23 Lessening (8)
24 Fix (4)

Down

1 Enter unlawfully (8)
2 Pied ___ of Hamelin: legendary person (5)
4 Nevertheless (3)
5 Teach to accept a belief uncritically (12)
6 Attributed to (7)
7 Sentimentality (4)
8 In a self-satisfied manner (12)
12 Animal enclosures (5)
13 Wore clothes on the catwalk (8)
15 Game played on a sloping board (7)
19 Woollen material like felt (5)
20 Mother (4)
22 Bristle-like appendage (3)

Puzzle 212

Across

7 Ten raised to the power 100 (6)
8 Third sign of the zodiac (6)
10 Readable (7)
11 Laud (5)
12 Ooze or leak slowly (4)
13 Magical incantation (5)
17 Senseless (5)
18 Swindle (4)
22 Garment with sleeves (5)
23 Bodyguards (7)
24 Gas with formula C2H6 (6)
25 Sounds off at length (6)

Down

1 Eternal (7)
2 Non-pedigree dog (7)
3 Uncertainty (5)
4 Exposes (7)
5 Young sows (5)
6 Cash registers (5)
9 Replied (9)
14 Combining (7)
15 Do something more quickly (5,2)
16 Carry on (7)
19 Remains of a fire (5)
20 Emits a breath of relief (5)
21 Range (5)

Puzzle 213

Across

1 Select; choose (4)
3 Roman leaders (8)
9 Deliberately impassive (7)
10 Doctrine (5)
11 In a persuasive manner (12)
13 Step down from a job (6)
15 Covered in cloth (6)
17 Circle amount (anag) (12)
20 Very masculine (5)
21 Between two objects (7)
22 Spattered with liquid (8)
23 Sound of a lion (4)

Down

1 Cosmetic treatment of the feet (8)
2 Series of linked metal rings (5)
4 Threaten (6)
5 Behavioural peculiarity (12)
6 Coincide partially (7)
7 Team (4)
8 Scallions (6,6)
12 Mileage tracker (8)
14 Uncomplaining (7)
16 Frail (6)
18 ___ acid: protein building block (5)
19 Flightless birds (4)

Crossword

Puzzle 214

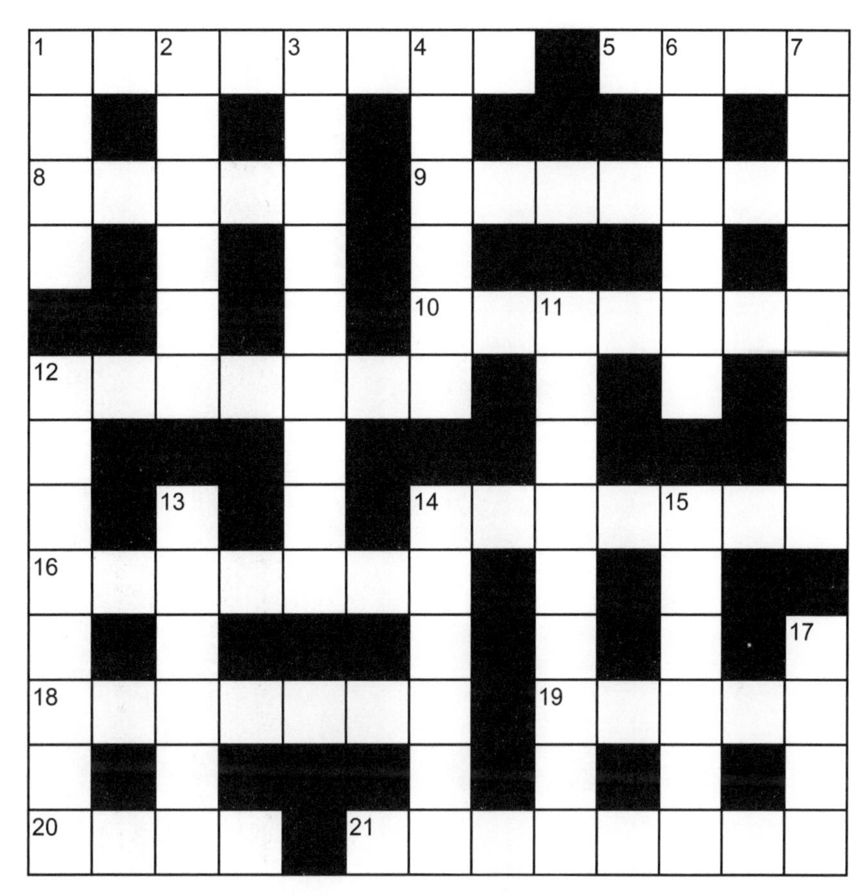

Across

1 Unexpected gain (8)
5 Opposite of low (4)
8 Group of eight (5)
9 Perils (7)
10 Perfect example of a quality (7)
12 Removed dirt (7)
14 Small-scale model (7)
16 Horse ridden by a knight (7)
18 Clap (7)
19 Coarse rock used for polishing (5)
20 Light fawn colour (4)
21 Trestles (anag) (8)

Down

1 Dense growth of trees (4)
2 Stinging plant (6)
3 Feeding up (9)
4 Lived with as a guest (6)
6 Refrigerator compartment (6)
7 Exaggerated emotion (8)
11 Wrong (9)
12 Private meeting (8)
13 Hinder (6)
14 Remove silt from a river (6)
15 Assert without proof (6)
17 Extras (cricket) (4)

Puzzle 215

Across

1 Hots (anag) (4)
3 Events that hinder progress (8)
9 Belgian city (7)
10 More mature (5)
11 Principal face of a building (12)
13 Move in haste (6)
15 Increases in size (6)
17 Loving (12)
20 In the company of (5)
21 Metal similar to platinum (7)
22 Gives a right to (8)
23 Long grass (4)

Down

1 Echinoderm with a distinctive shape (8)
2 Exceed (5)
4 Reveal (6)
5 Version of the blues (6-6)
6 Supplement to a will (7)
7 Painful or aching (4)
8 Boxing class division (12)
12 Admired and respected (8)
14 Candid (7)
16 Band of colour (6)
18 Live by (5)
19 Very strong wind (4)

Puzzle 216

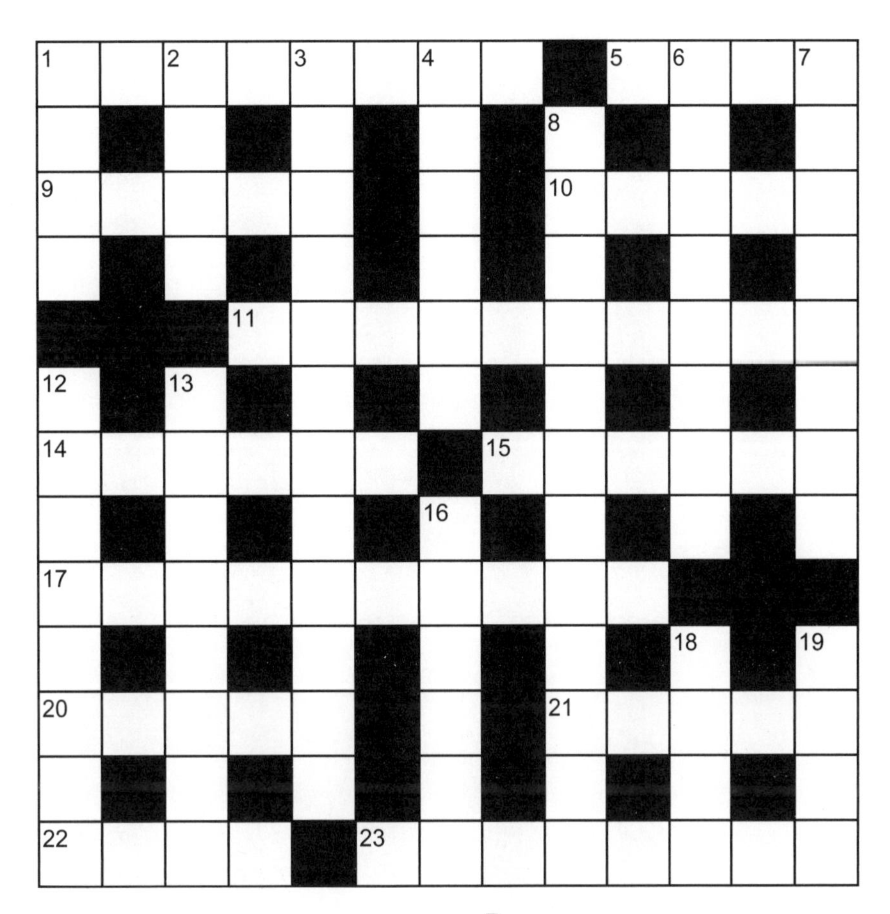

Across

1 Type of bag (8)
5 ___ Minnelli: US actress (4)
9 Coming after (5)
10 Extravagant dinner (5)
11 Final result (3,7)
14 Pointed projectiles (6)
15 Gazed (6)
17 Grumbled (10)
20 Group of lions (5)
21 Shrill sound (5)
22 Keeps on at (4)
23 Plump (4-4)

Down

1 Cabbagelike plant (4)
2 Creative disciplines (4)
3 Determined (6-6)
4 Moves very slowly (6)
6 Rushing (2,1,5)
7 Height (8)
8 Easily (12)
12 Cooking pot (8)
13 Making waves in hair (8)
16 Alyssa ___ : Phoebe in Charmed (6)
18 Italian acknowledgement (4)
19 Pottery material (4)

Puzzle 217

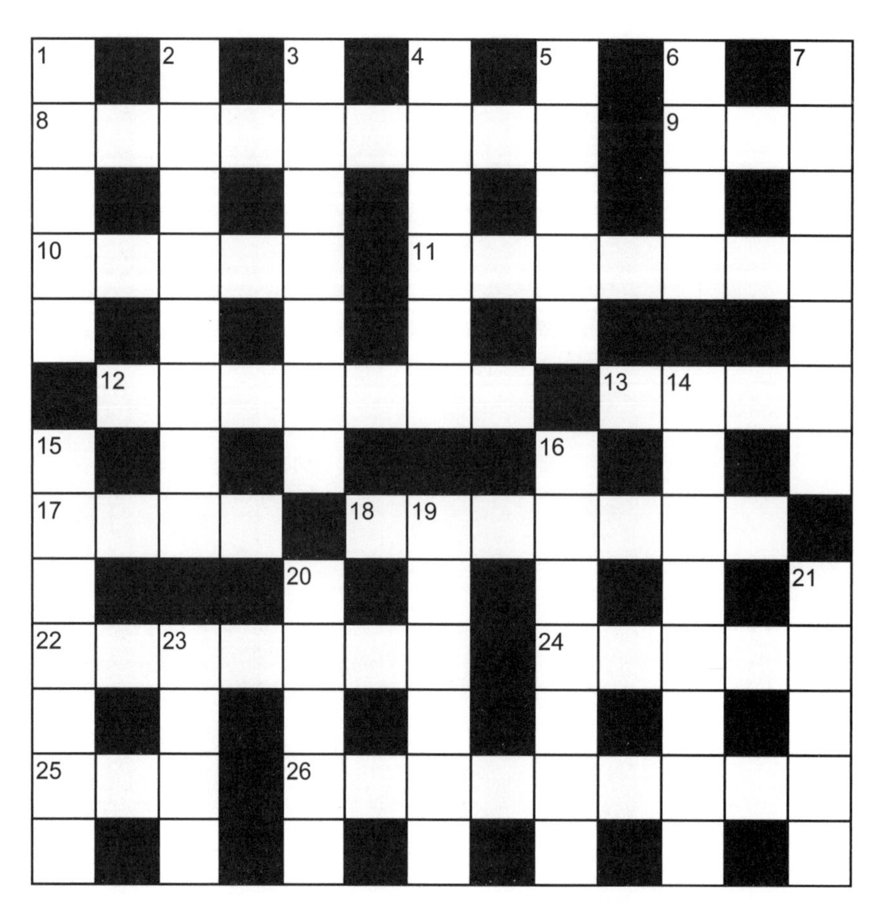

Across

- **8** Repeat (9)
- **9** Cease (3)
- **10** Spiked weapon (5)
- **11** Loud enough to be heard (7)
- **12** Hit hard (7)
- **13** Trickery (4)
- **17** Optimistic (4)
- **18** Enchanting (7)
- **22** Build in a certain place (7)
- **24** Gate fastener (5)
- **25** Space or interval (3)
- **26** Sweets on sticks (9)

Down

- **1** Outer layer of bread (5)
- **2** Difficult choices (8)
- **3** Patio area (7)
- **4** Control; regulate (6)
- **5** Looks after (5)
- **6** Plant used for flavouring (4)
- **7** Sticks to (7)
- **14** Idleness (8)
- **15** Portent (7)
- **16** Choice cut of beef (7)
- **19** ___ Berrabah: member of the Sugababes (6)
- **20** Sends out in the post (5)
- **21** Strategic board game (5)
- **23** Recording medium (4)

Puzzle 218

Across

1 Jovial (8)
5 Increase in size (4)
8 Clergyman (5)
9 Expressed audibly (7)
10 Formation of troops (7)
12 Routers (anag) (7)
14 Seems (7)
16 Protected (7)
18 Analyse (7)
19 Find out (5)
20 Observed (4)
21 Colouring glass or wood (8)

Down

1 Relocate (4)
2 Excessively ornate (of music) (6)
3 Made use of (9)
4 Loan shark (6)
6 Seldom (6)
7 Breadth (8)
11 The masses (3,6)
12 Sets off (8)
13 Injure (6)
14 Promotional material (6)
15 Opposite of an acid (6)
17 Cosy (4)

Puzzle 219

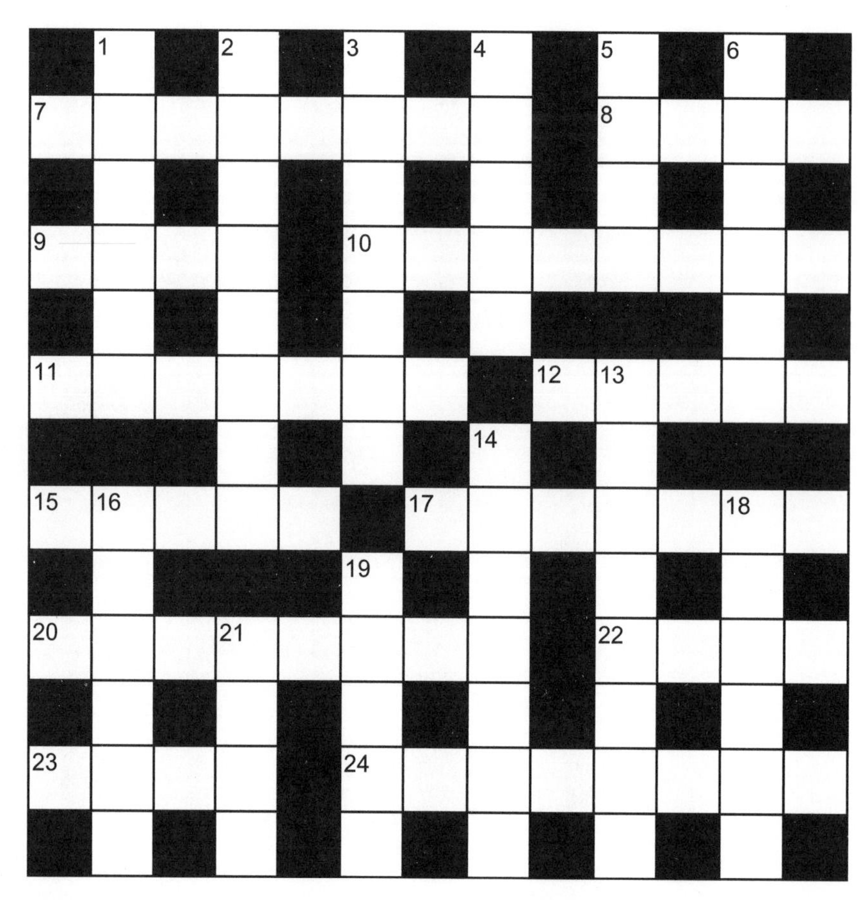

Across

7 Machine used to surf the internet (8)
8 Public disturbance (4)
9 Contented cat sound (4)
10 Eg hats and helmets (8)
11 Piece of jewellery (7)
12 Pierced by a bull's horn (5)
15 Things you buy; effects (5)
17 Where you watch films (7)
20 Wealthy (8)
22 Sullen (4)
23 Smile broadly (4)
24 Insisted upon (8)

Down

1 Measure of loudness (6)
2 Improved equipment (8)
3 Irritating; hankering (7)
4 Staple food (5)
5 Steep and rugged rock (4)
6 Place where something is set (6)
13 Exaggerated (8)
14 People harmed by criminal acts (7)
16 Type of lace-up shoe (6)
18 Keen insight (6)
19 Tall plants of the grass family (5)
21 ___ Del Rey: singer (4)

Crossword

Puzzle 220

Across

1 On the beach; on land (6)
4 Extravagant meals (6)
9 Official pardon (7)
10 Gold or silver in bulk (7)
11 Lazy person; layabout (5)
12 Burn with hot liquid (5)
14 Leases (5)
15 Tiny aquatic plants (5)
17 Australian arboreal marsupial (5)
18 Tidal wave (7)
20 Aquatic creature with prominent barbels (7)
21 Walks (6)
22 Impudent (6)

Down

1 In slow tempo (of music) (6)
2 Dealing with (8)
3 Vertical part of a step (5)
5 Interminable (7)
6 South Asian garment (4)
7 Autographed something for a fan (6)
8 Science of communications (11)
13 Grammatical case (8)
14 Meander (anag) (7)
15 Painter (6)
16 Walk nonchalantly (6)
17 Sailing ship (5)
19 Desire to act (4)

Puzzle 221

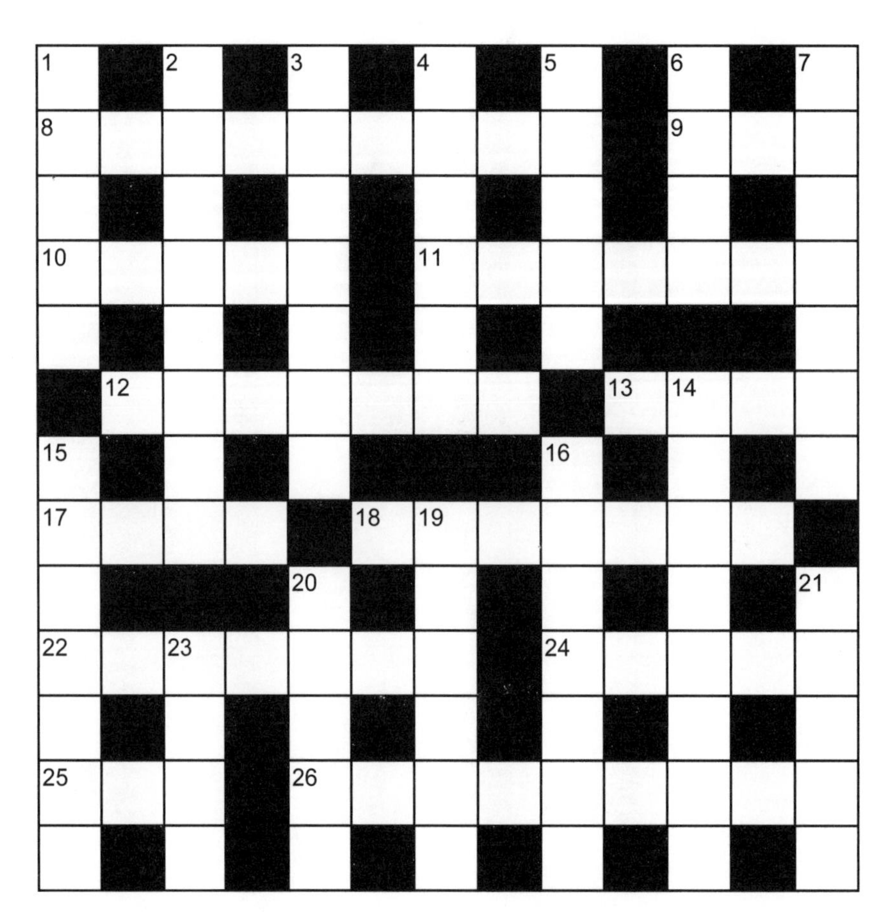

Across

8 Declaration of a marriage as null and void (9)
9 Deep anger (3)
10 Where tennis is played (5)
11 Painting medium (7)
12 Wears away (7)
13 Division of a hospital (4)
17 Injure (4)
18 Eg Borneo and Java (7)
22 Ditherer (7)
24 Sticky (5)
25 Slippery fish (3)
26 Advocate (9)

Down

1 Military walk (5)
2 Hamper (8)
3 Floating wreckage (7)
4 Mild or kind (6)
5 Remnant of a fallen tree (5)
6 Ready to eat (of fruit) (4)
7 Requests forcefully (7)
14 Daring (8)
15 Rich fish soup (7)
16 Humorous drawing (7)
19 Scratch (6)
20 Eg from Cork (5)
21 Aromatic resin (5)
23 Small mouse-like rodent (4)

Puzzle 222

Across

1 Name for New York City (3,5)
5 Make beer or ale (4)
9 Small tuned drum (5)
10 Intimate companion (5)
11 From now on (10)
14 Selfishness (6)
15 Not awake (6)
17 Enormous (10)
20 Triangular river mouth (5)
21 Clamorous (5)
22 Period of 365 days (4)
23 Exclamation of surprise (8)

Down

1 Young child (4)
2 Departed (4)
3 Opposite of amateur (12)
4 Propel with force (6)
6 Returned to type (8)
7 Pays homage to (8)
8 Antique; not modern (3-9)
12 Pageantry (8)
13 Mexican pancake (8)
16 Gaming tile with pips in each half (6)
18 Religious act (4)
19 Hair colourants (4)

Puzzle 223

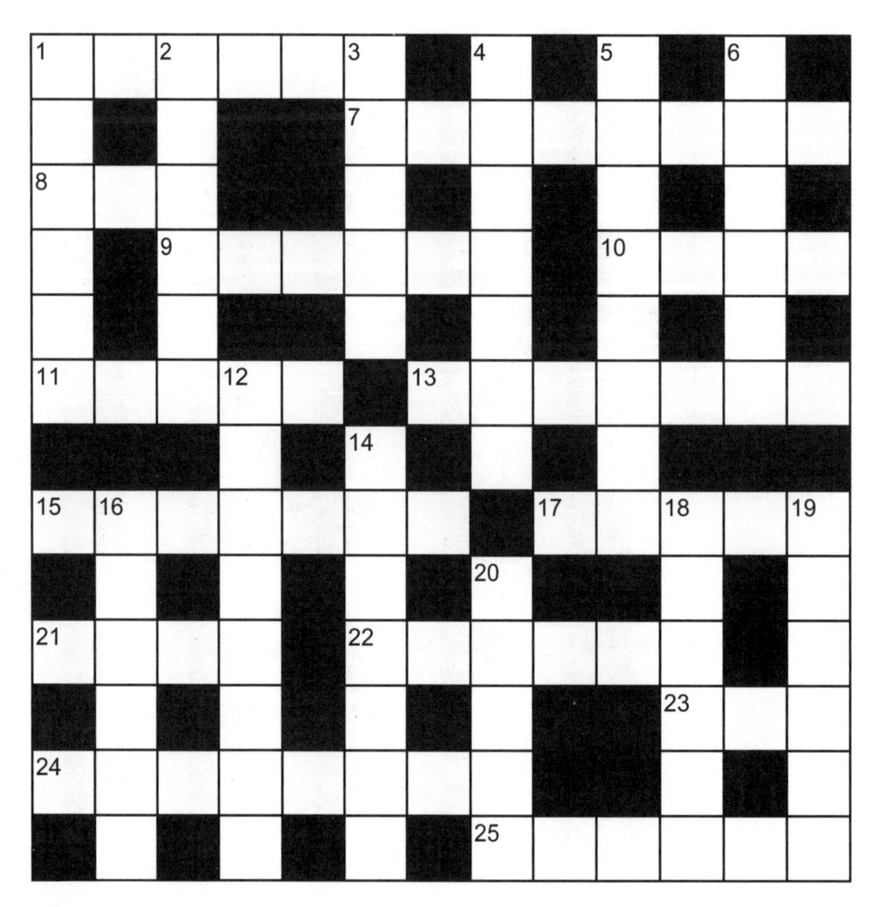

Across

- **1** Female sibling (6)
- **7** Substance used for polishing (8)
- **8** Ancient pot (3)
- **9** Start a fire (6)
- **10** Pulls a vehicle (4)
- **11** Nairobi is the capital here (5)
- **13** Break down chemically (7)
- **15** All together (2,5)
- **17** Tell off (5)
- **21** Word ending a prayer (4)
- **22** Poems; sounds alike (6)
- **23** Large beer cask (3)
- **24** Expression of gratitude (5,3)
- **25** Groups of lions (6)

Down

- **1** Parrot sound (6)
- **2** Deeply recessed (of someone's eyes) (6)
- **3** Attacks without warning (5)
- **4** Commanded (7)
- **5** Recondite (8)
- **6** Openly declared (6)
- **12** Longing (8)
- **14** Fish-eating birds of prey (7)
- **16** Insect larvae (6)
- **18** Expelled from office (6)
- **19** Activities (6)
- **20** Sticky sweet liquid (5)

Puzzle 224

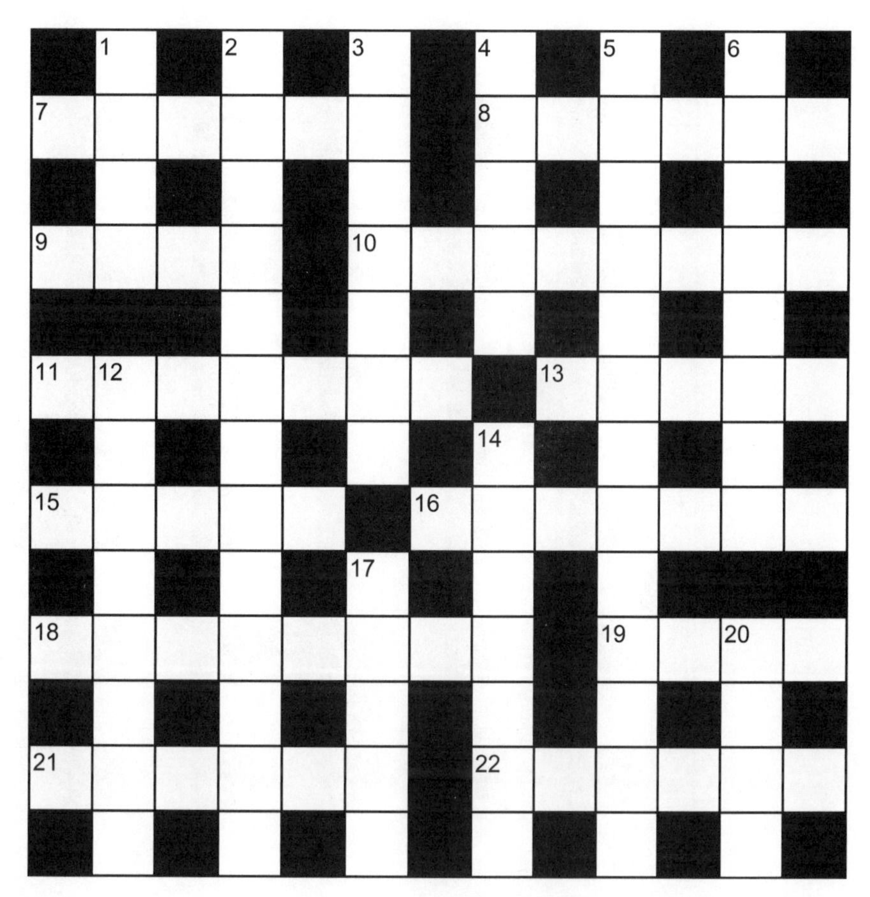

Across

7 Mix up (6)
8 Quiver (6)
9 Swerve (4)
10 Make more concentrated (8)
11 Answering correctly (7)
13 ___ Harding: Girls Aloud singer (5)
15 Gold ___ : award for coming first (5)
16 Eg using a straw (7)
18 Presiding officer (8)
19 Jar lids (4)
21 Large sign (6)
22 Takes fright (6)

Down

1 Source of inspiration (4)
2 Shortened forms of words (13)
3 Move downwards (7)
4 Supply sparingly; sandpiper (5)
5 Advertising by telephone (13)
6 One who steers a boat (8)
12 In the sky (8)
14 Root vegetables (7)
17 Smug smile (5)
20 Stride; rate of moving (4)

Puzzle 225

Across

1 Closing section of a piece of music (4)
3 Soft leather shoe (8)
9 Put in order (7)
10 Ben ___ : Scottish mountain (5)
11 Directions (12)
14 Diving bird (3)
16 Place where something happens (5)
17 Drunkard (3)
18 Electronic security device (7,5)
21 Rouse from sleep (5)
22 Delivers on a promise (7)
23 Gets ready (8)
24 Wetlands (4)

Down

1 Crucial (8)
2 Extinct birds (5)
4 Eccentric; strange (3)
5 Significant (12)
6 Money put aside for the future (7)
7 Kate ___ : British singer (4)
8 Lavish event (12)
12 Latin American dance (5)
13 Makes a list (8)
15 ___ down: apply oneself to a task (7)
19 Stand up (5)
20 Exchange (4)
22 Enemy (3)

Puzzle 226

Across

1 Metal worker (5)
4 Of doubtful honesty (informal) (5)
10 Premiership football club (7)
11 Faint southern constellation (5)
12 Word that identifies a thing (4)
13 Immediately after this (8)
16 Divers (anag) (6)
17 Oral (6)
20 Making (8)
21 Furnace (4)
23 Dietary roughage (5)
25 Spruce up (7)
26 Small white garden flower (5)
27 Coarse (5)

Down

2 Relating to men (9)
3 Colour lightly (4)
5 Hindered (8)
6 University teacher (3)
7 Having a human crew (6)
8 Moves through the air (5)
9 Give notice (4)
14 Printed for public sale (9)
15 Appendages on a bird's skin (8)
18 Protective layer (6)
19 Breathe in audibly (5)
20 Small restaurant (4)
22 A nobleman (4)
24 Bleat of a sheep (3)

Puzzle 227

Across

1 Endorsed (11)
9 Kick out (5)
10 Before the present (3)
11 Make less miserable (5)
12 Push gently (5)
13 Most jolly (8)
16 A desert in south-western Africa (8)
18 Representative; messenger (5)
21 Living in a city (5)
22 First woman (3)
23 Determine the number of (5)
24 Founded (11)

Down

2 Royal attendant (7)
3 Position on top of (7)
4 Trees with lobed leaves (6)
5 Gena Lee ___ : actress (5)
6 Antelope (5)
7 Not yet finished (11)
8 Supreme authority (11)
14 Military gestures (7)
15 Mandible (7)
17 Yearly (6)
19 Opinions (5)
20 Woody-stemmed plant (5)

Crossword

Puzzle 228

Across

1 ___ Moon: Character in Frasier (6)
7 Confidently optimistic (8)
8 Feline animal (3)
9 Seem (6)
10 Surplus (4)
11 Explore or examine (5)
13 Wicked look that causes harm (4,3)
15 Feeling positive (7)
17 Swing audibly through the air (5)
21 Modify (4)
22 Finish a telephone call (4,2)
23 Suitable (3)
24 Sticking together (8)
25 Purify then condense (6)

Down

1 Depart suddenly (6)
2 Edible plant tuber (6)
3 Trees (anag) (5)
4 Inscribe (7)
5 House with one storey (8)
6 Disorderly (6)
12 Inhales (8)
14 Shrub with tubular flowers (7)
16 More likely than not (4-2)
18 Deposit knowledge (6)
19 Youth ___ : accommodation provider (6)
20 Finished (5)

Puzzle 229

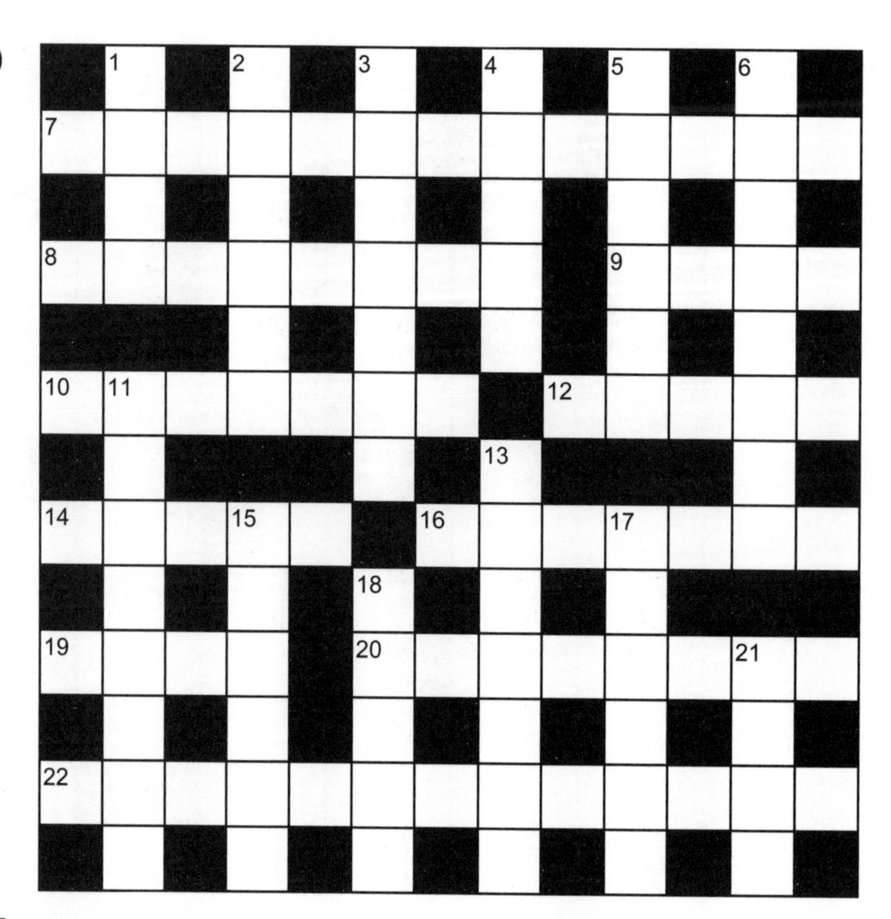

Across

7 Confirmation (13)
8 Relating to courts of law (8)
9 Move about aimlessly (4)
10 Knife (7)
12 Goodbye (Spanish) (5)
14 Dirty (5)
16 First light (7)
19 Soft creamy cheese (4)
20 The production and discharge of something (8)
22 Four-sided figure (13)

Down

1 Lead singer of U2 (4)
2 Part of a cannon behind the bore (6)
3 Corpulence (7)
4 Elegance; class (5)
5 Kept hold of (6)
6 Starchy edible tubers (8)
11 Sign of the zodiac (8)
13 Melodious (7)
15 Fears greatly (6)
17 Register of duties (6)
18 Denise ___ : British heptathlete (5)
21 Egg-shaped (4)

Crossword

Puzzle 230

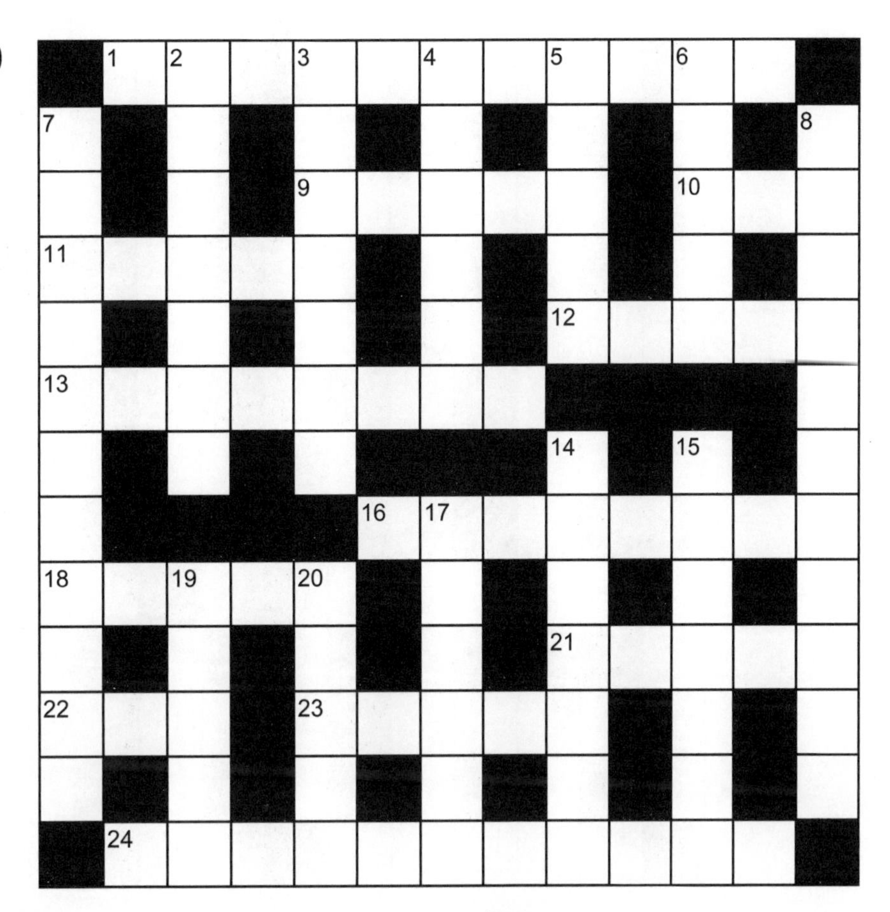

Across

1 Yearly celebration (11)
9 Ways or tracks (5)
10 By way of (3)
11 Town in Surrey (5)
12 Possessed (5)
13 Beat easily (8)
16 Capital of Finland (8)
18 Facial protuberances (5)
21 ___ Klum: supermodel (5)
22 Sound of a dove (3)
23 Put out a fire (5)
24 Mean (5-6)

Down

2 Not in any place (7)
3 Have a positive impact (7)
4 Large property with land; holding (6)
5 US R&B singer (5)
6 Torn apart (5)
7 Branch of physics (11)
8 Third awning (anag) (11)
14 Shuns (7)
15 Throw into disorder (7)
17 Surround (6)
19 Small seat (5)
20 Soft drinks (US) (5)

Puzzle 231

Across

1 ___ Ure: Ultravox singer (5)
4 Action words (5)
10 Trespass (7)
11 Elector (5)
12 Device sounding a warning (4)
13 Eg Usain Bolt and Mo Farah (8)
16 Applauded (6)
17 Begin to grow (6)
20 Act of treachery (8)
21 Pal (4)
23 Lean or thin (5)
25 Nationality of a citizen of Beijing (7)
26 Large indefinite amount (5)
27 Dr ___ : US writer (5)

Down

2 Forbid (9)
3 Dejected (4)
5 Wrapper for a letter (8)
6 Mouthpiece attached to a bridle (3)
7 Next after seventh (6)
8 Outdoor shelters (5)
9 ___ and cons: pluses and minuses (4)
14 Lacking force (9)
15 Excessively self-indulgent (8)
18 Meddle with (6)
19 Contest (5)
20 Shrub; uncultivated land (4)
22 Duration (4)
24 Small viper (3)

Crossword

Puzzle 232

Across

1 Heroic tale (4)
3 Harsh; grating (8)
9 Radioactive element (7)
10 Edge or border (5)
11 Conciliatory gift (3)
12 Water lily (5)
13 SI unit of luminous flux (5)
15 Conceal (5)
17 Ringing sound (5)
18 Allow (3)
19 Angry (5)
20 West Indian musical style (7)
21 Salutation (8)
22 ___ vera: used in cosmetics (4)

Down

1 Deep consideration of oneself (4-9)
2 Understand (5)
4 Cylindrical drum (3-3)
5 Immune (12)
6 Unpredictable (7)
7 Hidden store of valuables (8,5)
8 Action of moving a thing from its position (12)
14 Meatier (anag) (7)
16 Roman god of fire (6)
18 Folded back part of a coat (5)

Puzzle 233

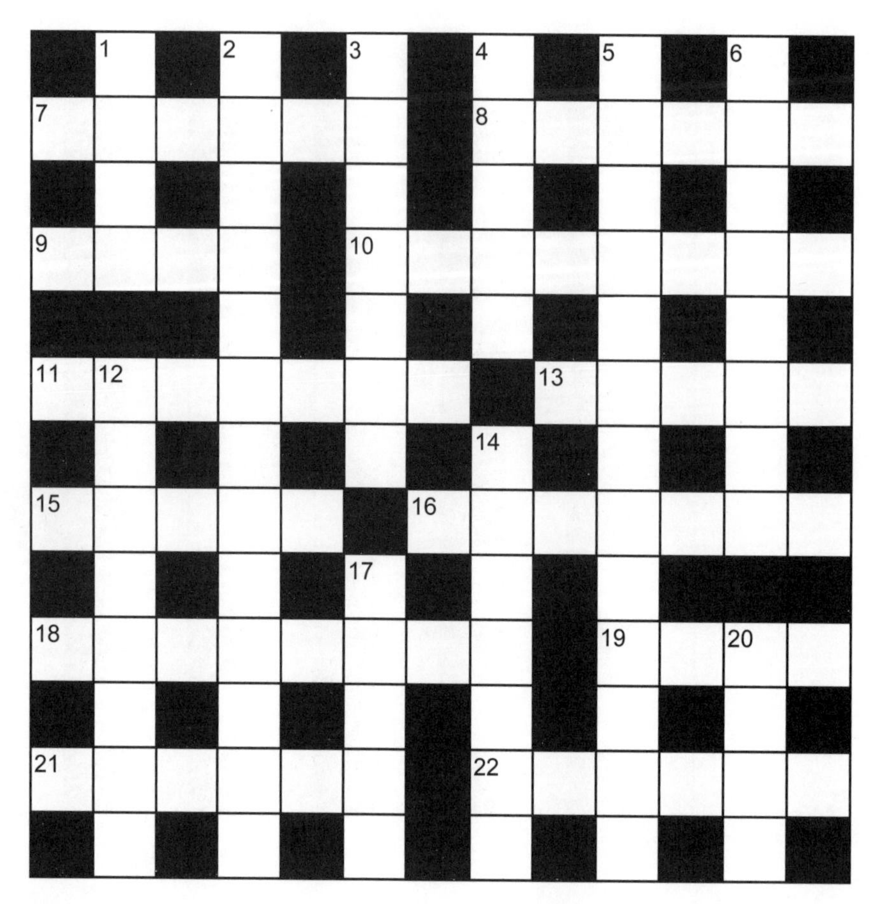

Across

7 Fighting instrument (6)
8 Official population count (6)
9 Game played on horseback (4)
10 Geniality (8)
11 Reptiles (7)
13 Caricature (5)
15 Palpitate (5)
16 Large area of land (7)
18 Musical wind instrument (8)
19 Robert De ___ : actor (4)
21 Occurring in spring (6)
22 Learned person (6)

Down

1 Short note or reminder (4)
2 Act of distribution (13)
3 Rebuffed; spurned (7)
4 Examines quickly (5)
5 Stoical; patient (13)
6 Shining (8)
12 Unscathed (8)
14 Extract (7)
17 Frustrates the plans of (5)
20 Devastation (4)

Crossword

Puzzle 234

Across

1 Cook meat in the oven (5)
4 Boats (5)
10 Workshop or studio (7)
11 Dried kernel of the coconut (5)
12 Eg petrol (4)
13 Extremely tall (8)
16 Clever or skilful (6)
17 Afloat (6)
20 Keep under control (8)
21 Father (4)
23 Strong thick rope (5)
25 Making sore by rubbing (7)
26 Oppress grievously (5)
27 Youngsters aged from 13 - 19 (5)

Down

2 Poetaster (anag) (9)
3 Earth (4)
5 Large Spanish estate (8)
6 Seed of an apple (3)
7 A palm tree (6)
8 Sing softly (5)
9 Tolled (4)
14 Impersonation (9)
15 Arguments (8)
18 Strong ringing sounds (6)
19 Lifting device (5)
20 Framework for holding things (4)
22 State of mental confusion (4)
24 Prevent (3)

Puzzle 235

Across

1 Stiff paper (4)
3 Multiplying by two (8)
9 Vapid (7)
10 Bunches (5)
11 Butterfly larvae (12)
13 US monetary unit (6)
15 Pay no attention to (6)
17 Study of human societies (12)
20 Promotional wording (5)
21 Eventually (7)
22 Liquids which dissolve other substances (8)
23 Travelled too quickly (4)

Down

1 Happen simultaneously (8)
2 Steer (anag) (5)
4 Establish by law (6)
5 Place of conflict (12)
6 Raging fire (7)
7 Lesion (4)
8 Easy to converse with (12)
12 Naive or sentimental (4-4)
14 Pertaining to the tongue (7)
16 Underside of an arch (6)
18 Spring flower (5)
19 Recedes (4)

Crossword

Puzzle 236

Across

1 Containing many inhabitants (8)
5 Cab (4)
8 Musical toy (5)
9 Not strict (7)
10 Funny (7)
12 Cleaned its feathers (of a bird) (7)
14 Rags (7)
16 Large fast warship (7)
18 Spouts (7)
19 Nearby (5)
20 Fastens a knot (4)
21 Remote; cut off (8)

Down

1 Fish (4)
2 Baffle (6)
3 Lack of accuracy (9)
4 Remove goods from a van (6)
6 Pertaining to vinegar (6)
7 Whole numbers (8)
11 Amoral (9)
12 Clearly defined area (8)
13 Drink greedily (6)
14 Has confidence in (6)
15 Send for sale overseas (6)
17 A plant grows from this (4)

Puzzle 237

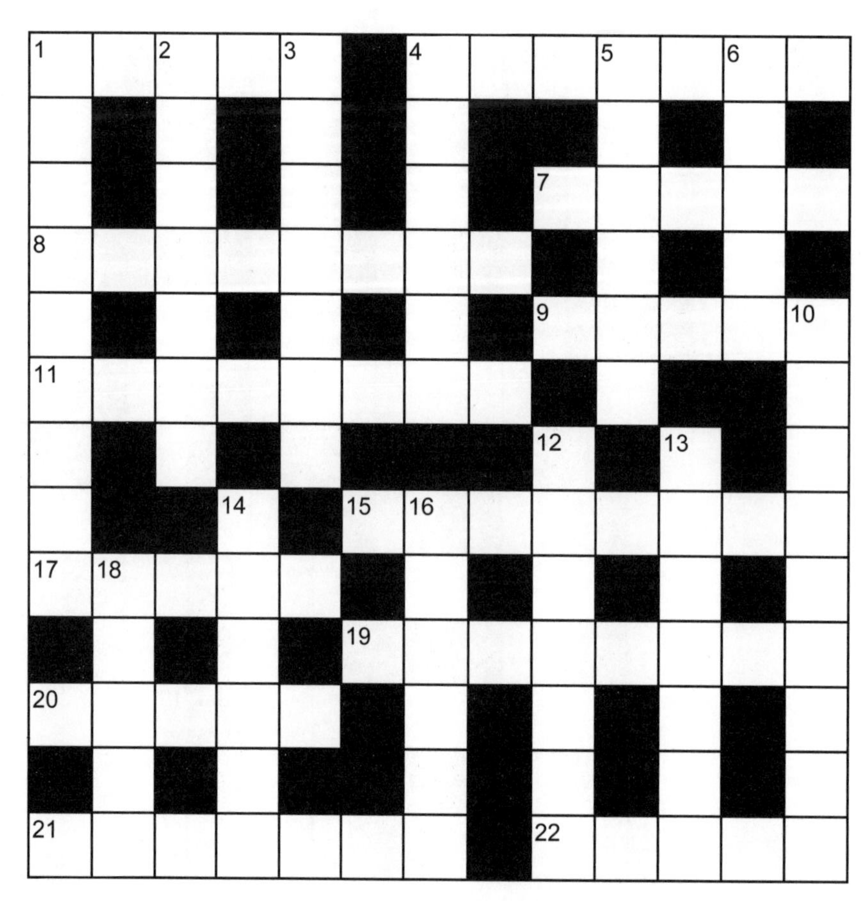

Across

1 Heavy noble gas (5)
4 Experiences anxiety (7)
7 ___ Agassi: former tennis star (5)
8 Act of leaving out (8)
9 Joe ___ : English presenter and actor (5)
11 Nuisance; unpleasant problem (8)
15 Act of moving around an axis (8)
17 Fill with high spirits (5)
19 A magical quality (8)
20 Distinguishing characteristic (5)
21 Showed a person to their seat (7)
22 Set piece in rugby (5)

Down

1 Percussion instrument (9)
2 Existing solely in name (7)
3 Male reporter (7)
4 Loud rushing noise (6)
5 Fame (6)
6 British noblemen (5)
10 Mesmerism (9)
12 Textiles (7)
13 Strong alcoholic spirit (7)
14 Walk with long steps (6)
16 Make a larger offer at auction (6)
18 Lingers furtively (5)

Puzzle 238

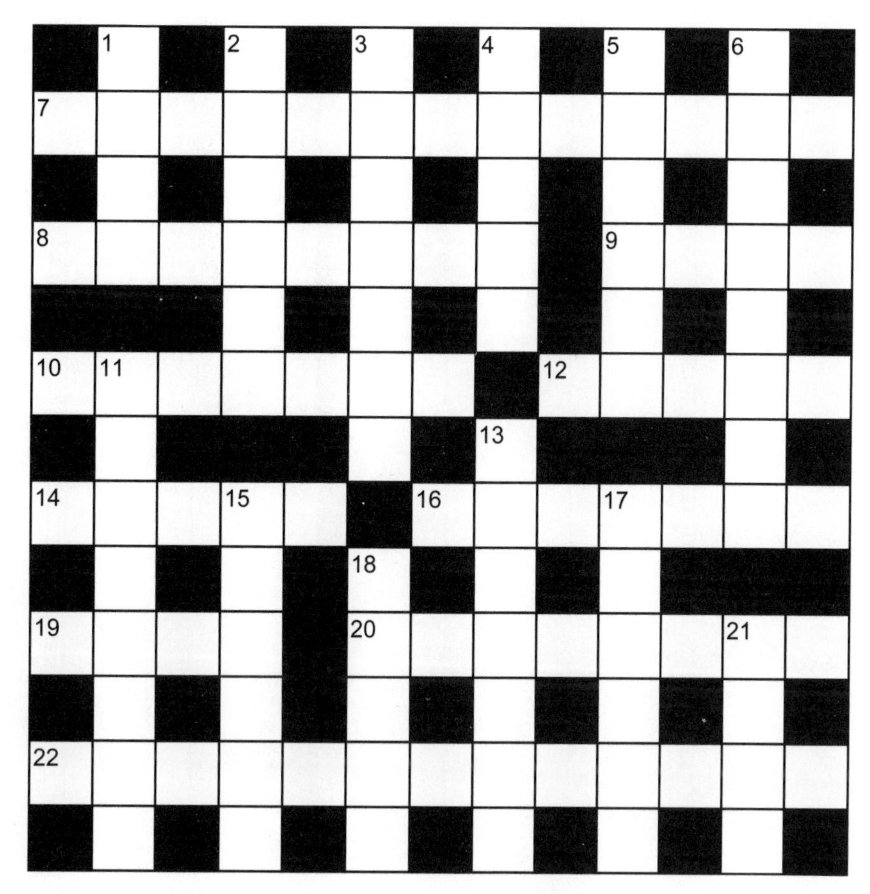

Across

7 Sweets (13)
8 Charm (8)
9 Resistance unit (pl) (4)
10 Cried plaintively (7)
12 Gave away (5)
14 Rushes along; skims (5)
16 Tragedy by Shakespeare (7)
19 Chances of winning (4)
20 Patrimony (8)
22 Tactically (13)

Down

1 Flaring star (4)
2 Continent (6)
3 Run with light steps (7)
4 Musical instrument with keys (5)
5 Doze (6)
6 Percussion sound (8)
11 Clarity (8)
13 Sheikhdom in the Persian Gulf (7)
15 Dreary (6)
17 Be disloyal to (6)
18 Very small amount (5)
21 Swallow eagerly (4)

Puzzle 239

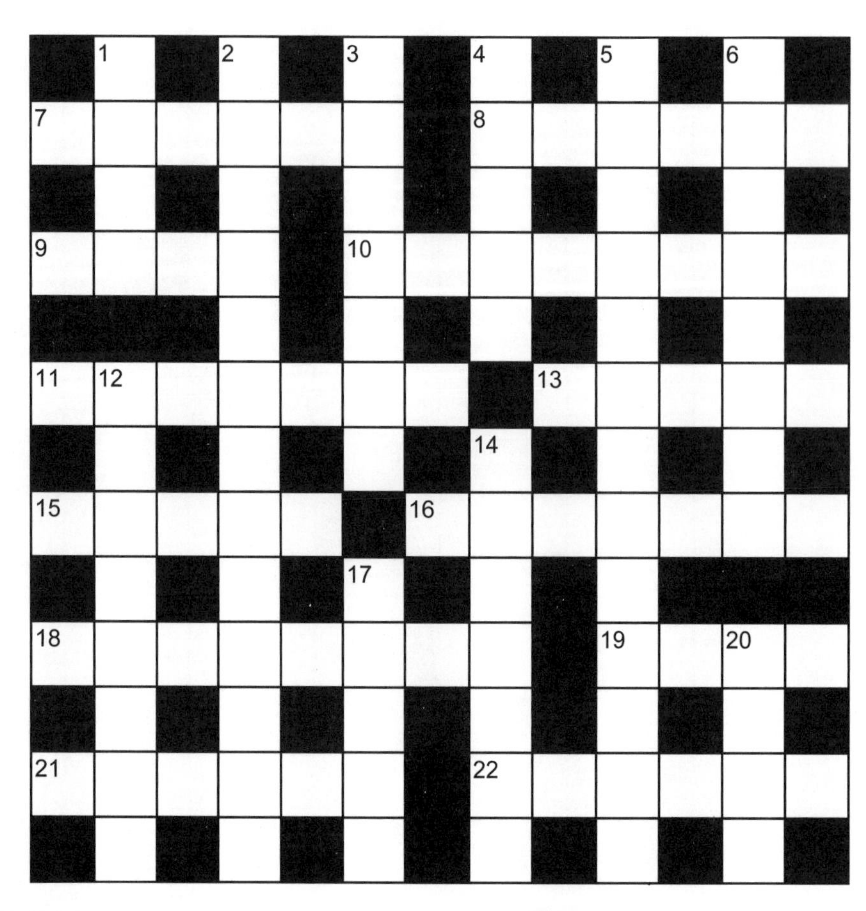

Across

7 Greater in height (6)
8 ___ Staunton: English actress (6)
9 Stylish and fashionable (4)
10 Eg physics and biology (8)
11 Spreads out (7)
13 ___ Piper: potato (5)
15 Woman getting married (5)
16 Precipitating (7)
18 At work (2-3-3)
19 Therefore (4)
21 Acrimonious (6)
22 Mythical monsters (6)

Down

1 Every (4)
2 Type of traditional photography (5-3-5)
3 Newly (7)
4 A finger or toe (5)
5 Rebirth in a new body (13)
6 Process of sticking to a surface (8)
12 Unreasonably anxious about (8)
14 Burrowing rodents (7)
17 ___ Ulvaeus: member of ABBA (5)
20 Unattractive (4)

Puzzle 240

Across

1 Ongoing disagreement (11)
9 Visual representation (5)
10 Not near (3)
11 Records (5)
12 Linear measures of three feet (5)
13 Lacking confidence (8)
16 Horse of light tan colour (8)
18 Principle of morality (5)
21 A woolly ruminant animal (5)
22 Come together (3)
23 Tortilla topped with cheese (5)
24 Brevity in expressing oneself (11)

Down

2 Distant settlement (7)
3 Divide into three parts (7)
4 Public speaker (6)
5 All (5)
6 More secure (5)
7 Innovative or pioneering (7,4)
8 Plant-eating insect (11)
14 Rainy season (7)
15 Repulsive (7)
17 Calculating machine (6)
19 Greeting (5)
20 Sceptic (5)

Puzzle 241

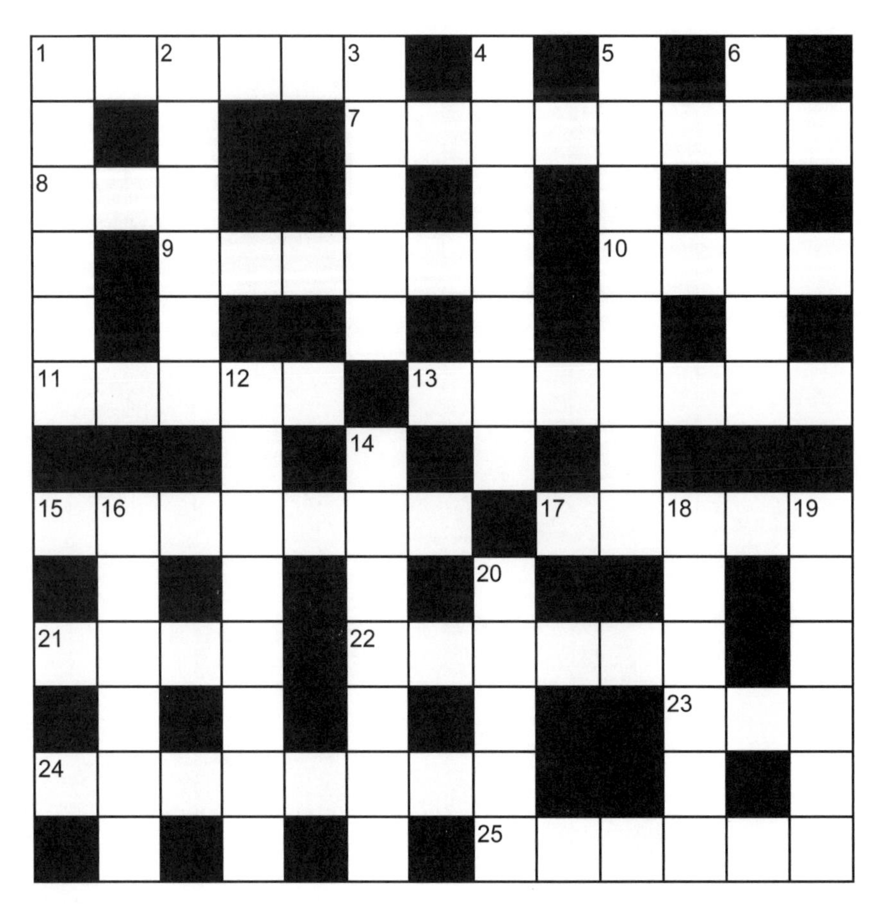

Across

1 Not genuine (6)
7 Fitting (8)
8 ___ Thurman: Kill Bill actress (3)
9 Type of sausage (6)
10 Greatest (4)
11 Mountain cry (5)
13 Diffusion of molecules through a membrane (7)
15 Listless (7)
17 Grind teeth together (5)
21 Skin irritation (4)
22 Collect or store (6)
23 Title of a married woman (3)
24 Sheets and pillowcases (8)
25 Lifting devices (6)

Down

1 Brave; courageous (6)
2 Wiped out (6)
3 Eg heart or liver (5)
4 Contrary to (7)
5 Resolute; obstinate (8)
6 Breakfast food (6)
12 Very delicate and thin (of china) (8)
14 Fixing; manipulating (7)
16 Part of a stamen (6)
18 Pilot (6)
19 Equine animals (6)
20 Old French currency (5)

Puzzle 242

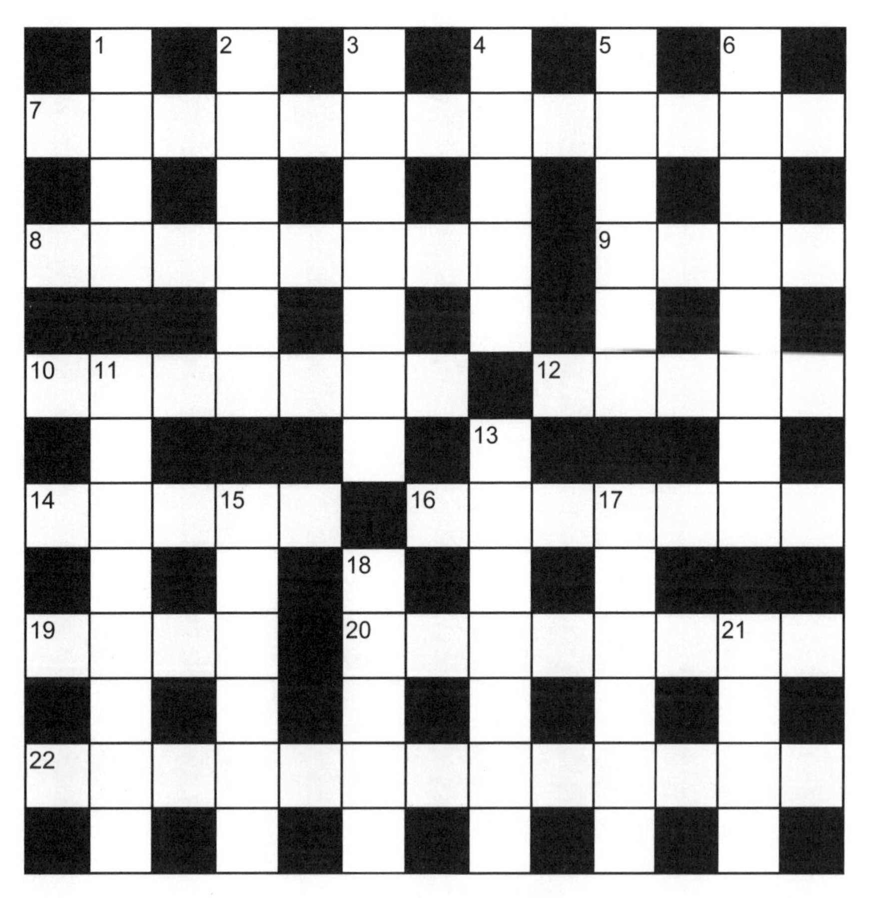

Across

7 Impulsively (13)
8 Moved forwards (8)
9 A parent's mother (4)
10 Make sour (7)
12 Chequered cloth (5)
14 Mark or wear thin (5)
16 Adolescent (7)
19 Concern; worry (4)
20 Based on reason (8)
22 American actor (6,7)

Down

1 Familiar name for a potato (4)
2 Ahead (6)
3 Embellish (7)
4 Shade (anag) (5)
5 Club (6)
6 Moving on the surface of water (8)
11 White crested parrot (8)
13 Unit of square measure (7)
15 Leave the nest (6)
17 Loops with running knots (6)
18 Golf clubs (5)
21 Unfortunately (4)

Puzzle 243

Across

1 Small sales stand (5)
4 Flow with a whirling motion (5)
10 Form a mental picture (7)
11 Striped animal (5)
12 Deliberately taunt (4)
13 Exploits to excess (8)
16 Avoids (6)
17 Gambol (6)
20 Changing (8)
21 Greek cheese (4)
23 Apprehended with certainty (5)
25 Escaping (7)
26 Implement used for cleaning (5)
27 Upper part of the leg (5)

Down

2 Lifeless (9)
3 List (anag) (4)
5 Great skill (8)
6 Mock (3)
7 Feasible (6)
8 Of great weight (5)
9 Short sleeps (4)
14 Material used to make glass reflective (9)
15 Marriages (8)
18 Rough and uneven (of a cliff) (6)
19 Derisive smile (5)
20 Ancient boats (4)
22 Succulent (4)
24 Blade for rowing a boat (3)

Puzzle 244

Across

1 Bats (anag) (4)
3 Likely to occur (8)
9 Eg flies and beetles (7)
10 Suit (5)
11 West Indian dance (5)
12 US state (7)
13 Push against gently with the nose (6)
15 Programme (6)
17 Division of the United Kingdom (7)
18 Smell (5)
20 Respond to (5)
21 Restrain (7)
22 Booked in advance (8)
23 Askew (4)

Down

1 Problem-solving method (5,3,5)
2 Broom made of twigs (5)
4 Scoundrel (6)
5 List of books referred to (12)
6 Clown (7)
7 Wastefully; lavishly (13)
8 Teacher (12)
14 Makes short and sharp turns (7)
16 Suggestion (6)
19 U-shaped curve in a river (5)

Puzzle 245

Across

1 Erase a mark from a surface (6)
4 Manic (6)
9 Had faith in (7)
10 Firmly establish (7)
11 Religious acts (5)
12 Snake (5)
14 Select class (5)
15 Fabric used to make jeans (5)
17 Up to the time when (5)
18 Promising young actress (7)
20 Took the place of (7)
21 Over there (6)
22 Participant in a game (6)

Down

1 Goes inside (6)
2 Ornamental jet of water (8)
3 Gives as a reference (5)
5 Final stage of a chess match (7)
6 Brass instrument (4)
7 Part of the eye (6)
8 Forever (2,9)
13 Increase greatly in number (8)
14 Imitate (7)
15 Disappointment (6)
16 Engineless aircraft (6)
17 Customary (5)
19 River in central England (4)

Puzzle 246

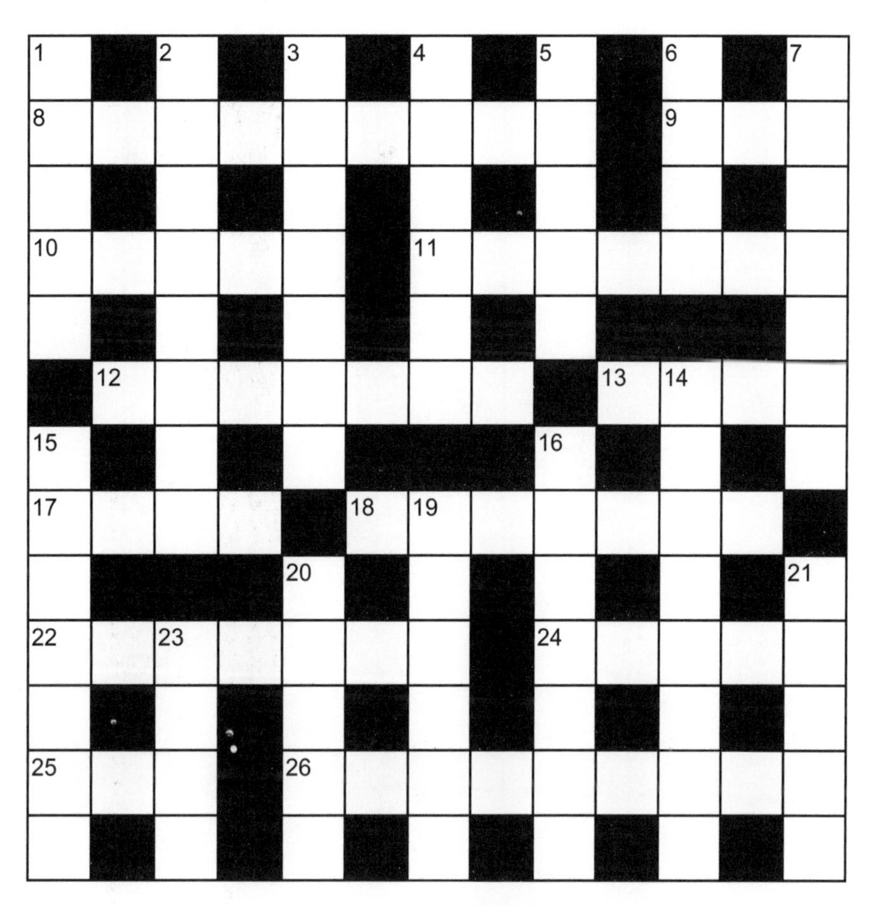

Across

8 Obviously (9)
9 Pasture; meadow (3)
10 Stared into space (5)
11 Exacted retribution (7)
12 Type of rock (7)
13 ___ Khan: British boxer (4)
17 Fertile type of soil (4)
18 Ejects a jet of liquid (7)
22 Surround with armed forces (7)
24 Legal process (5)
25 Organ of sight (3)
26 Space traveller (9)

Down

1 Join together (5)
2 Type of restaurant (8)
3 Curving (7)
4 Narrow passage of water (6)
5 Ancient harps (5)
6 Slow-moving garden mollusc (4)
7 Climbing tools (7)
14 Pertaining to measurement (8)
15 Talk foolishly (7)
16 Enunciation of speech (7)
19 Nauseous (6)
20 Barrier (5)
21 Schemes (5)
23 Prophet (4)

Puzzle 247

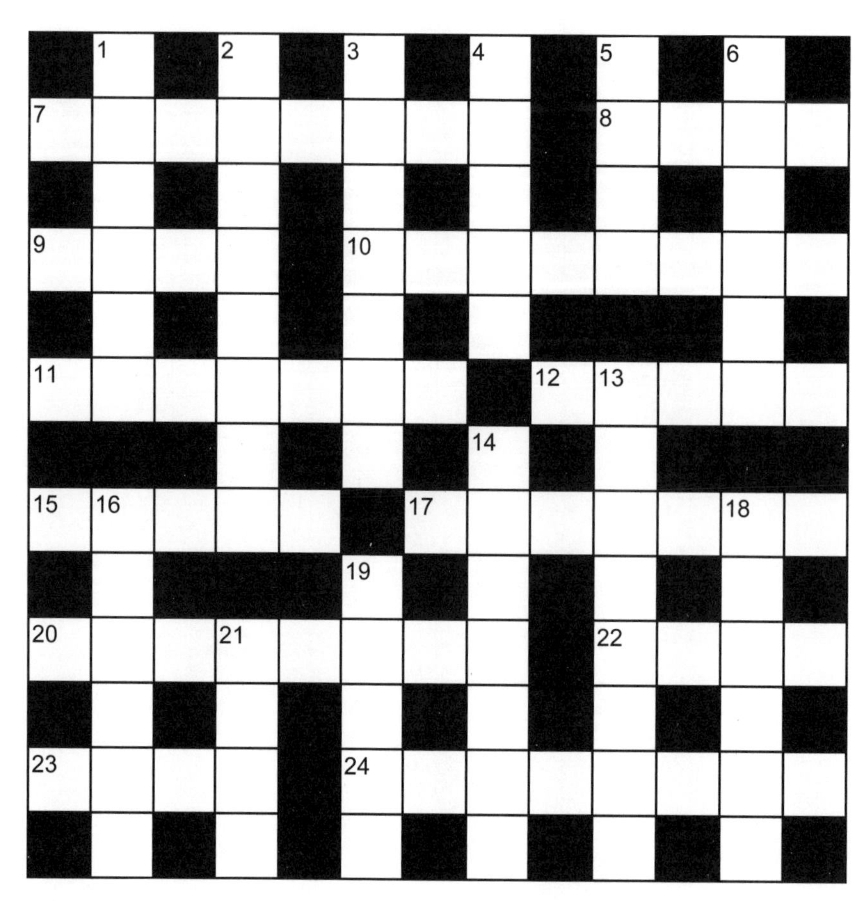

Across

7 Owner of an establishment providing lodgings (8)
8 Eager; keen (4)
9 Couple (4)
10 Comment at the bottom of a page (8)
11 Pouches (7)
12 Basic units of chemical elements (5)
15 Financial resources (5)
17 Feeling jealous (7)
20 Discern (8)
22 Part of an egg (4)
23 ___-Jacques Rousseau: philosopher (4)
24 Genteel and feminine in manner (8)

Down

1 Red salad fruit (6)
2 Type of leather (8)
3 Outsiders (7)
4 Sink; sag (5)
5 First light (4)
6 Single-celled alga (6)
13 Vehicle with three wheels (8)
14 Plans to do something (7)
16 Flattened out (6)
18 Different from (6)
19 Daft (5)
21 Food containers (4)

Puzzle 248

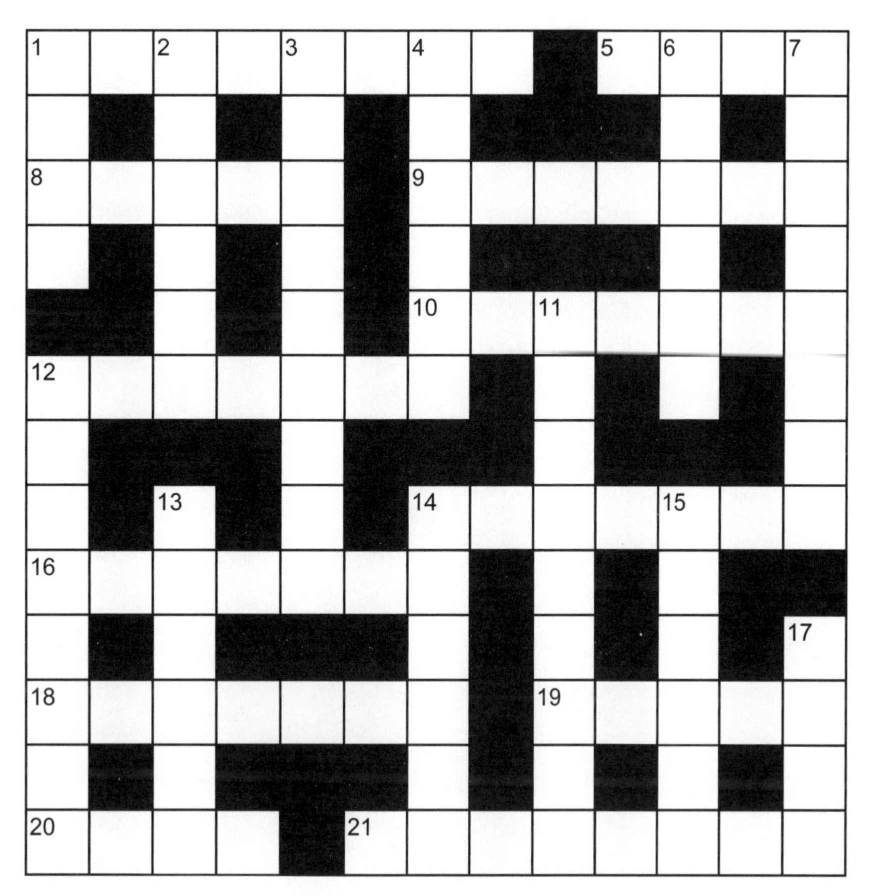

Across

1 Vision (8)
5 Moat (anag) (4)
8 ___ Schmidt: film starring Jack Nicholson (5)
9 Open-minded; given freely (7)
10 Quality of lacking transparency (7)
12 Small Eurasian crow (7)
14 US state (7)
16 Small bunch of flowers (7)
18 Young children (7)
19 Loop with a running knot (5)
20 The Christmas festival (4)
21 Worker (8)

Down

1 Long periods of history (4)
2 Excitingly strange (6)
3 Trespassing (9)
4 Insincere (6)
6 Lethargic (6)
7 SE Asian country (8)
11 Relating to the stomach (9)
12 Cheerily (8)
13 Of practical benefit (6)
14 Mineral used to make plaster of Paris (6)
15 Fashionable; exciting (6)
17 Allot justice (4)

Puzzle 249

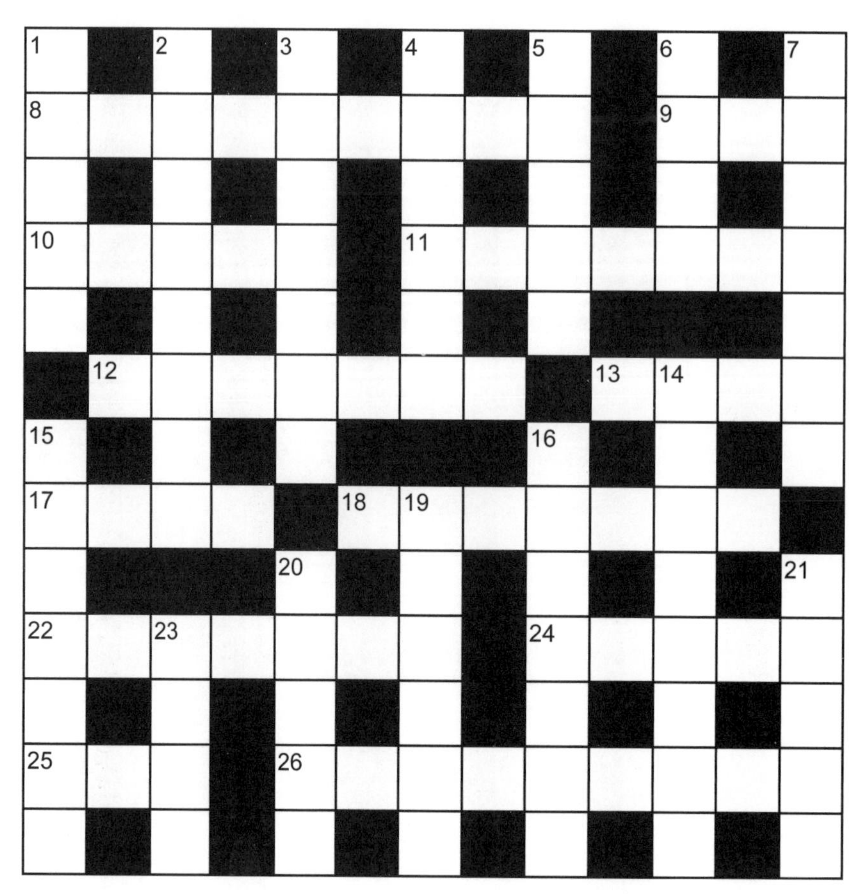

Across

8 Workman; shopkeeper (9)
9 Remove branches (3)
10 Early version of a document (5)
11 Provokes (7)
12 Outcasts from society (7)
13 Raised area of skin; swollen mark (4)
17 Stringed instrument (4)
18 Having a large belly (7)
22 Able to read minds (7)
24 Circumference (5)
25 Large deer (3)
26 Oscillate (9)

Down

1 Examine (5)
2 Large waterfall (8)
3 Free from doubt (7)
4 Mischievous (6)
5 Natural talent (5)
6 Move swiftly and lightly (4)
7 Letter (7)
14 Extremely delicate (8)
15 Smacked (7)
16 People of noble birth (7)
19 Increase over time (6)
20 Act of stealing (5)
21 Taming of the ___ : Shakespeare play (5)
23 Wooden crosspiece attached to animals (4)

Crossword

Puzzle 250

Across

1 People not ordained (5)
4 ___ owl: common Eurasian owl (5)
10 Insanitary (7)
11 Piece of furniture (5)
12 Ale (4)
13 Driver of a horse-drawn carriage (8)
16 Barking loudly (6)
17 Twist together (6)
20 Young plant (8)
21 Celebration; festivity (4)
23 Mountain range in South America (5)
25 Extinguish a candle (4,3)
26 Nationality of Stanislas Wawrinka (5)
27 Dull colours (5)

Down

2 Typical example of a thing (9)
3 Adolescent (4)
5 Ruler who has absolute power (8)
6 Arrest (3)
7 Confused noise (6)
8 Spy (5)
9 Seabird (4)
14 Moving seasonally (of a bird) (9)
15 Considers in detail (8)
18 Makes a bill law (6)
19 Rebuffs (5)
20 Sewing join (4)
22 Not sweet (4)
24 Ground condensation (3)

Puzzle 251

Across

1 Actor's part in a film (4)
3 Official orders (8)
9 Uncovers (7)
10 Petite (5)
11 Employer (5)
12 Virtuoso solo passage (7)
13 Christening (6)
15 Photographic equipment (6)
17 Release someone from duty (7)
18 Trite (anag) (5)
20 Confuse (5)
21 Wealthy businessperson (7)
22 Boating (8)
23 Requests (4)

Down

1 Crude but effective (5,3,5)
2 Arboreal primate (5)
4 Region of France (6)
5 Drawback (12)
6 Person learning a skill (7)
7 Conscious knowledge of oneself (4-9)
8 Separation; alienation (12)
14 Tuneful (7)
16 Language spoken in Berlin (6)
19 Rips (5)

Crossword

Puzzle 252

Across

1 Savage (6)
4 Open declaration of affirmation (6)
9 Reindeer (7)
10 Shine like a star (7)
11 Crucial person or point (5)
12 Tones (anag) (5)
14 Suspend; prevent (5)
15 Rope with a running noose (5)
17 Easy to understand (5)
18 Pancreatic hormone (7)
20 Idealist; visionary (7)
21 Enjoy greatly (6)
22 Sport Andy Murray plays (6)

Down

1 Arm muscle (6)
2 Straightens out (8)
3 Scope or extent (5)
5 Guest (7)
6 Part of a candle (4)
7 Most recent (6)
8 Beyond acceptability (3,2,6)
13 Sample for medical testing (8)
14 US currency (pl) (7)
15 Linger aimlessly (6)
16 Decorates (6)
17 Feudal vassal (5)
19 Exchange for money (4)

Puzzle 253

Across

1 End of a railway route (8)
5 Among (4)
9 Light downy particles (5)
10 Tarns (anag) (5)
11 Build up (10)
14 Edible pulse (6)
15 Bowed string instruments (6)
17 Amazing (10)
20 Move slowly (5)
21 Giggle (5)
22 Playthings (4)
23 US name for the aubergine (8)

Down

1 Petty quarrel (4)
2 Destroy (4)
3 Contagiously (12)
4 Quantity you can hold (6)
6 By hand (8)
7 Distribute (8)
8 A type of error in speech (8,4)
12 Neat and smart (5-3)
13 Unstable (8)
16 Border (6)
18 Distinctive atmosphere created by a person (4)
19 Close (4)

Puzzle 254

Across

1 Saving from danger (8)
5 Manure (4)
8 Held on to something tightly (5)
9 Variegated (7)
10 Adopt or support a cause (7)
12 Lived in (7)
14 Side of a coin bearing the head (7)
16 Aquatic invertebrates (7)
18 Uncertain (7)
19 Consumer of food (5)
20 Freedom from difficulty or hardship (4)
21 Spiritually symbolic (8)

Down

1 Large stone (4)
2 Causes (anag) (6)
3 Moving to a higher class (9)
4 Bit sharply (6)
6 Planet (6)
7 Dish of rice with fish and eggs (8)
11 Making timely preparation for the future (9)
12 Restore confidence to (8)
13 Compels to do something (6)
14 Fish-eating bird of prey (6)
15 Simple; unrefined (6)
17 By word of mouth (4)

Puzzle 255

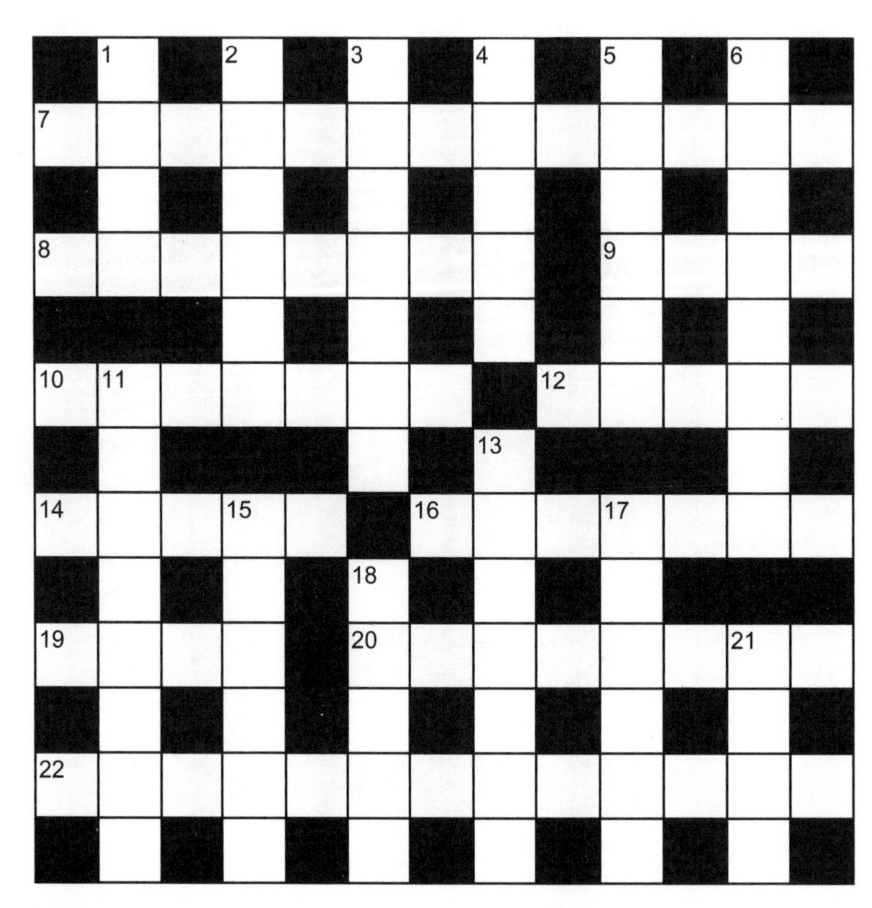

Across

7 Easily angered (5-8)
8 Disadvantage (8)
9 Country whose capital is Havana (4)
10 Small storage rooms or cupboards (7)
12 Double fold in a garment (5)
14 Bitterly pungent (5)
16 Mapped out in advance (7)
19 Knowledge (abbrev) (4)
20 Device that sends a rocket into space (8)
22 State of extreme happiness (7,6)

Down

1 Singe; burn (4)
2 Moves like a baby (6)
3 Capital of the US state of Georgia (7)
4 Hazy (5)
5 Writing implement (6)
6 Pliable sheet of material (8)
11 Permits to do something (8)
13 Farm implements (7)
15 Removed creases from clothes (6)
17 Sugary flower secretion (6)
18 Ostentatious glamour (5)
21 Saw; observed (4)

Crossword

Puzzle 256

Across

1 Cut a small notch in (5)
4 Cooks slowly in liquid (5)
10 Jumping athlete (7)
11 Wild dog of Australia (5)
12 Slanting; crooked (4)
13 Woodwind instrument (8)
16 Dried grape (6)
17 Entirely lacking (6)
20 Confine (8)
21 Before long (4)
23 Flinch away in pain (5)
25 Release (7)
26 Remains (5)
27 Bands worn around the waist (5)

Down

2 Rooms for young children (9)
3 Select from a large amount (4)
5 Larval frogs (8)
6 Came first (3)
7 Follow-up drink (6)
8 Liberates (5)
9 Guided journey (4)
14 Substance that reduces perspiration (9)
15 Strongly (8)
18 Small inflatable boat (6)
19 Make a search (5)
20 Argues (4)
22 Smoke passage (4)
24 Item for catching fish (3)

Puzzle 257

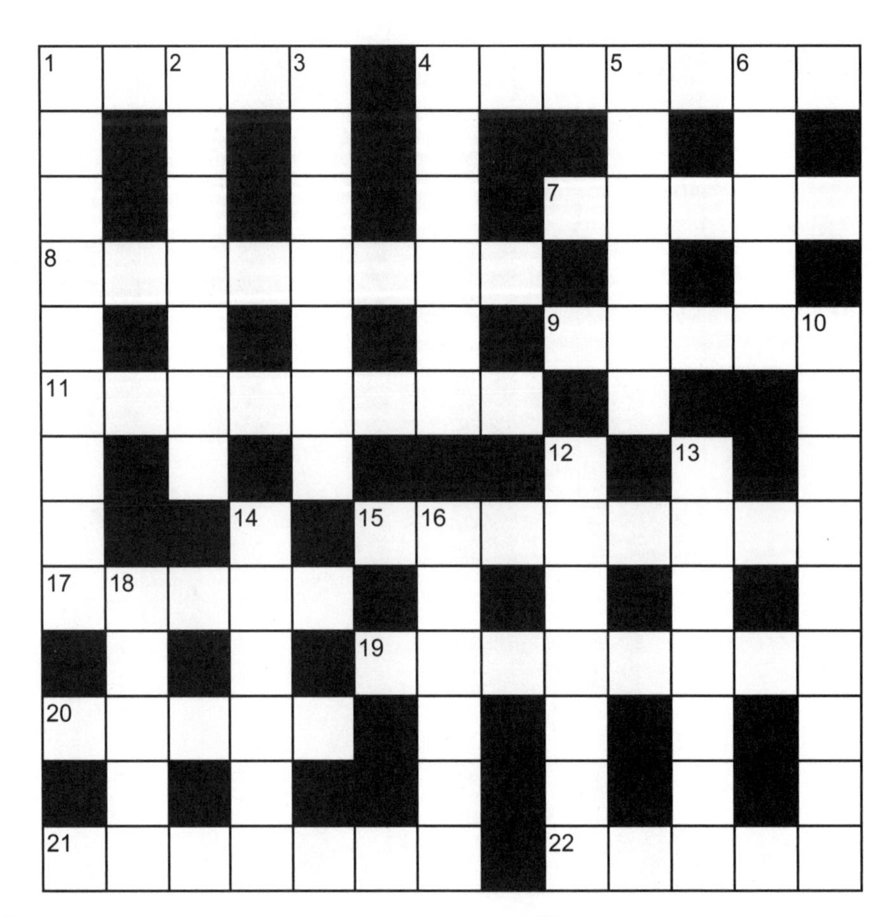

Across

1 Expect (5)
4 Repeats from memory (7)
7 Sudden constriction (5)
8 Coerce into doing something (8)
9 Streamlined (5)
11 Brushing the coat of (an animal) (8)
15 Vivid and brilliant (of a colour) (8)
17 ___ Presley: US singer (5)
19 Took in (food) (8)
20 Relating to a city (5)
21 Sets fire to (7)
22 Respected person in a field (5)

Down

1 Sum (9)
2 Juicy soft fruit (7)
3 Ancient war galley (7)
4 Keep hold of (6)
5 Leaping antelope (6)
6 Follow on from (5)
10 Very low (of a price) (5-4)
12 Planned one's actions (7)
13 ___ Spears: US singer (7)
14 Minimal bathing suit (6)
16 Isolationists (6)
18 Not telling the truth (5)

Puzzle 258

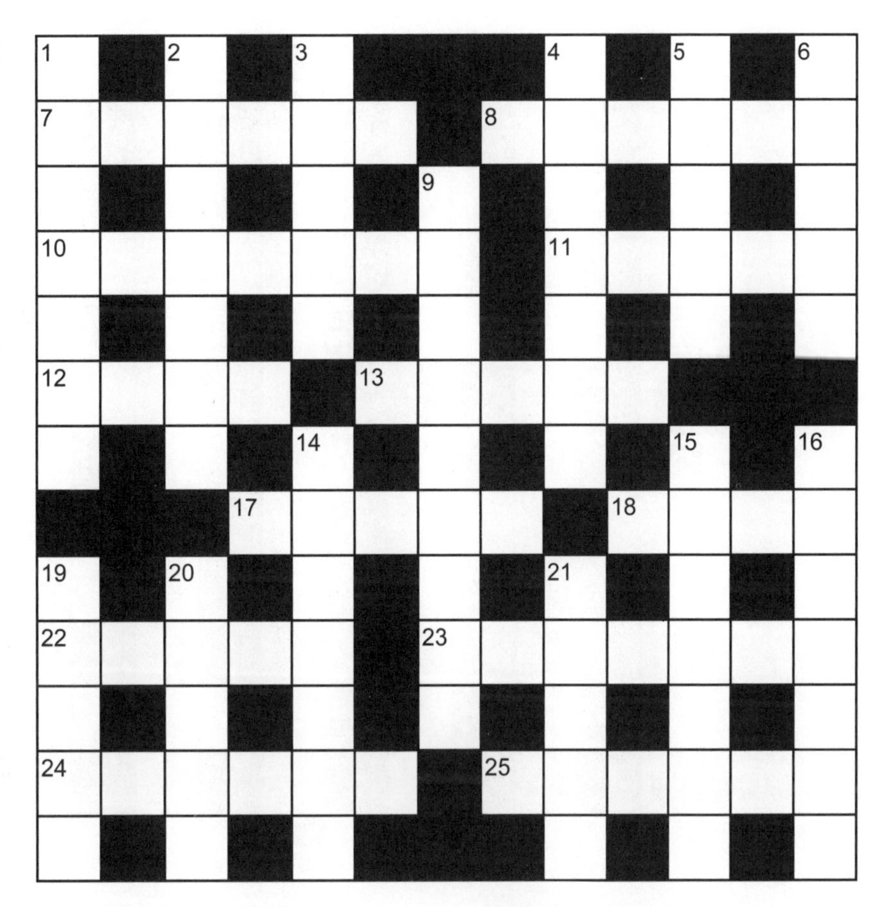

Across

7 Talks excessively about one's talents (6)
8 Fierce woman (6)
10 Stations where journeys end (7)
11 Voting compartment (5)
12 Small symbol or graphic (4)
13 Watched secretly (5)
17 Warning sound (5)
18 Hale (anag) (4)
22 Small arm of the sea (5)
23 Statements of intent to harm (7)
24 One appointed to administer a state (6)
25 One's environment (6)

Down

1 Refrain from (7)
2 Brave fighter (7)
3 Elevated step (5)
4 Takes small bites (7)
5 Reception room in a large house (5)
6 Variety of strong coffee (5)
9 Different in kind (9)
14 Thin coating of metal (7)
15 Large Israeli city (3,4)
16 Magnified view (5-2)
19 Headdress worn by a bishop (5)
20 Nick ___ : politician (5)
21 Circle a planet (5)

Puzzle 259

Across

1 Hydrocarbon found in petroleum spirit (6)
4 Performing on stage (6)
9 Relating to Oxford (7)
10 Vent for molten lava (7)
11 Large quantities of paper (5)
12 Our planet (5)
14 Woodland god (5)
15 The reproduction of sound (5)
17 Part of (5)
18 Island in the West Indies (7)
20 Pulling at (7)
21 Happenings (6)
22 Ukrainian port (6)

Down

1 Smells (6)
2 Insincere and dishonest (3-5)
3 Metal spikes (5)
5 Device for cooling (7)
6 Tiny amount (4)
7 Waterproof overshoe (6)
8 Examine in detail (11)
13 Curative medicines; sets right (8)
14 Ask for; try to obtain (7)
15 Renounce an oath (6)
16 Figure of speech (6)
17 Gaped (anag) (5)
19 Created (4)

Puzzle 260

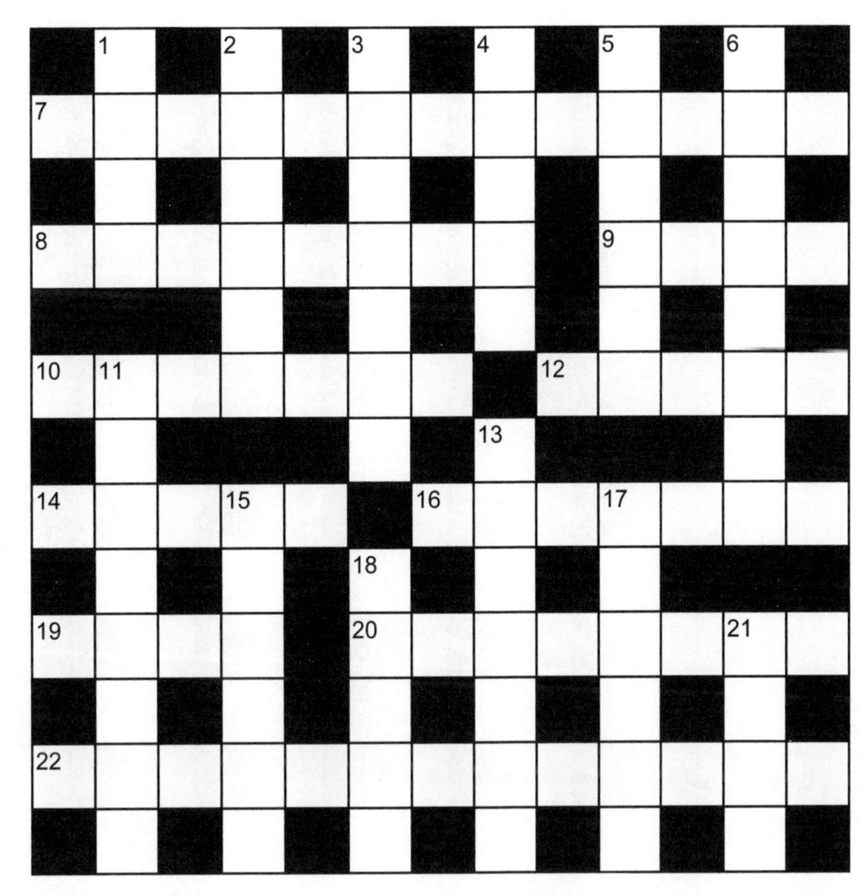

Across

7 Prescience (13)
8 Peacemaker (8)
9 Big cat (4)
10 Upward slopes (7)
12 Vibrated (5)
14 Uses a keyboard (5)
16 Primates (7)
19 Silvery-white metallic element (4)
20 Electrical component (8)
22 Horror film directed by M. Night Shyamalan (3,5,5)

Down

1 Settee (4)
2 Repeat from memory (6)
3 Demands forcefully (7)
4 Eg an Oscar or Grammy (5)
5 Well-being (6)
6 Science of soil management (8)
11 Window in a roof (8)
13 Beetroot soup (7)
15 Forgive for a fault (6)
17 Locked lips with someone (6)
18 Person acting as a deputy (5)
21 Kiln (4)

Puzzle 261

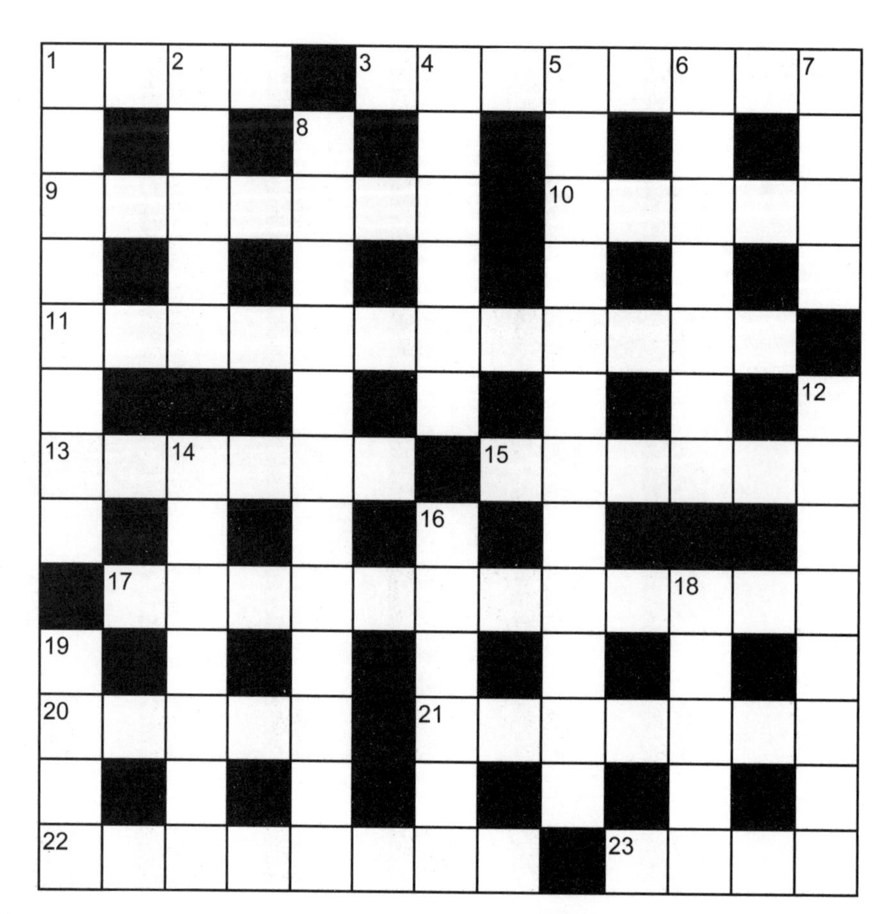

Across

1 Young lions (4)
3 Science of classification (8)
9 Itemising (7)
10 Teacher (5)
11 Complete destruction (12)
13 Soaks in liquid (6)
15 Type of muscle (6)
17 Duplication (12)
20 Browned bread (5)
21 Country whose capital is Reykjavik (7)
22 Vacations (8)
23 Exercise venues (4)

Down

1 Cave in (8)
2 Buffalo (5)
4 Attendants upon God (6)
5 Fully extended (12)
6 Choices (7)
7 Three feet (4)
8 Joyously unrestrained (4-8)
12 Explosive shells (8)
14 Look something over (7)
16 Nervously (6)
18 Where one finds Rome (5)
19 Engrave with acid (4)

Crossword

Puzzle 262

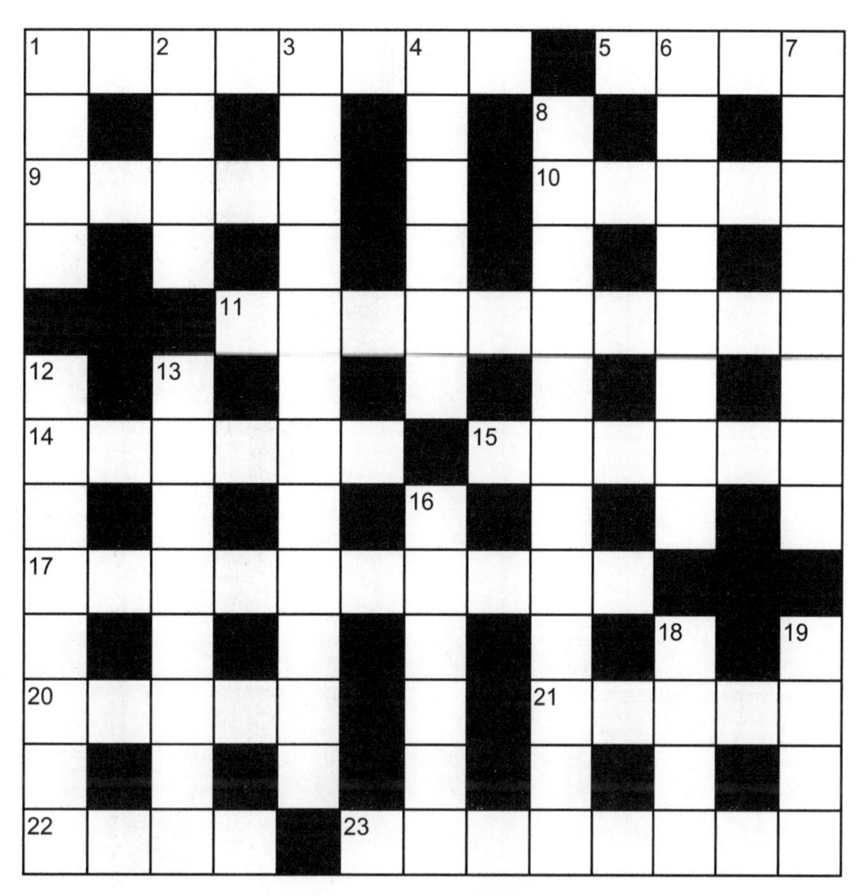

Across

1 Treatment of the hands (8)
5 Extent of a surface (4)
9 Acknowledged; assumed (5)
10 Prophet (5)
11 Organised (10)
14 Hold in high esteem (6)
15 Clear from a charge (6)
17 Having a favourable outcome (10)
20 Impersonator (5)
21 Bring together (5)
22 One less than ten (4)
23 Supplemental part of a book (8)

Down

1 Wizard (4)
2 Dark blue colour (4)
3 Body of voters in a specified region (12)
4 Regain (6)
6 Extremely thorough (8)
7 Extreme bitterness (8)
8 Expensive clothes (5,7)
12 Male journalists (8)
13 Astronaut (8)
16 Not awake (6)
18 Temperate (4)
19 Medium-sized feline (4)

Puzzle 263

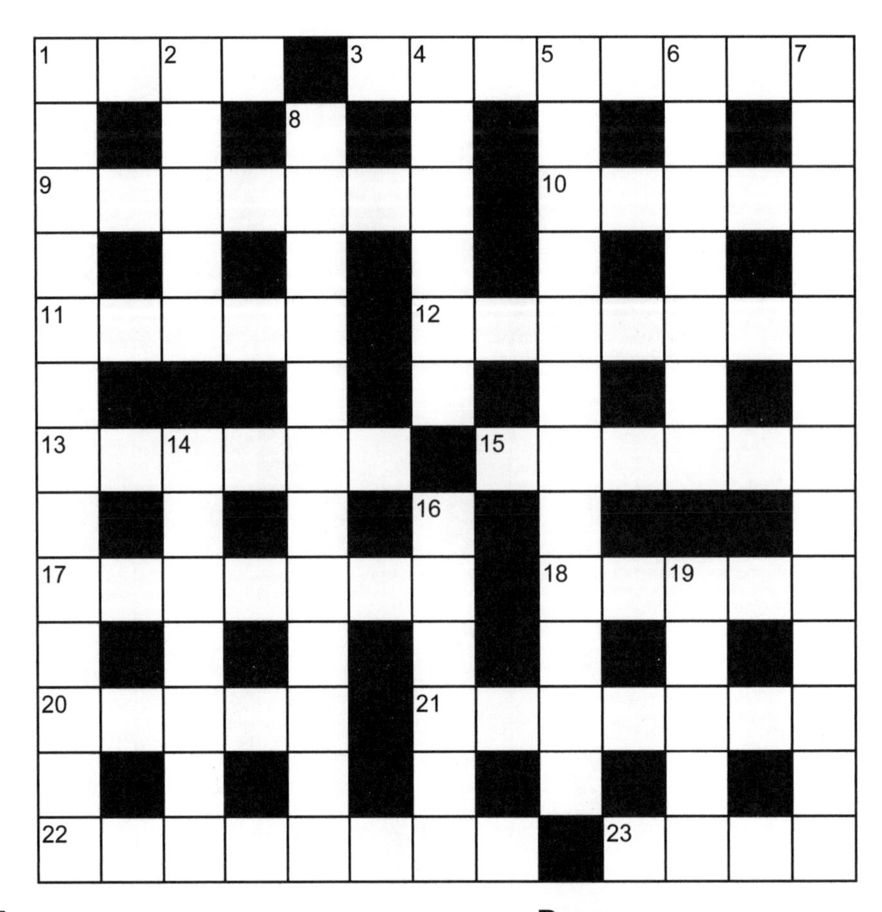

Across

1 Ballot choice (4)
3 Taught (8)
9 Open-meshed material (7)
10 Parts in a play (5)
11 Send money (5)
12 Joined together (7)
13 Form of church prayer (6)
15 ___ Cuthbert: actress (6)
17 Reduce the volume (7)
18 Phantasm (5)
20 Accustom to something (5)
21 Driving out (7)
22 Finance department (8)
23 ___ Blyton: writer (4)

Down

1 Voice projection artist (13)
2 ___ pole: tribal emblem (5)
4 Type of canoe (6)
5 Heart specialist (12)
6 Totals up (7)
7 Deprived (13)
8 Clarity (12)
14 Commendation (7)
16 Situated within a building (6)
19 The Hunter (constellation) (5)

Puzzle 264

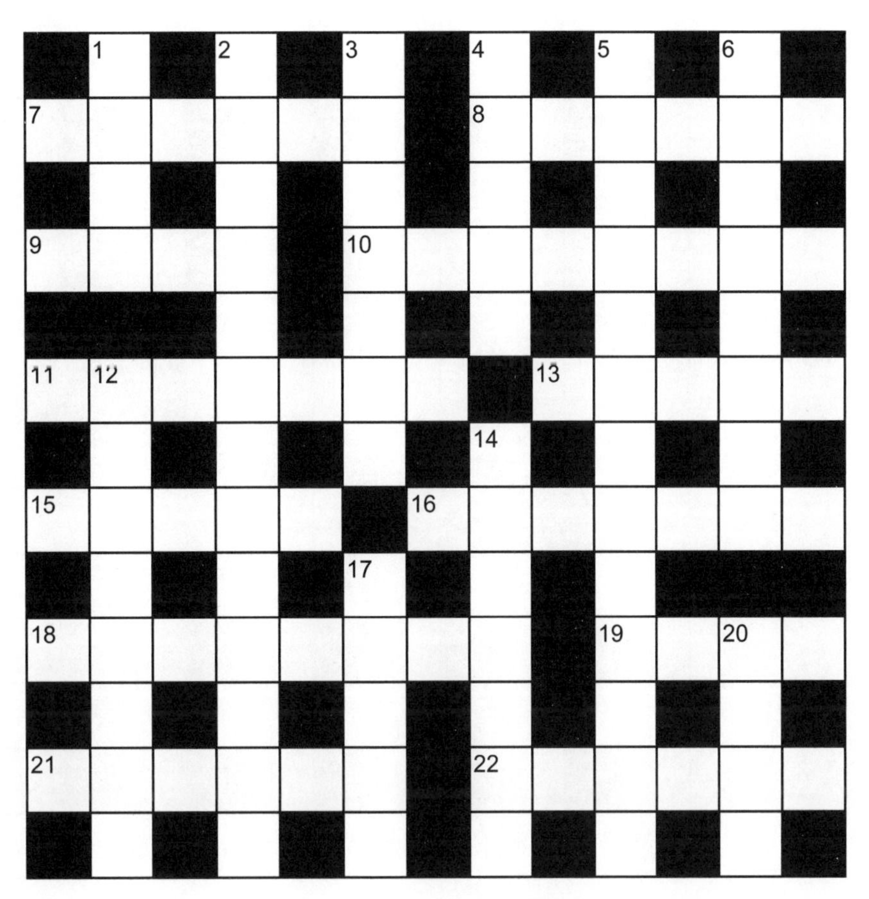

Across

7 Statue base (6)
8 Conceit (6)
9 Mischievous god in Norse mythology (4)
10 Shortage (8)
11 Photography technique (7)
13 Scamps (5)
15 Make a god of (5)
16 Demureness (7)
18 Courgette (US) (8)
19 Immerse in liquid (4)
21 Attitude or body position (6)
22 Detestable (6)

Down

1 Adult male singing voice (4)
2 Petty (13)
3 Pursuing (7)
4 Pertaining to birds (5)
5 Chronologically misplaced (13)
6 Written laws (8)
12 Sufficient (8)
14 Visual display unit (7)
17 Lobed glandular organ (5)
20 Greenish-blue colour (4)

Puzzle 265

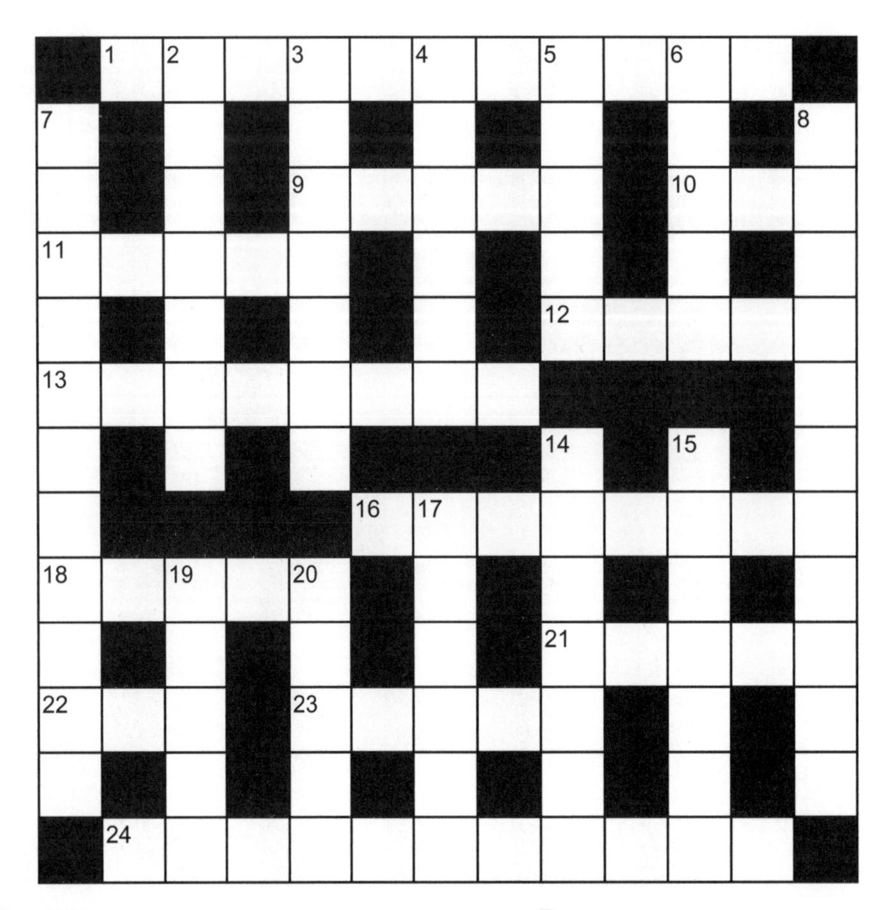

Across

1 Able to be used (11)
9 Male duck (5)
10 Four-wheeled road vehicle (3)
11 Crunch; wear down (5)
12 Dish of mixed vegetables (5)
13 Ability to meet liabilities (8)
16 Relinquish a throne (8)
18 Measuring stick (5)
21 Cleans (5)
22 Creative activity (3)
23 High-pitched noises (5)
24 Demolition (11)

Down

2 Pasta pockets (7)
3 Hugs (7)
4 Sloping (of a typeface) (6)
5 Asserts; affirms (5)
6 Nearby (5)
7 Dictatorial (11)
8 One who held a job previously (11)
14 Inclination (7)
15 A very skilled performer (7)
17 Flat-bottomed rowing boat (6)
19 Metric unit of capacity (5)
20 Machine; automaton (5)

Crossword

Puzzle 266

Across

1 Run-down and in poor condition (6)
5 ___ Barker: former tennis star (3)
7 Data entered into a system (5)
8 Outburst of anger (7)
9 Network points where lines intersect (5)
10 Woke up (8)
12 Small hole (6)
14 Fine cloth (6)
17 Floating masses of frozen water (8)
18 Dens (5)
20 Decanting (7)
21 ___ Armstrong: cyclist (5)
22 Cereal plant (3)
23 ___ Cole: Girls Aloud star (6)

Down

2 Progress (7)
3 Saddled with a heavy load (8)
4 Puns (anag) (4)
5 Examines in detail (7)
6 Elusive (7)
7 Urge into action (5)
11 Device for spraying paint (8)
12 Opposite of later (7)
13 Ennoble (7)
15 Necessity (7)
16 Long flower-stalk (5)
19 Beach constituent (4)

Puzzle 267

Across

1 Not singular (6)
5 Insole (anag) (6)
8 Insect stage (4)
9 Person who rebels (8)
10 Fairy (5)
11 Iron lever (7)
14 Process of worsening (13)
16 Gets out (7)
18 Brilliant and clear (5)
20 Imitator (8)
22 Part of a plant (4)
23 Depression from a meteor impact (6)
24 Strike repeatedly (6)

Down

2 Awfulness (9)
3 Understand (7)
4 Eg an arm or leg (4)
5 Bookish (8)
6 Tough fibrous tissue (5)
7 Lyric poem (3)
12 Detest (9)
13 Top quality (of a hotel) (4-4)
15 Set of three things (7)
17 Dole out (5)
19 Seize (4)
21 Russian space station (3)

Puzzle 268

Across

1 Made officially valid (8)
5 Vigour (4)
9 Delicious (5)
10 Small bottles (5)
11 Shameful (10)
14 Young people (6)
15 Hinder (6)
17 Eg Shakespeare (10)
20 Spin quickly (5)
21 Long-legged wading bird (5)
22 Pull abruptly (4)
23 Stiff coarse hairs (8)

Down

1 ___ Ifans: Welsh actor in Notting Hill (4)
2 Large and scholarly book (4)
3 Unseen observer (3,2,3,4)
4 Breathe out (6)
6 Argued logically (8)
7 Completely preoccupied with (8)
8 Excessive stress (12)
12 Compassion (8)
13 Random change (8)
16 Flammable material used to light a fire (6)
18 At a low temperature (4)
19 Seek (anag) (4)

Puzzle 269

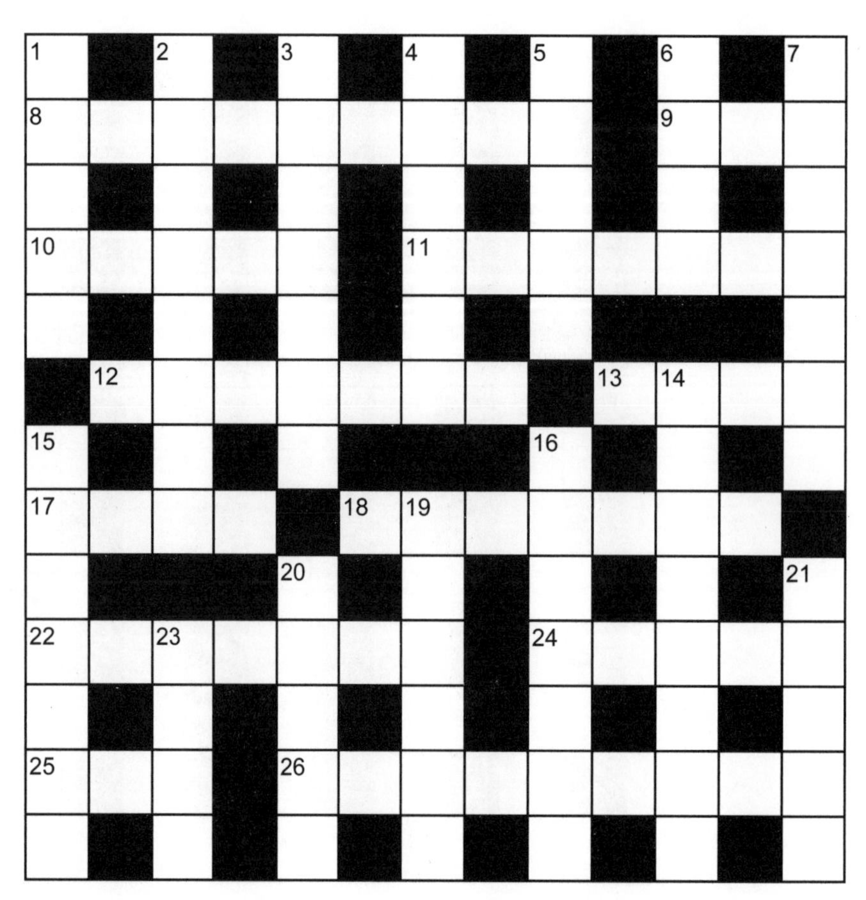

Across

8 Unhurried (9)
9 Opposite of in (3)
10 Loutish person (5)
11 Collapse inwards (7)
12 Untidy (7)
13 Touch (4)
17 International exhibition (4)
18 Earthly (7)
22 Stored away (7)
24 Cut a joint of meat (5)
25 Longing (3)
26 Barrier for stopping traffic (9)

Down

1 Tactical manoeuvres (5)
2 Drink consumed before bed (8)
3 Prompting device for a TV presenter (7)
4 Trust or faith in (6)
5 Graceful young woman (5)
6 Benicio del ___ : actor (4)
7 Swears (7)
14 Dancing hall (8)
15 Jumpers (7)
16 Inactive pill (7)
19 Trying experience (6)
20 Appeal (5)
21 Smells strongly (5)
23 Spots (4)

Crossword

Puzzle 270

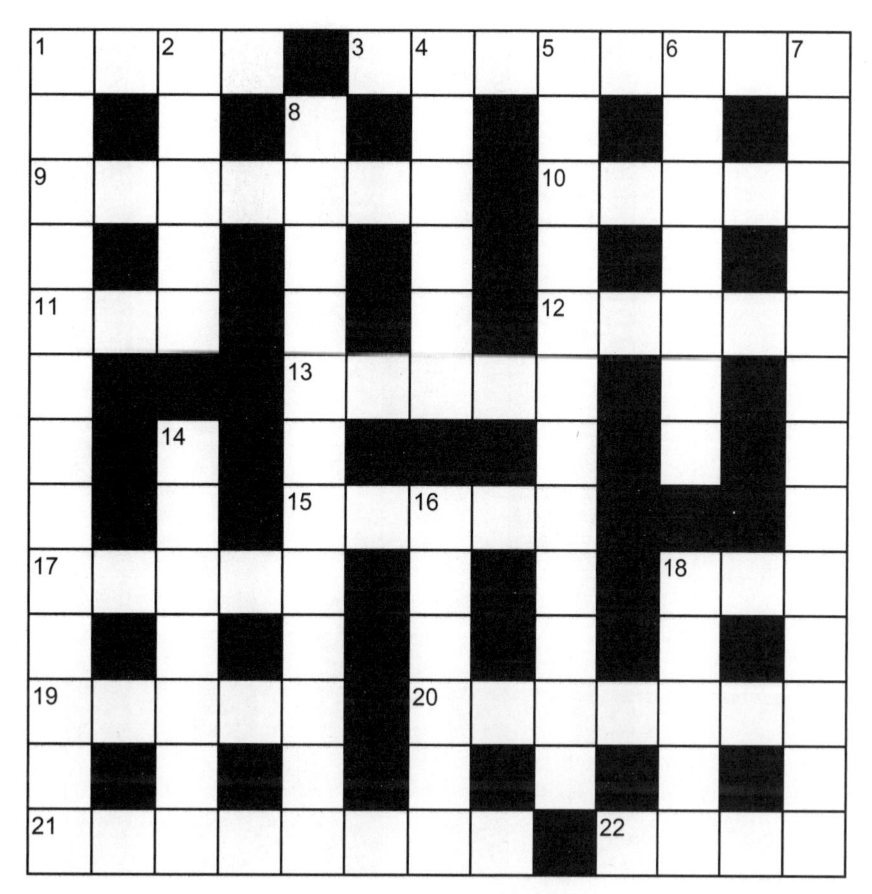

Across

1 Curved shapes (4)
3 Went along to an event (8)
9 Dolorous (7)
10 Public transport vehicles (5)
11 Container for a drink (3)
12 Eg the Thames (5)
13 Bart's father in the Simpsons (5)
15 Takes a break (5)
17 Positively charged electrode (5)
18 Umpire (abbrev) (3)
19 Speed music is played at (5)
20 Regeneration (7)
21 Strongholds (8)
22 Military unit (4)

Down

1 Not living up to expectations (13)
2 Muscular contraction (5)
4 ___ powder: bathroom item (6)
5 Awkward (12)
6 Deny any responsibility for (7)
7 Suspiciously (13)
8 Unofficially (3,3,6)
14 Eyelet placed in a hole (7)
16 Plant used in salads (6)
18 Oarsman (5)

Puzzle 271

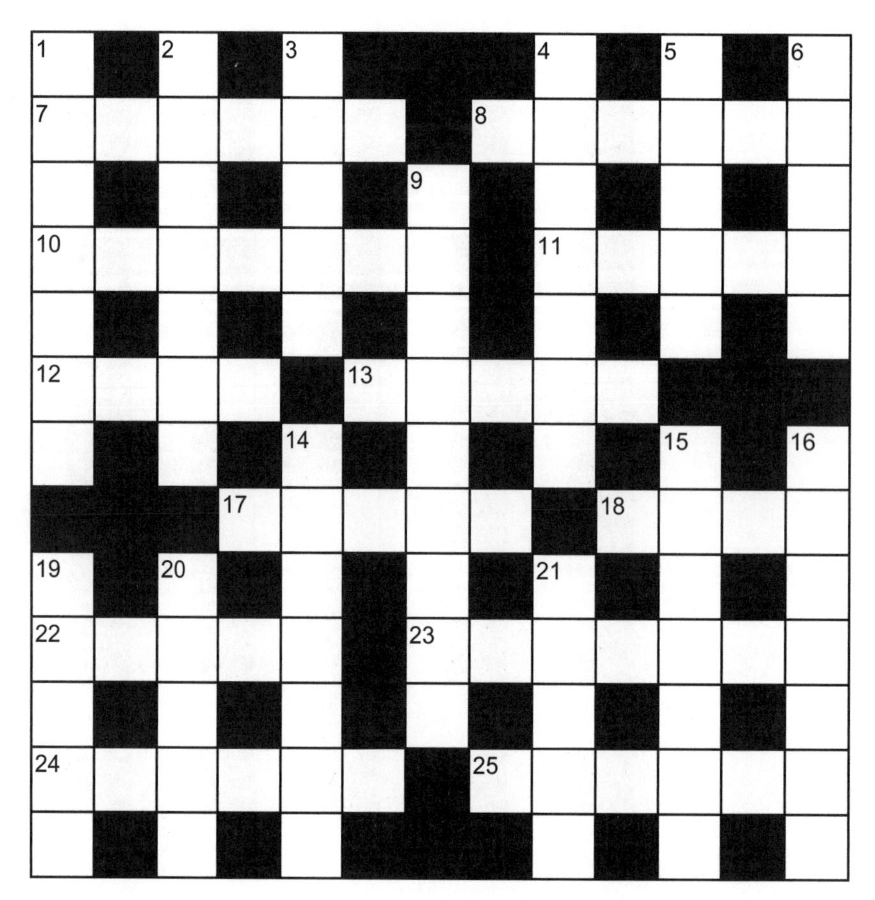

Across

7 True skin (6)
8 Extract meaning from (6)
10 Flat highland (7)
11 Long cloud of smoke (5)
12 Corner (4)
13 Underground railway (5)
17 Utter repetitively (5)
18 Capital of Norway (4)
22 Device that splits light (5)
23 Minute cavity in organic tissue (7)
24 Support; help (6)
25 Demand forcefully to have something (6)

Down

1 Formally approved (7)
2 Accuse of a wrong (7)
3 Erased (5)
4 Moderates; mitigates (7)
5 Position or point (5)
6 Round cap (5)
9 Exploding star (9)
14 Comic film with Jim Carrey and Cameron Diaz (3,4)
15 Baltic country (7)
16 Originality (7)
19 Disgust (5)
20 Top degree mark (5)
21 Perfume (5)

Crossword

Puzzle 272

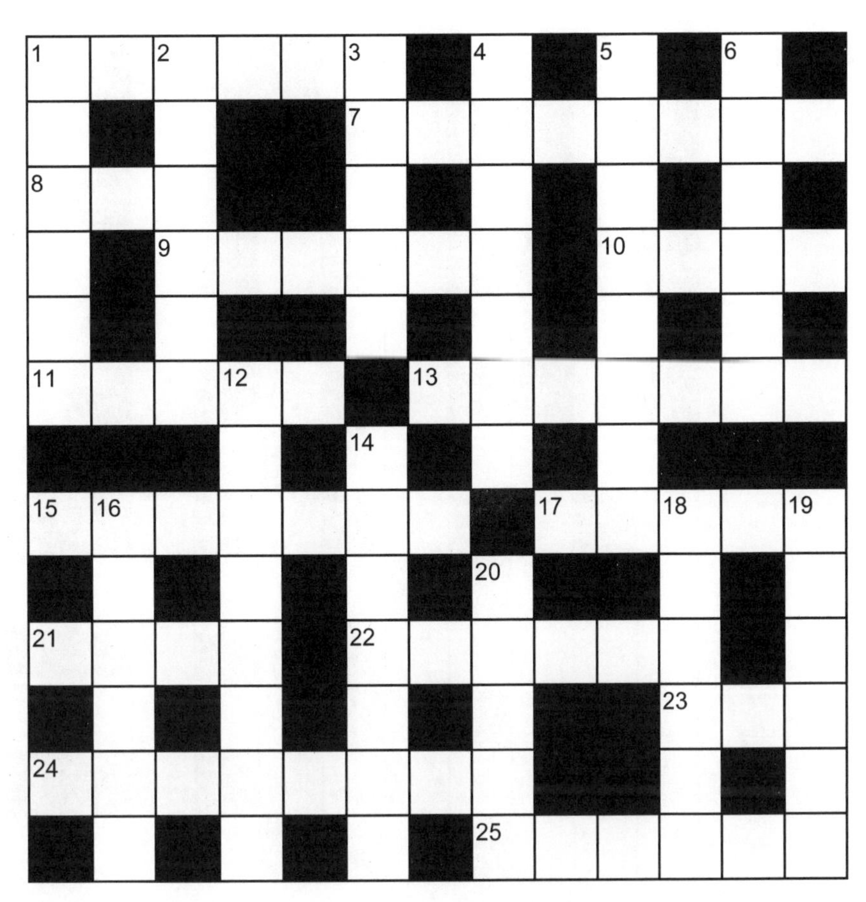

Across

1 ___ acid: lemon juice constituent (6)
7 Peacemaker (8)
8 Opposite of no (3)
9 Generic term for a martial art (4,2)
10 Female sheep (pl) (4)
11 ___ Izzard: stand-up comedian (5)
13 Disturb (7)
15 Looked up to (7)
17 Lukewarm (5)
21 Type of house (abbrev) (4)
22 US rapper (6)
23 Cry of a cat (3)
24 Remaining; surplus (8)
25 By word of mouth (6)

Down

1 Wolflike wild dog (6)
2 Assigned a piece of work (6)
3 Freight (5)
4 Sudden increase (7)
5 Holder of invention rights (8)
6 Building material (6)
12 Begin (8)
14 Merit (7)
16 Increase; extend (6)
18 Projecting part of a saddle (6)
19 Lethargic; sleepy (6)
20 Extremely small (prefix) (5)

Puzzle 273

Across

1 Large sticks (6)
5 Drink a little (3)
7 Clod of turf (5)
8 Suitor (7)
9 Dressed to the ___ : elaborately clothed (5)
10 Household chore (8)
12 Fanciful; delightful (6)
14 Centre (6)
17 Increase rapidly (8)
18 Nationality of Louis Walsh (5)
20 Act of reading carefully (7)
21 Simple earrings (5)
22 Bind (3)
23 Mineral used in fertiliser (6)

Down

2 A child beginning to walk (7)
3 Eg Daniel or Matthew (8)
4 ___ Lendl: ex-tennis player (4)
5 Rendered senseless (7)
6 Expect; suppose to be true (7)
7 Imbibed (5)
11 Until now (8)
12 Excess of liabilities over assets (7)
13 Oval shape (7)
15 Washing sponges (7)
16 Leaps (5)
19 Sixty minutes (4)

Puzzle 274

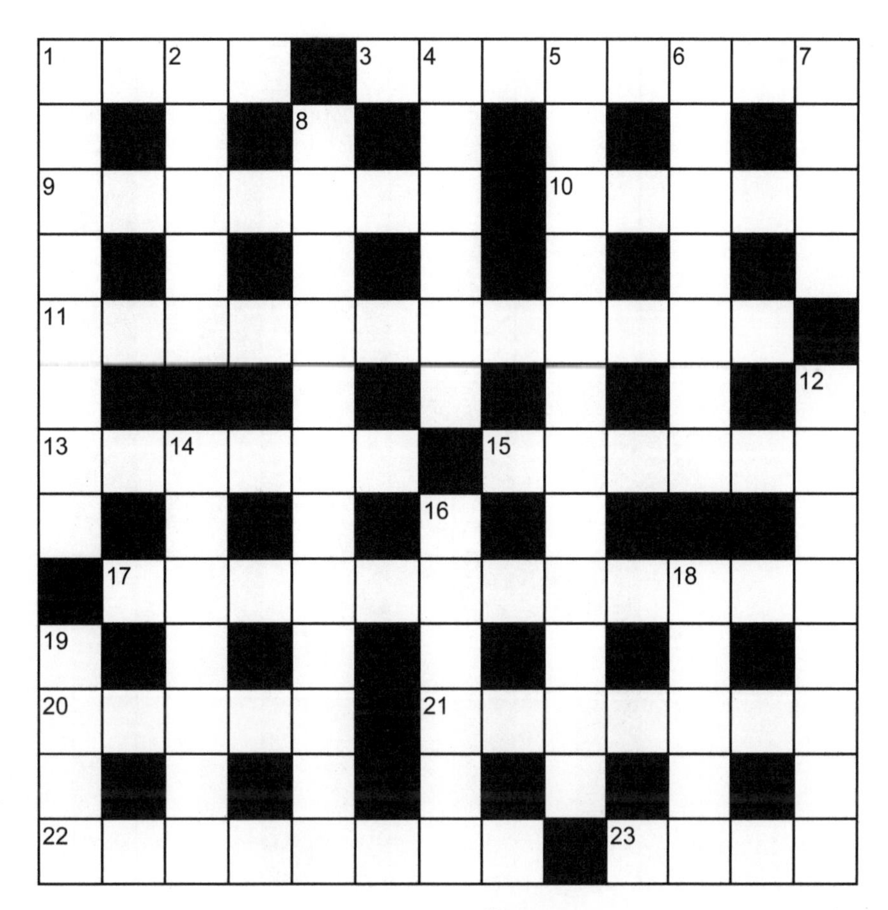

Across

1 Young female (4)
3 Curved sword (8)
9 Attains (7)
10 Female relatives (5)
11 Occult (12)
13 Foolish behaviour (6)
15 Ruler (6)
17 Inventiveness (12)
20 Loud resonant noise (5)
21 Shock with wonder (7)
22 Remaining (8)
23 Writing instruments (4)

Down

1 Someone skilled in shooting (8)
2 Waterlogged ground (5)
4 Relaxed and informal (6)
5 Calculations of dimensions (12)
6 Drinking vessel (7)
7 Prickly plant with fragrant flowers (4)
8 Cheated someone financially (5-7)
12 Disperse (anag) (8)
14 Weaves; clothing (7)
16 Stout-bodied insect (6)
18 Draw or bring out (5)
19 Skin mark from a wound (4)

Puzzle 275

Across

1 Risky (6)
4 Large edible gourd (6)
9 Have as a part (7)
10 Bicycle stunt (7)
11 Combines (5)
12 Card game (5)
14 Wireless (5)
15 Bend (5)
17 Ashley ___ : actress (5)
18 Playful musical compositions (7)
20 Convent (7)
21 Large quantity (6)
22 Fish with thick lips (6)

Down

1 Leaders (6)
2 Forebear (8)
3 Hints (5)
5 Quick musical tempo (7)
6 Roll of photographic film (4)
7 Wet (6)
8 Causing bafflement (11)
13 Fictional ugly creatures (8)
14 Go back over a route (7)
15 Gambling house (6)
16 Biochemical catalyst (6)
17 Possessor (5)
19 Posterior (4)

Crossword

Puzzle 276

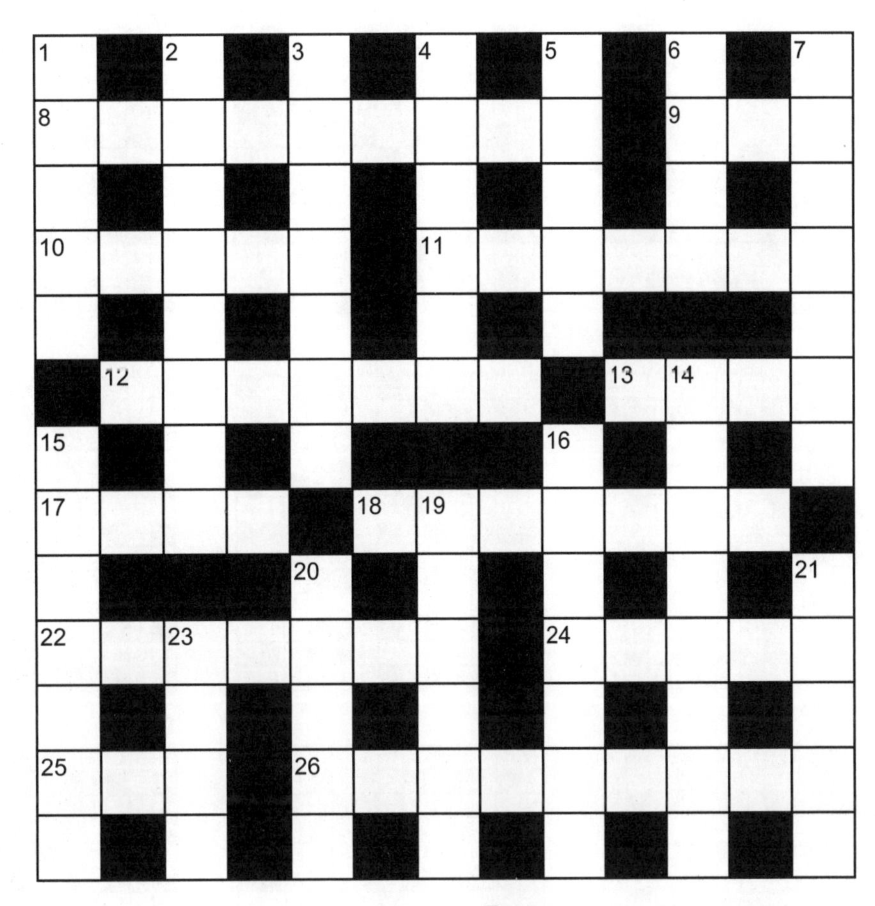

Across

8 Test again (2-7)
9 ___ McKellen: actor (3)
10 Take away by force (5)
11 Organs (7)
12 Composed or serious manner (7)
13 Carlos ___ : former tennis player (4)
17 Semi-precious agate (4)
18 Pursuer (anag) (7)
22 Inert gaseous element (7)
24 Moved slowly (5)
25 Mixture of gases we breathe (3)
26 Flag on a ship (4,5)

Down

1 Russell ___ : Gladiator actor (5)
2 Tranquillity (8)
3 Hitting a ball in cricket (7)
4 Small gate (6)
5 Curves (5)
6 Remain or stay somewhere (4)
7 Uncommon (7)
14 Small-scale musical drama (8)
15 Male labourer (7)
16 Rule of personal conduct (7)
19 Wicked (6)
20 Cigarette ends (5)
21 Ringo ___ : one of the Beatles (5)
23 Spun thread used for knitting (4)

Solutions

1.

C	A	V	E	A	T			S		A	S	H
	I			A		D	I	C	E	D		A
E	M	B	A	R	G	O		A		A		N
	L			D		E		N	O	M	A	D
D	E	L	I	V	E	R	Y			A		L
	S			A		S		S		N		E
E	S	C	O	R	T		S	T	A	T	U	S
M		O		K		C		A			N	
B		N			E	L	E	G	A	N	C	E
R	I	N	K	S		E		N			A	
A		E		O		A	B	A	L	O	N	E
C		C	A	B	I	N		N			N	
E	F	T		S			S	T	R	A	Y	S

2.

G	A	S	P		P	A	R	M	E	S	A	N
L		C		D		G		I		T		O
A	M	A	T	E	U	R		S	U	R	G	E
C		M		M		E		R		E		L
I	M	P	R	O	V	E	M	E	N	T	S	
E				N		D		P		C		B
R	E	S	I	S	T		A	R	T	H	U	R
S		W		T		T		E				I
	H	A	I	R	D	R	E	S	S	I	N	G
E		L		A		A		E		D		H
V	A	L	E	T		S	I	N	G	L	E	T
E		O		E		H		T		E		E
N	O	W	A	D	A	Y	S		E	D	E	N

3.

	P	A	R	C	H		W	H	I	P	S	
S		C		O		T		O		I		W
U	N	C	O	V	E	R		M	A	N	T	A
M		E		E		E		E				F
M	O	S	S		T	W	I	L	I	G	H	T
I		S		S		S		A		U		
T	R	I	B	E	S		E	N	G	A	G	E
		O		A		T		D		R		R
K	I	N	G	S	T	O	N		F	A	R	M
I				O		U		J		N		I
S	U	S	A	N		C	R	O	U	T	O	N
S		E		A		H		K		E		E
	S	W	E	L	L		T	E	N	E	T	

4.

G	E	T	S		B	A	S	I	L	I	C	A
O		U		P		D		N		N		S
L	U	N	C	H	E	D		D	U	C	A	T
D		I		I		L		I		L		O
E	X	C	E	L		E	L	A	T	I	O	N
N				H		S		N		N		I
J	A	C	K	A	L		O	S	I	E	R	S
U		A		R		I		U				H
B	I	T	U	M	E	N		M	U	F	T	I
I		C		O		C		M		A		N
L	O	H	A	N		O	B	E	Y	I	N	G
E		E		I		M		R		L		L
E	N	R	I	C	H	E	S		E	S	P	Y

5.

S	E	L	E	C	T		U		D		A	
U		I			A	L	T	H	O	U	G	H
B	I	N			N		E		L		A	
D		N	A	P	K	I	N		D	E	S	K
U		E			S		S		R		S	
E	L	T	O	N		M	I	N	U	T	I	A
			V		P		L		M			
S	E	N	E	G	A	L		U	S	U	R	Y
	X		R		R		D			P		I
S	T	E	T		A	M	U	L	E	T		E
	R		A		D		O			A	I	L
D	A	R	K	R	O	O	M			K		D
	S		E		X		O	T	H	E	R	S

6.

	C		M		C		S		D		S	
D	Y	N	A	M	O		P	O	E	T	I	C
	A		G		L		I		P		N	
A	N	O	N		O	U	T	W	E	I	G	H
			I		N		E		N		U	
S	E	T	F	R	E	E		A	D	E	L	E
	X		I		L		P		A		A	
P	E	A	C	H		R	O	B	B	E	R	S
	R		E		W		T		I			
U	T	E	N	S	I	L	S		L	O	C	O
	I		T		N		H		I		A	
L	O	L	L	E	D		O	C	T	A	V	E
	N		Y		Y		T		Y		A	

7.

S		A		C		M		B		Z		A
P	A	N	T	O	M	I	M	E		E	B	B
A		A		N		N		L		B		Y
W	E	L	L	S		U	M	L	A	U	T	S
N		Y		U		T		Y				M
	S	T	I	L	L	E	R		D	I	V	A
A		I		T				H		N		L
R	A	C	Y		R	E	S	E	R	V	E	
C				S		N		R		E		C
H	O	L	S	T	E	R		M	I	N	E	R
E		I		A		I		I		T		I
R	U	E		L	O	C	A	T	I	O	N	S
S		D		L		H		S		R		P

8.

S	O	D	A		A	R	R	E	S	T	E	D
A		I		S		A		X		H		E
N	O	T	I	C	E	S		P	R	O	V	E
D		T		R		H		E		R		M
W	H	O	L	E	H	E	A	R	T	E	D	
I				E		S		I		A		B
C	O	S	I	N	E		N	E	B	U	L	A
H		H		W		E		N				C
	H	O	R	R	O	R	S	T	R	U	C	K
S		W		I		A		I		N		W
C	R	O	F	T		S	T	A	M	I	N	A
U		F		E		E		L		T		R
D	E	F	O	R	E	S	T		D	Y	E	D

9.

E	S	C	R	O	W		R	I	F	F	L	E
	T		A		I		I		A		O	
D	A	F	T		L	E	V	I	T	A	T	E
	M		I		Y		E		T			
S	P	O	O	N		S	T	A	Y	I	N	G
	D		N		D		I				U	
Q	U	E	S	T	I	O	N	N	A	I	R	E
	T				N		G		V		T	
T	Y	P	H	O	O	N		P	I	O	U	S
			E		S		B		A		R	
C	A	R	A	P	A	C	E		T	O	I	L
	Y		L		U		R		O		N	
C	E	N	S	O	R		G	A	R	A	G	E

10.

	B	A	D	G	E		G	R	A	F	T	
T		M		R		B		E		A		V
E	M	O	T	I	V	E		C	A	N	D	O
M		R		P		F		E				I
P	O	P	S		P	O	L	I	S	H	E	D
T		H		D		G		V		O		
S	C	O	R	E	R		B	E	D	B	U	G
		U		F		F		S		G		R
M	A	S	T	E	R	E	D		B	O	R	E
O				N		T		S		B		E
A	R	M	E	D		I	N	H	A	L	E	D
T		A		E		D		I		I		Y
	S	P	A	R	S		S	P	I	N	S	

11.

	T		O		D		W		J		F	
C	O	I	F	F	U	R	E		A	W	E	D
	B		F		T		E		W		A	
H	A	T	S		I	N	D	U	S	T	R	Y
	G		H		F		S				E	
C	O	C	O	N	U	T		G	I	L	D	S
			R		L		S		G			
R	E	B	E	L		S	T	A	N	D	B	Y
	L				M		A		I		U	
S	I	G	N	P	O	S	T		T	O	G	A
	J		A		U		U		I		L	
H	A	S	P		S	T	R	A	N	G	E	R
	H		E		E		E		G		S	

12.

	C		L		T		A		M		D	
B	O	L	E	R	O		S	T	A	T	I	C
	I		V		U		K		S		S	
C	L	U	E		C	R	E	O	S	O	T	E
			L		H		W		A		A	
C	I	R	C	L	E	D		S	C	A	N	T
	M		R		D		C		H		C	
S	P	O	O	K		A	L	B	U	M	E	N
	R		S		A		A		S			
C	O	N	S	U	M	E	R		E	L	M	S
	P		I		E		I		T		E	
V	E	R	N	O	N		O	U	T	L	A	W
	R		G		D		N		S		N	

Solutions

13.

■	E	■	U	■	R	■	F	■	P	■	D	■
A	M	A	N	D	A	■	A	P	I	A	R	Y
■	I	■	A	■	M	■	L	■	E	■	A	■
A	R	I	D	■	P	A	S	T	R	A	M	I
■	■	■	U	■	A	■	E	■	C	■	A	■
C	O	L	L	E	G	E	■	K	E	A	T	S
■	U	■	T	■	E	■	E	■	B	■	I	■
S	T	E	E	L	■	E	X	T	R	A	C	T
■	B	■	R	■	S	■	H	■	O	■	■	■
C	R	E	A	M	T	E	A	■	S	A	G	S
■	E	■	T	■	O	■	U	■	N	■	I	■
M	A	K	E	D	O	■	S	T	A	I	R	S
■	K	■	D	■	P	■	T	■	N	■	L	■

14.

M	O	B	S	■	B	R	O	U	H	A	H	A
I	■	A	■	R	■	E	■	N	■	V	■	G
S	I	S	T	E	R	S	■	A	M	O	U	R
C	■	T	■	S	■	I	■	C	■	C	■	E
E	J	E	C	T	■	D	I	C	T	A	T	E
L	■	■	■	A	■	E	■	E	■	D	■	A
L	E	A	G	U	E	■	A	P	L	O	M	B
A	■	R	■	R	■	G	■	T	■	■	■	L
N	A	R	R	A	T	E	■	A	P	P	L	E
E	■	A	■	T	■	N	■	B	■	I	■	N
O	U	N	C	E	■	O	B	L	I	Q	U	E
U	■	G	■	U	■	M	■	E	■	U	■	S
S	H	E	R	R	I	E	S	■	B	E	D	S

15.

B	U	C	K	■	U	N	C	O	V	E	R	S
O	■	H	■	A	■	A	■	N	■	P	■	E
B	L	E	N	D	E	R	■	O	S	I	E	R
W	■	E	■	M	■	R	■	M	■	C	■	F
H	I	P	P	O	P	O	T	A	M	U	S	■
I	■	■	■	N	■	W	■	T	■	R	■	U
T	I	T	B	I	T	■	S	O	L	E	M	N
E	■	R	■	S	■	G	■	P	■	■	■	N
■	M	O	T	H	E	R	T	O	N	G	U	E
S	■	W	■	M	■	O	■	E	■	E	■	E
T	H	E	R	E	■	T	W	I	N	N	E	D
O	■	L	■	N	■	T	■	A	■	R	■	E
P	O	S	I	T	I	O	N	■	F	E	U	D

16.

■	F	R	O	G	S	■	C	R	O	W	D	■
T	■	A	■	O	■	B	■	E	■	I	■	L
A	N	T	E	N	N	A	■	M	A	N	N	A
R	■	I	■	G	■	R	■	O	■	■	■	Z
G	L	O	W	■	O	B	T	U	S	E	L	Y
E	■	N	■	R	■	S	■	N	■	X	■	■
T	R	A	D	E	R	■	S	T	U	P	I	D
■	■	L	■	C	■	G	■	S	■	R	■	E
P	L	E	T	H	O	R	A	■	H	E	A	P
I	■	■	■	A	■	I	■	H	■	S	■	O
P	O	W	E	R	■	S	P	O	U	S	E	S
S	■	A	■	G	■	T	■	S	■	E	■	E
■	T	R	E	E	S	■	H	E	A	D	Y	■

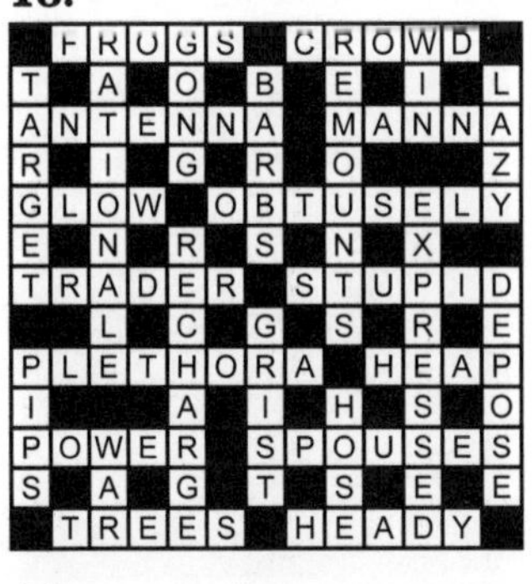

17.

■	A	L	T	E	R	N	A	T	I	V	E	■
U	■	I	■	S	■	E	■	A	■	O	■	S
N	■	D	■	C	R	E	A	M	■	C	O	T
P	O	L	K	A	■	D	■	E	■	A	■	R
A	■	E	■	P	■	L	■	S	O	L	V	E
L	I	S	T	E	N	E	D	■	■	■	■	N
A	■	S	■	E	■	■	■	C	■	C	■	U
T	■	■	■	■	B	A	L	L	Y	H	O	O
A	M	B	L	E	■	S	■	E	■	A	■	U
B	■	E	■	R	■	S	■	M	Y	T	H	S
L	A	D	■	A	M	I	D	E	■	T	■	L
E	■	I	■	S	■	S	■	N	■	E	■	Y
■	I	M	M	E	D	I	A	T	E	L	Y	■

18.

C	R	I	S	P	S	■	■	E	■	A	S	K
■	E	■	■	O	■	I	D	L	E	S	■	N
O	V	A	T	I	O	N	■	K	■	S	■	E
■	E	■	■	N	■	L	■	S	C	U	B	A
C	L	A	P	T	R	A	P	■	■	A	■	D
■	R	■	■	I	■	Y	■	S	■	G	■	E
B	Y	L	I	N	E	■	S	H	I	E	L	D
A	■	A	■	G	■	P	■	O	■	■	E	■
T	■	M	■	■	S	A	T	U	R	D	A	Y
T	U	B	E	S	■	P	■	L	■	■	D	■
L	■	A	■	H	■	A	N	D	R	O	I	D
E	■	D	R	O	L	L	■	E	■	■	N	■
S	E	A	■	E	■	■	G	R	U	N	G	E

19.

D	■	W	■	U	■	■	■	A	■	R	■	A
I	N	H	A	L	E	■	O	F	F	E	N	D
S	■	E	■	T	■	D	■	F	■	E	■	U
C	O	T	E	R	I	E	■	A	N	V	I	L
O	■	H	■	A	■	C	■	B	■	E	■	T
R	U	E	S	■	P	E	E	L	S	■	■	■
D	■	R	■	G	■	I	■	E	■	R	■	C
■	■	■	S	E	T	T	S	■	D	A	S	H
B	■	H	■	N	■	F	■	B	■	D	■	E
U	S	A	G	E	■	U	N	A	L	I	K	E
S	■	N	■	R	■	L	■	S	■	A	■	T
H	O	O	R	A	Y	■	V	I	E	N	N	A
Y	■	I	■	L	■	■	■	C	■	S	■	H

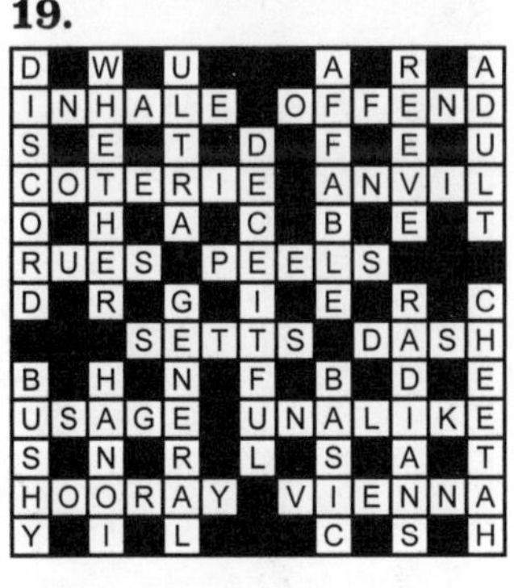

20.

E	A	T	S	■	P	U	G	I	L	I	S	M
X	■	A	■	F	■	N	■	M	■	M	■	I
P	O	M	P	O	U	S	■	P	I	P	E	S
A	■	E	■	R	■	U	■	E	■	E	■	C
N	O	D	■	M	■	R	■	R	O	A	C	H
S	■	■	■	A	L	E	R	T	■	C	■	I
I	■	R	■	L	■	■	■	I	■	H	■	E
V	■	E	■	D	I	V	A	N	■	■	■	V
E	A	G	L	E	■	E	■	E	■	B	O	O
N	■	R	■	H	■	R	■	N	■	R	■	U
E	N	E	M	Y	■	S	U	C	C	E	S	S
S	■	S	■	D	■	E	■	E	■	V	■	L
S	U	S	P	E	N	D	S	■	L	E	V	Y

21.

F	■	C	■	S	■	■	■	M	■	K	■	A
A	D	A	P	T	S	■	B	I	T	I	N	G
L	■	R	■	A	■	A	■	S	■	W	■	I
S	O	P	H	I	S	M	■	S	K	I	L	L
E	■	E	■	D	■	P	■	I	■	S	■	E
L	A	T	E	■	T	H	A	N	E	■	■	■
Y	■	S	■	A	■	I	■	G	■	L	■	R
■	■	■	G	R	U	B	S	■	V	I	V	A
F	■	S	■	T	■	I	■	F	■	G	■	I
R	U	L	E	D	■	A	B	A	S	H	E	D
O	■	Y	■	E	■	N	■	C	■	T	■	E
S	O	L	A	C	E	■	F	E	L	L	E	R
T	■	Y	■	O	■	■	■	D	■	Y	■	S

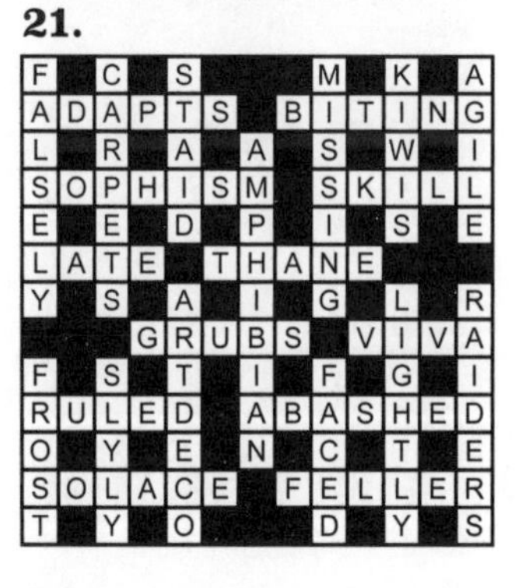

22.

D	O	R	I	C	■	O	M	I	N	O	U	S
E	■	E	■	A	■	C	■	■	O	■	M	■
A	■	Q	■	P	■	E	■	B	O	B	B	Y
F	A	U	L	T	I	L	Y	■	D	■	R	■
E	■	I	■	I	■	O	■	B	L	O	A	T
N	A	T	I	V	I	T	Y	■	E	■	■	E
I	■	E	■	E	■	■	■	C	■	R	■	S
N	■	■	A	■	P	A	R	A	K	E	E	T
G	R	U	F	F	■	N	■	S	■	F	■	I
■	U	■	F	■	D	Y	E	S	T	U	F	F
O	P	E	R	A	■	O	■	O	■	G	■	I
■	E	■	A	■	■	N	■	C	■	E	■	E
R	E	C	Y	C	L	E	■	K	E	E	P	S

23.

I	C	E	D	■	A	S	S	E	M	B	L	E
M	■	R	■	P	■	I	■	M	■	E	■	N
P	R	O	L	O	N	G	■	P	I	L	O	T
R	■	D	■	S	■	H	■	H	■	L	■	E
E	V	E	R	T	■	E	N	A	M	O	U	R
S	■	■	■	G	■	D	■	T	■	W	■	T
S	Q	U	A	R	E	■	S	I	E	S	T	A
I	■	P	■	A	■	P	■	C	■	■	■	I
O	V	E	R	D	U	E	■	A	R	S	O	N
N	■	N	■	U	■	S	■	L	■	U	■	M
I	N	D	I	A	■	E	C	L	I	P	S	E
S	■	E	■	T	■	T	■	Y	■	E	■	N
M	E	D	I	E	V	A	L	■	T	R	O	T

24.

■	O	■	I	■	M	■	S	■	H	■	M	■
S	W	A	N	K	Y	■	O	R	E	G	O	N
■	E	■	C	■	S	■	L	■	L	■	D	■
I	N	T	O	■	T	H	I	R	T	E	E	N
■	■	■	N	■	E	■	D	■	E	■	R	■
S	H	I	V	E	R	S	■	B	R	E	A	M
■	I	■	E	■	Y	■	M	■	S	■	T	■
R	E	I	N	S	■	T	I	C	K	L	E	S
■	R	■	I	■	A	■	C	■	E	■	■	■
L	A	V	E	N	D	E	R	■	L	A	K	E
■	T	■	N	■	A	■	O	■	T	■	I	■
H	I	C	C	U	P	■	B	L	E	N	D	S
■	C	■	E	■	T	■	E	■	R	■	S	■

Solutions

25.

C	A	G	E		T	R	I	M	A	R	A	N
H		I		K		O		O		E		E
I	N	A	N	I	T	Y		T	E	M	P	T
V		N		N		A		I		N		S
A	N	T	E	D	I	L	U	V	I	A	N	
L				E		E		A		N		C
R	E	C	O	R	D		S	T	A	T	O	R
Y		H		G		S		I				A
	C	A	T	A	S	T	R	O	P	H	I	C
B		N		R		E		N		E		K
L	I	C	I	T		L	E	A	K	A	G	E
O		E		E		L		L		T		R
C	A	L	E	N	D	A	R		W	H	Y	S

26.

P	O	K	E		D	E	T	A	I	L	E	D
A		R		C		A		F		E		I
R	I	O	T	O	U	S		T	H	I	E	F
T		N		N		I		E		S		F
I	N	A	P	T		N	U	R	T	U	R	E
C				R		G		T		R		R
U	N	S	E	A	T		T	H	I	E	V	E
L		P		D		H		O				N
A	V	A	R	I	C	E		U	N	C	U	T
R		N		C		R		G		A		I
I	N	G	O	T		E	C	H	I	D	N	A
T		L		E		I		T		G		T
Y	I	E	L	D	I	N	G		N	E	V	E

27.

R	E	N	O	U	N	C	E		S	P	U	R
A		O		N		H		U		H		E
V	I	S	O	R		O		N	E	A	R	S
E		H		E		I		I		N		I
			F	A	S	C	I	N	A	T	E	D
P		S		S		E		T		A		I
A	U	T	H	O	R		N	E	L	S	O	N
N		A		N		A		R		M		G
C	A	M	P	A	I	G	N	E	R			
A		P		B		O		S		A		R
K	R	I	L	L		U		T	O	R	C	H
E		N		E		T		E		I		Y
S	A	G	E		W	I	N	D	L	A	S	S

28.

R	E	B	E	L	S		C	A	S	I	N	G
E		U		U		W		L		D		L
M	A	Z	U	R	K	A		R		O		O
O		Z		I		T	R	E	L	L	I	S
V	O	W	E	D		E		A				S
E		O				R		D	A	F	F	Y
		R		B	U	M	P	Y		I		
M	E	D	I	A		E				G		S
A				G		L		M	O	U	N	T
S	H	A	M	P	O	O		U		R		A
C		L		I		N	U	L	L	I	F	Y
O		E		P		S		E		N		E
T	I	C	K	E	R		A	S	C	E	N	D

29.

A	B	R	A	D	E			Y		C	U	R
	E			A		S	E	O	U	L		E
A	N	O	D	Y	N	E		G		O		A
	E			L		P		A	N	T	I	C
P	A	R	T	I	S	A	N			H		T
	T			G		L		R		E		O
R	H	Y	T	H	M		L	E	S	S	E	R
E		E		T		O		S			N	
P		L			P	R	E	T	E	N	C	E
R	E	L	A	X		C		O			R	
O		I		M		A	C	R	O	N	Y	M
O		N	E	E	D	S		E			P	
F	O	G		N			E	D	I	C	T	S

30.

N	U	T	S		F	A	N	A	T	I	C	S
U		O		P		R		L		D		E
T	A	X	F	R	E	E		P	A	Y	E	E
R		I		E				H		L		M
I	N	C	O	M	P	A	R	A	B	L	E	
E				E		B		B		I		A
N	O	W		D	R	O	N	E		C	O	N
T		A		I		D		T				Y
	B	R	O	T	H	E	R	I	N	L	A	W
L		M		A				C		A		H
A	V	E	R	T		B	R	A	M	B	L	E
M		S		E		U		L		E		R
A	N	T	I	D	O	T	E		G	L	E	E

31.

	M	I	S	C	H	I	E	V	O	U	S	
E		N		E		M		E		T		R
M		S		L	A	P	S	E		T	E	E
B	I	T	E	S		E		R		E		S
R		A		I		L		S	T	R	O	P
O	U	T	B	U	R	S	T					I
I		E		S				G		H		R
D					A	U	T	O	M	A	T	A
E	R	R	O	R		N		N		L		T
R		U		I		C		D	U	B	A	I
E	O	N		F	O	L	I	O		E		O
R		I		L		E		L		R		N
	U	N	D	E	R	S	T	A	N	D	S	

32.

U	P	S	H	O	T		P	O	S	I	T	S
	R		E		I		O		P		A	
F	E	A	R		C	U	D	D	L	I	N	G
	D		S		K		I		I			
R	A	K	E	S		L	A	P	T	O	P	S
	T		L		F		T				R	
C	O	N	F	L	A	G	R	A	T	I	O	N
	R				M		Y		U		T	
P	Y	R	A	M	I	D		F	R	I	E	D
			N		L		K		M		S	
S	C	A	N	S	I	O	N		O	A	T	S
	R		E		E		A		I		E	
L	Y	N	X	E	S		P	A	L	T	R	Y

33.

S	E	T	T	L	E		A	S	S	E	T	S
T		A		E		I		T		L		C
U	N	C	H	A	I	N		I		S		E
F		I		C		G	A	L	L	E	O	N
F	E	T	C	H		R		T				E
S		U				E		O	A	S	E	S
		R		O	L	D	E	N		I		
R	E	N	A	L		I				L		P
E				Y		E		P	A	L	E	R
F	I	R	E	M	E	N		H		I		A
U		E		P		T	R	A	C	E	R	Y
G		E		U		S		S		S		E
E	F	F	U	S	E		N	E	T	T	E	D

34.

F	O	O	T	B	A	L	L		G	R	I	D
O		A		E		A		I		E		I
P	E	T	A	L		R		N	O	U	N	S
S		H		O		D		T		N		A
			S	W	E	E	T	E	N	I	N	G
G		D		T		R		L		O		R
L	A	U	G	H	S		P	L	U	N	G	E
A		R		E		K		I		S		E
D	R	A	W	B	R	I	D	G	E			
R		T		E		M		I		P		M
A	R	I	E	L		O		B	U	L	L	Y
G		O		T		N		L		E		T
S	I	N	G		P	O	L	Y	M	A	T	H

35.

S		R		A				S		V		B
K	N	O	L	L	S		T	H	R	I	L	L
E		O		L		M		A		N		O
T	O	M	B	O	L	A		K	A	Y	A	K
C		I		Y		E		E		L		E
H	E	E	L		A	L	O	U	D			
Y		R		C		S		P		N		T
			P	O	S	T	S		S	O	L	O
A		T		P		R		N		X		U
S	C	R	A	P		O	L	I	V	I	E	R
P		O		E		M		G		O		I
E	A	T	E	R	Y		S	H	O	U	T	S
N		S		S				T		S		T

36.

S	P	E	E	D		U	N	T	R	U	T	H
T		V		I		G			E		R	
I		E		O		A		C	A	N	O	N
M	E	N	A	C	I	N	G		R		V	
U		I		E		D		J	E	W	E	L
L	I	N	E	S	M	A	N		D			E
A		G		E				F		S		G
N			S		L	I	B	R	E	T	T	I
T	A	S	K	S		M		E		I		S
	B		I		S	P	I	T	E	F	U	L
C	O	U	L	D		O		F		F		A
	V		L			S		U		E		T
M	E	S	S	A	G	E		L	U	N	G	E

Solutions

37.

U	P	O	N		D	E	S	P	O	T	I	C
N		I		O		N		I		H		O
A	L	L	E	L	E	S		T	H	O	R	N
C		E		Y		U		T		U		T
C	A	D		M		E		E	A	G	L	E
O				P	O	S	E	R		H		N
U		S		I				P		T		T
N		P		C	O	B	R	A				E
T	Y	I	N	G		O		T		A	N	D
A		N		A		N		T		W		N
B	R	O	O	M		O	P	E	R	A	T	E
L		F		E		B		R		R		S
E	F	F	U	S	I	O	N		J	E	T	S

38.

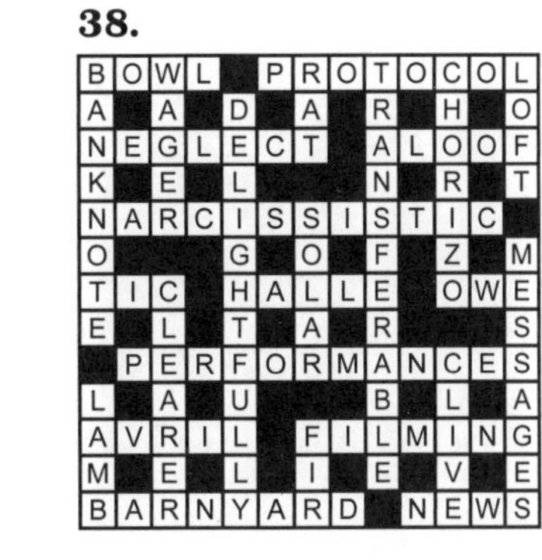

39.

40.

I	G	U	A	N	A		O		O		F	
N		N			S	O	F	T	B	A	L	L
C	H	I			L		F		S		O	
I		S	T	E	A	L	S		C	O	R	E
T		O			N		I		U		I	
E	R	N	I	E		A	D	O	R	I	N	G
			D		C		E		E			
A	L	G	E	B	R	A		A	D	D	E	R
	O		N		O		P			E		O
S	C	U	T		C	O	R	G	I	S		C
	K		I		H		O			I	L	K
D	E	A	F	N	E	S	S			R		E
	T		Y		T		E	F	F	E	C	T

41.

R	A	S	P		N	A	T	A	T	I	O	N
E		T		C		R		L		N		E
C	O	U	L	O	M	B		P	O	S	E	S
L		F		N		O		H		U		T
U	N	F	A	V	O	U	R	A	B	L	E	
S				A		R		N		T		G
E	A	S	E	L	S		C	U	R	S	O	R
S		N		E		I		M				E
	C	O	N	S	I	S	T	E	N	T	L	Y
R		R		C		O		R		O		N
A	N	K	L	E		B	R	I	S	T	L	E
T		E		N		A		C		A		S
S	A	L	U	T	A	R	Y		A	L	M	S

42.

I	M	P	A	C	T		C	O	V	E	R	S
	O		Q		U		A		O		E	
G	U	R	U		N	O	S	E	D	I	V	E
	S		A		E		T		K			
S	E	A	T	S		J	A	K	A	R	T	A
	T		I		G		W				A	
P	R	A	C	T	I	C	A	L	J	O	K	E
	A				U		Y		U		E	
U	P	R	A	I	S	E		S	P	E	A	R
			L		E		T		I		W	
C	H	U	T	Z	P	A	H		T	O	A	D
	E		A		P		O		E		Y	
E	N	T	R	E	E		M	O	R	A	S	S

43.

	P		S		A		T		T		S	
S	E	A	W	A	T	E	R		R	O	T	E
	A		I		H		U		U		I	
B	R	A	N		L	E	N	I	E	N	C	Y
	L		G		E		K				K	
A	S	S	I	S	T	S		G	U	I	S	E
			N		E		L		N			
J	U	D	G	E		T	I	D	D	L	E	R
	N				C		M		E		N	
S	C	O	T	F	R	E	E		R	E	D	S
	O		I		I		A		A		I	
G	I	R	D		M	E	D	I	C	I	N	E
	L		Y		E		E		T		G	

44.

45.

O	F	T	E	N		C	A	R	P	O	R	T
V		E		I		O			H		O	
E		N		T		R		C	O	L	O	N
R	E	D	E	P	L	O	Y		E		M	
D		R		I		N		O	B	E	Y	S
R	A	I	N	C	O	A	T		E			A
A		L		K				E		E		R
F			Q		R	H	E	T	O	R	I	C
T	O	R	U	S		U		H		A		A
	C		A		A	R	K	A	N	S	A	S
R	E	A	R	S		T		N		I		T
	A		T			L		O		N		I
E	N	D	O	R	S	E		L	O	G	I	C

46.

	P	O	L	Y	T	E	C	H	N	I	C	
O		S		A		N		U		D		F
U		T		W	A	V	E	R		E	T	A
T	A	L	O	N		I		L		A		S
S		E		I		E		S	P	L	A	T
T	H	R	E	N	O	D	Y					F
A		S		G				C		A		O
N					I	N	T	R	U	D	E	R
D	O	C	K	S		A		I		D		W
I		E		L		T		M	A	R	I	A
N	I	L		U	N	I	T	S		E		R
G		L		S		O		O		S		D
	N	O	T	H	I	N	G	N	E	S	S	

47.

	T		A		H		D		G		I	
D	O	U	B	L	E	D	E	A	L	I	N	G
	W		L		A		I		I		F	
I	N	V	O	L	V	E	S		T	R	O	Y
			O		I		T		C		R	
C	O	M	M	E	N	D		R	H	Y	M	E
	V				G		D				E	
R	E	U	S	E		S	I	L	V	E	R	Y
	R		T		H		S		I			
A	V	E	R		E	X	P	L	O	R	E	S
	I		A		L		L		L		R	
F	E	L	I	C	I	T	A	T	I	O	N	S
	W		N		X		Y		N		E	

48.

A	U	K	S		B	A	L	A	N	C	E	D
I		I		E		D		S		E		U
R	E	L	A	X	E	D		T	I	D	E	S
E		N		H				O		I		T
D	E	S	P	A	I	R	I	N	G	L	Y	
A				U		E		I		L		F
L	A	W		S	A	V	E	S		A	W	L
E		R		T		U		H				O
	C	A	B	I	N	E	T	M	A	K	E	R
T		N		V				E		A		I
R	O	G	U	E		T	E	N	U	R	E	S
E		L		L		O		T		M		T
E	V	E	R	Y	O	N	E		S	A	W	S

Solutions

49.

```
#BALMY#REEFS#
W#S#E#F#S#E#J
APPEASE#CONGO
R#A#T#I#A###H
MARS#EGYPTIAN
E#T#D#N#I#N##
DIADEM#INDEED
##M#C#S#G#B#I
PREFECTS#DROP
A###N#O#R#I#P
SHOUT#CHARADE
S#A#L#K#T#T#D
#GREYS#FETES#
```

50.

```
#TRACKRECORD#
C#E#O#E#L#I#S
O#T#PADRE#OAT
NERVY#D#A#J#A
G#A#I#E#TWANG
REIGNING####E
E#N#G###P#A#F
S####RECLINER
SHRUB#N#A#T#I
M#E#O#A#ICING
AFT#WOMEN#G#H
N#R#I#E#L#E#T
#ROLEPLAYING#
```

51.

```
EXPOSURE#HALO
V#R#A#E###U#V
ERECT#CRUMPLE
S#S#I#O###A#R
##E#S#ITALICS
FATEFUL#N#R#E
E###I###A###A
E#N#E#OBLONGS
LOURDES#G#E##
I#G###C#E#V#H
NIGERIA#SKATE
G#E###R#I#D#R
SITE#ESCAPADE
```

52.

```
WEPT#EUPHORIA
A#I#L#T#O#E#I
LOCKOUT#METER
K#K#S#E#E#U#W
IVY#T#R#LARGO
N###PISTE#N#R
G#C#R###S#S#T
S#O#OPENS###H
THUMP#N#N#PHI
I#R#E#J#E#E#N
CRIER#OSSICLE
K#E#T#I#S#A#S
SPRAYING#GNUS
```

53.

```
LOSER#SERMONS
I#C#O#C##E#A#
P#A#M#R#WALTZ
SURFACED#D#A#
T#I#N#E#ROLLS
INNOCENT#W##H
C#G#E###O#B#A
K##C#ARGUMENT
SCORE#I#T#L#T
#H#O#ADDITIVE
VALUE#G#N#N#R
#I#C##E#G#D#E
ORPHANS#SWARD
```

54.

```
F#B#A###R#J#S
ORANGE#HEROIC
R#L#A#E#S#I#O
MOLLIFY#TANGO
I#A#N#E#A#T#P
NODS#COLTS###
G#S#L#P#E#D#F
###CASES#GOBI
A#F#G#N#I#O#R
PRONG#ENSURES
P#R#I#R#L#M#T
LUCENT#RECALL
Y#E#G###T#N#Y
```

55.

```
#F#S#B#S#G#T#
DISTRUST#AIRY
#L#A#C#I#R#A#
FLAG#KICKBACK
#E#N#L#K###E#
STEAMER#HARSH
###T#S#S#C###
HAYEK#SPECIFY
#M###B#I#U#A#
FORSWEAR#RICE
#U#A#G#I#A#I#
TRON#ASTUTELY
#S#E#N#S#E#E#
```

56.

```
CITY#MASSAGED
A#A#I#N#T#O#I
RECENCY#RUSKS
A#I#T#W#A#H#H
MATHEMATICAL#
E###L#Y#G#W#E
LASTLY#SHEKEL
S#I#I#H#T###O
#EXAGGERATION
B#T#E#L#W#V#G
ALIGN#PIANOLA
S#E#C#E#Y#R#T
HOSTELRY#LYRE
```

57.

```
SCALDING#PUMA
I#I#I#E#M#N#S
CODES#E#YAWNS
K#E#A#D#T#I#I
###SPEECHLESS
C#S#P#D#O#L#T
ARCHER#SLEDGE
U#E#A#A#O#Y#D
CENTRIFUGE###
U#A#I#F#I#S#B
SIREN#O#CHOIR
E#I#G#R#A#F#A
SLOT#IDOLATRY
```

58.

```
COMA#CRIMINAL
H#E#E#E#A#I#I
RESTFUL#STRUT
Y#S#F#I#S#V#T
SPY#E#E#PEARL
A###REFER#N#E
N#B#V###O#A#M
T#I#EMBED###E
HOLES#E#U#FOR
E#L#C#A#C#L#M
MAIZE#CAESURA
U#O#N#O#D#T#I
MONOTONE#HEED
```

59.

```
LOGGER#INFECT
E#R#M#E#E#X#I
PHALANX#B#A#N
T#F#I#PLUMMET
OFFAL#R#L###E
N#I###E#APHID
##T#PASSE#U##
HAIKU#S###R#P
I###M#I#RURAL
SCORPIO#I#Y#A
S#W#K#NAPKINS
E#E#I#S#E#N#M
SIDING#ENIGMA
```

60.

```
#CONSTRUCTED#
M#B#Y#U#O#R#D
O#E#SOBER#URE
UPSET#R#D#P#S
L#I#E#I#SETUP
INTIMACY####O
N#Y#S###D#M#N
R####VINEYARD
OTHER#N#V#R#E
U#U#E#F#OUTEN
GOB#CREST#I#C
E#B#A#S#E#N#Y
#SYMPATHETIC#
```

Solutions

61.

```
BISECT PRAYER
E Y A D E O U
SAMURAI S G G
I M O LETTING
DWELL A O   E
E T   P RAGED
  R TRIBE R  
LAYER D   U M
I   A A CAMEO
GOURMET I B U
A L M ENGULFS
N N E D A E S
DEARLY CRUSOE
```

62.

```
SCALES BERATE
 L U W O O E 
FIRM INDECENT
 E B M Y K   
KNEAD TWISTED
 T G E O   L 
DEMONSTRATION
 L   C K E Q 
REDHEAD VACUA
   O R K C E 
TARRAGON HONK
 I D O E E C 
ODDEST WARDEN
```

63.

```
 W F I E I S 
SHOOIN MYRIAD
 I L T P R N 
OPAL ENTREATY
   O N Y C I 
HOGWASH TOGAS
 L T E C V G 
SIGHT SOMEHOW
 V R G R R   
DEBONAIR AIMS
 O U U U B I 
SINGED POLICY
 L H Y T E E 
```

64.

```
RUCK STRIKING
E R C U N T O
INEXACT DIEGO
N D P O E R D
FLOOR REFRAIN
O   I S E T A
RELICS INGEST
C U I L S   U
ENCLOSE INTER
M K U A B R E
EXITS DULLARD
N E L E E C L
TARRYING STAY
```

65.

```
S P M L C P P
HALLIWELL EAU
O A S G E A L
WATER INFORMS
S I U O T   A
 ANGLING OMIT
D U E   S A E
EMMY SPLURGE 
S   D L M E B
SANGRIA MOLAR
E U A N A L A
RUM MOTORCARS
T B A S Y N S
```

66.

```
FEDORA S C P 
A A  BACCARAT
DUN  A A N G 
I DAMSEL OBOE
N E  H D N D 
GERMS AEOLIAN
   I S D A   
MAGNETS SWORE
 N O E D   BN
STIR WHENCE S
 L I A N  YOU
FEATURES  E E
 R Y D EXUDED
```

67.

```
CAVERN WARMUP
O A A P C A A
NOURISH T G R
C L S OCULIST
UNTIE T A   L
R I   O RANGY
  N RUGBY I  
MAGMA R   N M
A   S A ARENA
KETCHUP M T R
I I E HOUSING
N E R S S E I
GARISH NEESON
```

68.

```
P M R   E A S
ROOTED ASYLUM
O R G C Q O A
VIOLATE USHER
O C L A I A T
KICK TSARS   
E O I E E S A
   AMPLE HUES
B A P E S F P
LADLE SCUFFLE
O D T S G E C
CROCUS CARROT
K N S   R S S
```

69.

```
POPE CRYSTALS
E O T O A S A
RESURGE CUSHY
F I A   R A S
OSTENTATIOUS 
R   S R L L G
MOO PURGE TAR
S C A O G   A
 NARROWMINDED
P R E   O R I
ANION PLUMAGE
T N C I S I N
HEAVYSET GNAT
```

70.

```
CHOOSE THROWN
U N I P O C E
BREADTH S H A
I L L OUTWEAR
SPIRE T I   E
M N   O LAIRD
  E SEGUE N  
STREW R   S E
A   E A PUPIL
FLAREUP A I U
E S T HUNDRED
T I E Y D E E
YEARNS CANDID
```

71.

```
 P E C S O R 
OUTSTRIP NEAR
 N P A E C S 
DINE CONTEMPT
 S C K T   E 
CHOICES MAIDS
   A D C N   
BULLS BREEZES
 N   M O C A 
STENCILS DARK
 I O S S O N 
WEAR THEATRES
 S M Y D E R 
```

72.

```
HELIUM Y L A 
A U  ELEVATES
VAN  D L B R 
I GENIAL RAID
N E  C O A A 
GASES SWADDLE
   P R S O   
UNAIDED ARRAY
 I D D C  I E
OGRE TILING O
 H M A E  HUM
ETHIOPIA  T A
 S C E REASON
```

Solutions

73.

A	N	T	E		T	H	R	O	T	T	L	E
C		R		S		A		V		R		X
C	H	I	P	P	E	R		E	V	I	T	A
O		E		I		D		R		V		G
M	U	S	I	C		L	A	S	T	I	N	G
P				K		Y		I		A		E
A	B	R	O	A	D		A	M	B	L	E	R
N		E		N		A		P				A
I	N	S	I	D	E	S		L	I	S	Z	T
M		C		S		I		I		O		E
E	Q	U	I	P		D	E	F	I	N	E	D
N		E		A		E		Y		A		L
T	A	R	T	N	E	S	S		P	R	E	Y

74.

L		G		P		A		H		G		B
A	V	A	I	L	A	B	L	E		R	I	O
Y		U		A		O		N		U		U
B	A	N	D	Y		D	E	C	I	B	E	L
Y		T		I		E		E				D
	I	L	L	N	E	S	S		A	C	H	E
A		E		G				T		I		R
D	U	T	Y		O	U	T	W	A	R	D	
J				P		N		O		C		T
O	B	E	L	I	S	K		S	O	L	V	E
U		G		T		I		O		I		A
R	I	G		O	I	N	T	M	E	N	T	S
N		Y		N		D		E		G		E

75.

T	R	U	M	P	S			T		A	N	T
	E			L		P	A	R	E	D		W
O	V	E	R	A	L	L		A		I		E
	I			N		E		P	U	P	A	E
E	V	E	N	T	U	A	L			O		T
	A			A		S		I		S		E
C	L	I	N	I	C		E	N	D	E	A	R
H		G		N		S		F			U	
I		N			D	E	M	O	L	I	S	H
L	E	I	G	H		R		R			T	
L		T		E		V	A	M	P	I	R	E
E		E	X	I	L	E		E			A	
D	U	D		R			E	D	I	B	L	E

76.

S	C	A	L	A	R		D	E	L	U	D	E
	U		E		E		E		O		U	
A	P	E	X		A	N	C	H	O	R	E	D
	B		I		M		R		K			
B	O	T	C	H		F	E	A	S	T	E	D
	A		O		E		P				C	
P	R	O	N	U	N	C	I	A	T	I	O	N
	D				S		T		O		N	
E	S	C	A	P	E	D		S	W	O	O	N
			U		M		W		A		M	
F	L	E	X	I	B	L	E		R	A	I	N
	O		I		L		N		D		S	
T	W	I	N	G	E		T	O	S	S	E	S

77.

	N		S		A		W		I		S	
D	I	S	P	A	S	S	I	O	N	A	T	E
	N		L		S		D		J		R	
L	A	T	I	T	U	D	E		U	N	I	T
			N		R		N		R		C	
C	A	N	T	E	E	N		P	E	T	T	Y
	G				D		D				L	
M	I	X	U	P		R	E	P	L	A	Y	S
	T		N		S		V		A			
B	A	R	B		P	L	A	T	Y	P	U	S
	T		E		R		L		I		R	
B	O	U	N	T	I	F	U	L	N	E	S	S
	R		T		G		E		G		A	

78.

S	L	A	L	O	M		N		A		I	
T		L			E	V	O	L	V	I	N	G
E	M	U			Z		T		O		V	
W		M	U	Z	Z	L	E		I	D	E	A
E		N			O		P		D		R	
D	R	I	F	T		S	A	T	I	A	T	E
			A		B		D		N			
F	L	A	T	O	U	T		A	G	R	E	E
	A		I		R		V			E		S
S	T	A	G		S	T	I	T	C	H		T
	E		U		A		L			A	A	H
I	N	T	E	G	R	A	L			S		E
	T		D		Y		A	N	C	H	O	R

79.

L	I	N	G	U	I	S	T		M	E	L	T
O		O		N		C		M		M		E
S	I	T	U	P		R		A	L	B	U	M
E		E		R		A		T		I		E
			C	O	M	P	E	T	I	T	O	R
A		C		F		S		E		T		I
C	H	O	P	I	N		P	R	I	E	S	T
A		N		T		A		O		R		Y
D	E	C	L	A	S	S	I	F	Y			
E		E		B		S		F		L		F
M	E	R	Y	L		O		A	G	A	P	E
I		T		E		R		C		T		N
C	O	O	S		S	T	I	T	C	H	E	D

80.

S	K	I	E	S		A	F	F	A	I	R	S
W		M		U		D			N		I	
E		I		P		R		H	I	T	C	H
E	X	T	E	R	I	O	R		M		C	
T		A		E		I		M	A	G	I	C
E	S	T	I	M	A	T	E		L			R
N		E		O				S		O		O
E			A		B	R	I	C	K	B	A	T
R	U	N	G	S		A		A		L		C
	N		L		S	K	I	T	T	I	S	H
A	D	D	E	D		I		T		G		E
	U		A			N		E		E		T
H	E	M	M	I	N	G		R	A	S	P	Y

81.

	B		U		D		S		W		N	
T	R	A	N	S	E	C	T		A	L	U	M
	O		K		V		I		R		A	
S	K	I	N		O	R	N	A	M	E	N	T
	E		O		T		G				C	
C	R	A	W	L	E	R		W	A	R	E	S
			N		D		K		V			
C	H	A	S	E		B	I	V	O	U	A	C
	U				G		N		C		R	
U	N	I	C	O	R	N	S		A	I	D	S
	T		U		A		M		D		E	
K	E	E	P		D	R	A	G	O	O	N	S
	R		S		E		N		S		T	

82.

D	E	B	U	N	K		S	P	O	R	T	S
I		A		A		H		E		O		H
V	E	R	T	I	G	O		A		L		O
I		N		V		M	U	F	F	L	E	R
D	R	A	P	E		E		O				T
E		C				O		W	A	S	P	S
		L		B	A	S	I	L		T		
K	N	E	E	L		T				A		C
N				A		A		A	C	C	R	A
O	B	J	E	C	T	S		N		C		V
C		O		K		I	N	G	R	A	T	E
K		E		E		S		R		T		I
S	H	Y	I	N	G		T	Y	C	O	O	N

83.

	K	N	O	W	S		S	P	O	K	E	
A		O		I		G		E		I		T
B	U	R	G	L	A	R		D	O	D	G	E
I		M		L		O		A				A
D	I	A	L		S	W	I	N	D	L	E	R
E		T		L		S		T		I		
S	E	I	Z	E	D		A	I	R	B	U	S
		V		C		Q		C		R		P
C	H	E	S	T	N	U	T		C	A	L	L
A				U		A		F		R		A
B	O	W	E	R		C	R	I	T	I	C	S
S		E		E		K		N		E		H
	B	E	E	R	S		L	E	A	S	H	

84.

E	A	R	N		O	M	N	I	V	O	R	E
N		O		U		Y		N		R		N
L	A	M	E	N	T	S		T	R	A	D	E
I		E		D		T		R		T		R
G	O	O		E		I		O	W	I	N	G
H				R	A	C	E	D		O		E
T		C		A				U		N		T
E		O		C	U	B	I	C				I
N	I	N	T	H		E		T		D	E	C
M		V		I		M		O		I		A
E	L	I	D	E		U	N	R	A	V	E	L
N		C		V		S		Y		E		L
T	O	T	T	E	R	E	D		G	R	E	Y

Solutions

85.

```
OARS#SHOUTING
B#U#O#E#N#C#U
SAMOVAR#FIERY
I#B#E###L#P#S
DIAGRAMMATIC#
I###E#E#T#C#I
ALL#SLANT#KEN
N#A#T#N#E###C
#SCRIPTWRITER
S#O#M###I#I#E
WANDA#BONANZA
A#I#T#Y#G#G#S
MACKEREL#GENE
```

86.

```
MISLAY#OBJECT
A#U#H#S#A#V#H
TABLEAU#D#I#E
R#S#A#PEDDLER
ILIAD#E#E###O
X#D###R#BASIN
##E#ADMIT#Q##
EIDER#A###U#R
X###M#R#CHIDE
HUMMOCK#O#R#L
A#O#U#EMPORIA
L#N#R#T#E#E#Y
EPONYM#ADULTS
```

87.

```
#T#S#E#O#C#C#
DOGLEG#PHOTON
#R#E#G#A#U#W#
ANTI#HOLINESS
###G#E#S#T#L#
ARCHWAY#BEGIN
#E#T#D#R#R#P#
SCOOT#BELFAST
#E#F#H#S#E###
MISHMASH#IVOR
#V#A#U#A#T#U#
LENNON#PLEASE
#R#D#T#E#R#T#
```

88.

```
OLDEST#SUPPLE
R#Y#T#D#N#O#N
BENZENE#D#S#T
I#A#M#FURTHER
TIMES#E#E###A
S#I###N#SWOOP
##S#PECKS#U##
COMMA#E###T#A
H###R#L#TACOS
ACTUATE#E#L#S
S#E#B#SYRIANA
E#A#L#S#R#S#I
SALTED#HANSEL
```

89.

```
S#K#T#M#R#A#A
THIGHBONE#MET
E#N#I#S#R#M#T
PAGES#ANYMORE
S#S#T#I#L###M
#CHALICE#CHOP
U#I#E###T#U#T
NIPS#WIGWAMS#
B###D#N#I#A#S
OVERACT#RANCH
U#A#C#E#L#I#A
NOR#HARVESTED
D#L#A#N#D#Y#E
```

90.

```
IONS#THOROUGH
N#O#B#I#E#N#A
FITTEST#QUAIL
I#E#L#H#U#W#F
NASAL#EPITAPH
I###I#R#R#R#E
THOUGH#GENEVA
E#P#E#A#M###R
SPHERES#EXALT
I#E#E#T#N#C#E
MELON#HATCHED
A#I#C#M#S#E#L
LEAPYEAR#EDDY
```

91.

```
RABBIT#EJECTS
U#R#N#E#U#A#L
PHOENIX#M#S#U
E#C#E#PEACHES
RACER#E#N###H
T#O###D#JEMMY
##L#HAITI#I##
NOISE#T###N#B
U###X#I#DISCO
CHICAGO#E#T#T
L#S#G#UNEARTH
E#I#O#S#M#E#E
INSANE#OSTLER
```

92.

```
INFAMOUS#OWLS
M#A#E#P###I#C
PACKS#BEGONIA
S#I#M#E###I#R
##A#E#ARSENIC
CULPRIT#P#G#E
I###I###A###L
S#F#S#COGENCY
THERMAL#H#I##
E#N###E#E#C#P
RECOVER#TOKYO
N#E###G#T#E#O
SOSO#CYLINDER
```

93.

```
SOLECISM#SPAR
E#O#O#T#O#R#E
COVEN#R#VIOLA
T#E#S#I#E#D#G
###MISFORTUNE
V#R#D#E#I#C#N
IMAGES#INVENT
N#I#R#M#D#R#S
CONTAGIOUS###
I#F#B#S#L#S#G
BRAWL#C#GRILL
L#L#Y#U#E#G#A
ELLA#REDDENED
```

94.

```
INJURING#EDAM
R#U#O#E###R#A
ODDLY#UTILITY
N#G#A#T###F#O
##E#L#EJECTOR
DOSSIER#C#S#E
E###S###O###S
E#E#T#ASSERTS
REVISED#Y#A##
L#A###V#S#B#N
INDULGE#TABOO
K#E###N#E#L#D
ENDS#STAMPEDE
```

95.

```
#SPLAY#YELPS#
O#N#E#S#X#I#B
CHEROOT#PATER
U#U#N#I#A###A
LIME#BLINDING
A#A#P#E#D#M##
ROTORS#PEOPLE
##I#E#D#D#E#N
SYCAMORE#PROD
W###I#U#H#I#U
AWAKE#GLAMOUR
B#R#R#S#I#U#E
#SKIED#CLASH#
```

96.

```
#D#E#A#B#S#L#
POSSIBLY#OVEN
#C#P#S#L#U#A#
LIMO#CLAPPING
#L#U#O#W###E#
PERSONS#KINDS
###A#D#P#C###
MAPLE#ELDERLY
#D###C#A#C#O#
IDEALIST#REST
#L#W#N#E#E#I#
LEIA#CONTAINS
#D#Y#H#S#M#G#
```

Solutions

97.

	S		R		T		A		G		G	
B	O	T	U	L	I	S	M		L	E	A	P
	D		S		P		I		U		L	
W	I	S	H		P	O	T	B	E	L	L	Y
	U		H		I		Y				O	
I	M	P	O	U	N	D		L	I	M	P	S
			U		G		P		M			
S	C	A	R	Y		S	U	M	M	I	N	G
	L				S		R		A		I	
D	O	O	R	S	T	O	P		T	U	B	E
	S		I		A		O		U		B	
V	E	A	L		K	E	S	T	R	E	L	S
	S		L		E		E		E		E	

98.

F	O	W	L		F	R	E	S	H	M	A	N
R		H		D		O		U		O		O
E	D	I	F	I	C	E		B	I	D	E	S
E		R		S				S		I		Y
W	A	L	K	I	N	G	S	T	I	C	K	
I				N		L		A		U		P
L	I	T		T	I	E	I	N		M	A	R
L		R		E		B		T				E
	S	I	N	G	L	E	M	I	N	D	E	D
O		F		R				A		I		I
V	O	L	G	A		T	I	T	A	N	I	C
I		E		T		O		E		A		T
D	A	R	K	E	N	E	D		A	R	M	S

99.

D		S		P		W		B		S		P
I	N	T	R	U	S	I	V	E		W	O	O
O		U		N		G		L		I		L
D	O	M	E	D		W	R	I	G	G	L	E
E		B		I		A		E				N
	A	L	L	T	I	M	E		A	B	E	T
F		E		S				E		A		A
R	U	D	E		H	A	P	P	I	L	Y	
I				F		B		I		L		R
G	U	Z	Z	L	E	R		G	N	O	M	E
A		E		O		U		R		O		A
T	E	A		E	X	P	L	A	I	N	E	D
E		L		S		T		M		S		S

100.

C	O	S	Y		T	W	E	N	T	I	E	S
I		H		S		A		I		T		T
R	O	E	B	U	C	K		G	U	A	V	A
C		L		B		E		H		L		C
U	N	F	I	T		N	A	T	T	I	L	Y
M				E		S		C		A		F
F	L	U	R	R	Y		G	L	A	N	C	E
E		N		R		A		O				R
R	E	L	O	A	D	S		T	H	I	N	G
E		O		N		S		H		N		U
N	O	V	A	E		U	S	E	L	E	S	S
C		E		A		R		S		P		O
E	N	D	A	N	G	E	R		S	T	U	N

101.

H	I	D	D	E	N		B	L	O	W	U	P
U		A		X		P		A		E		I
S	H	I	A	T	S	U		N		R		A
T		Q		R		L	E	C	T	E	R	N
L	A	U	R	A		L		E				O
E		I				T		T	E	S	T	S
		R		A	C	H	E	S		T		
S	L	I	N	G		E				I		S
I				R		P		T	U	M	M	Y
T	O	P	S	O	I	L		A		U		D
C		E		U		U	P	S	I	L	O	N
O		C		N		G		T		U		E
M	I	K	A	D	O		M	E	A	S	L	Y

102.

A	M	U	S	E	D			G		I	N	K
	A			V		E	X	A	M	S		N
P	R	E	S	E	N	T		F		S		I
	C			N		H		F	A	U	L	T
T	O	M	A	T	O	E	S			E		T
	N			F		R		N		R		E
N	I	M	B	U	S		D	O	W	S	E	R
I		E		L		S		N			L	
B		M			E	P	I	S	O	D	E	S
B	R	E	A	K		E		E			G	
L		N		I		C	Y	N	I	C	A	L
E		T	R	A	C	K		S			N	
R	H	O		N			F	E	I	N	T	S

103.

D	E	C	R	E	A	S	E		B	O	U	T
A		O		N		H		U		U		I
M	O	T	E	T		R		N	O	T	E	D
E		S		H		U		D		D		I
			T	U	M	B	L	E	D	O	W	N
P		I		S		S		R		O		E
H	O	R	R	I	D		U	S	U	R	P	S
Y		R		A		W		T		S		S
S	L	I	P	S	T	R	E	A	M			
I		G		T		I		F		G		I
Q	U	A	S	I		T		F	R	O	W	N
U		T		C		E		E		O		C
E	W	E	R		P	R	U	D	E	N	C	E

104.

D	R	E	N	C	H			C		C	U	T
	E			O		E	B	O	N	Y		O
A	V	A	I	L	E	D		O		C		U
	I			U		I		T	I	L	E	R
D	E	C	I	M	A	T	E			I		N
	W			B		S		F		S		E
O	S	I	R	I	S		S	U	L	T	R	Y
Y		N		A		E		S			E	
S		H			A	D	H	E	S	I	V	E
T	H	A	W	S		I		L			E	
E		L		M		F	E	A	T	U	R	E
R		E	P	O	X	Y		G			T	
S	I	R		G			D	E	F	U	S	E

105.

H	I	L	A	R	I	T	Y		B	R	O	W
I		E		U		U		A		E		H
D	R	A	W	N		R		C	A	D	R	E
E		K		O		K		C		F		R
			A	F	T	E	R	I	M	A	G	E
A		H		T		Y		D		C		V
C	L	O	T	H	E		R	E	N	E	G	E
H		O		E		S		N		D		R
I	L	L	U	M	I	N	A	T	E			
L		I		I		I		A		D		P
L	E	G	A	L		V		L	E	O	N	A
E		A		L		E		L		D		L
S	A	N	G		P	L	A	Y	R	O	O	M

106.

U	P	S	I	D	E			H		D	A	D
	R			I		B	E	I	G	E		I
C	O	U	N	S	E	L		F		V		E
	T			P		U		I	N	E	R	T
T	E	N	D	E	R	E	D			L		A
	C			R		S		O		O		R
S	T	R	E	S	S		S	N	A	P	P	Y
A		O		E		R		E			E	
S		U			K	I	L	O	W	A	T	T
H	I	G	H	S		G		N			U	
I		H		A		H	O	O	K	I	N	G
M		E	G	R	E	T		N			I	
I	N	N		K			Z	E	B	R	A	S

107.

N	O	R	S	E		P	A	N	D	E	R	S
E		E		X		O			E		A	
G		Q		A		K		A	B	U	Z	Z
L	A	U	N	C	H	E	D		R		O	
I		I		T		R		P	I	E	R	S
G	O	R	M	L	E	S	S		S			T
E		E		Y				C		T		R
N			M		S	E	M	O	L	I	N	A
T	W	A	I	N		T		N		M		T
	E		N		C	H	I	C	K	P	E	A
B	A	T	I	K		I		O		A		G
	R		M			C		R		N		E
E	S	T	A	T	E	S		D	E	I	S	M

108.

	T		A		D		S		S		M	
F	R	A	G	R	A	N	T		L	O	U	D
	A		R		S		U		I		S	
C	U	T	E		H	I	N	D	M	O	S	T
	M		E		I		G				E	
S	A	P	I	E	N	T		C	H	I	L	L
			N		G		S		A			
S	I	N	G	S		G	A	R	N	I	S	H
	N				W		G		D		T	
D	W	E	L	L	I	N	G		M	O	O	N
	A		A		N		I		A		R	
X	R	A	Y		K	I	N	G	D	O	M	S
	D		S		S		G		E		Y	

Solutions

109.

C	O	P	E		A	T	Y	P	I	C	A	L
L		I		U		I		R		H		A
E	X	T	I	N	C	T		E	V	A	N	S
M		C		V		T		D		T		H
A	C	H	I	E	V	E	M	E	N	T	S	
T				R		R		C		E		E
I	C	O	N	I	C		P	E	A	R	L	Y
S		V		F		T		S				E
	D	E	L	I	Q	U	E	S	C	E	N	T
A		R		A		R		O		L		O
C	R	U	M	B		B	U	R	R	I	T	O
M		S		L		O		S		O		T
E	L	E	M	E	N	T	S		U	T	A	H

110.

	A		P		E		S		S		P	
A	L	T	E	R	N	A	T	I	V	E	L	Y
	L		E		A		I		E		U	
C	Y	C	L	I	C	A	L		L	A	M	E
			E		T		T		T		B	
W	E	A	R	I	E	D		G	E	N	I	E
	R				D		E				N	
T	U	L	I	P		I	M	P	I	N	G	E
	P		M		A		P		N			
S	T	U	B		M	E	A	N	D	E	R	S
	I		I		B		T		U		E	
D	O	U	B	L	E	C	H	E	C	K	E	D
	N		E		R		Y		E		K	

111.

S	O	N	A	T	A		A		B		R	
E		U			C	O	N	V	E	N	E	S
D	I	D			O		I		R		P	
U		G	E	N	R	E	S		I	T	E	M
C		E			N		E		B		A	
E	A	S	E	S		R	E	J	E	C	T	S
			Q		T		D		R			
E	S	T	U	A	R	Y		V	I	S	T	A
	P		A		A		O			T		S
F	O	U	L		N	O	B	O	D	Y		S
	T		I		S		E			L	I	E
S	T	A	T	I	O	N	S			E		S
	Y		Y		M		E	X	I	S	T	S

112.

Z		D		A				M		P		M
A	F	I	E	L	D		W	I	N	O	N	A
M		S		O		F		S		S		D
B	A	S	H	F	U	L		H	O	S	T	A
E		E		T		O		A		E		M
Z	I	N	G		S	W	E	P	T			
I		T		A		E		S		C		B
			A	D	O	R	E		T	U	T	U
I		E		V		B		R		R		O
M	U	M	B	A		E	P	I	T	A	X	Y
A		B		N		D		N		T		A
G	R	E	E	C	E		A	S	T	E	R	N
O		R		E				E		S		T

113.

	S	M	E	L	T		S	C	A	R	P	
T		A		O		F		O		O		B
R	E	G	A	L	I	A		L	I	B	E	L
O		N		L		M		U				U
J	E	E	P		P	E	R	M	E	A	T	E
A		T		D		D		B		P		
N	A	I	L	E	D		E	U	R	E	K	A
		S		F		S		S		R		G
C	O	M	M	E	N	C	E		N	I	G	H
A				R		A		W		O		A
T	A	K	E	R		R	E	R	E	D	O	S
S		I		A		S		A		I		T
	K	N	O	L	L		S	P	E	C	S	

114.

	R		S		S		S		S		D	
Q	U	I	C	K	T	E	M	P	E	R	E	D
	N		A		A		O		C		R	
T	E	R	R	I	F	I	C		T	H	I	N
			E		F		K		O		S	
B	O	L	S	T	E	R		F	R	A	I	L
	R				D		E				O	
L	I	S	T	S		L	A	N	D	I	N	G
	G		H		T		R		I			
P	I	E	R		H	A	N	D	S	O	M	E
	N		E		U		I		U		I	
M	A	L	A	D	M	I	N	I	S	T	E	R
	L		D		B		G		E		N	

115.

C	O	A	R	S	E		A	D	J	U	S	T
A		C		T		D		E		S		I
N	A	I	R	O	B	I		C		E		T
A		D		R		S	C	A	N	D	A	L
D	U	R	U	M		T		N				E
A		A				A		T	E	R	M	S
		I		O	U	S	T	S		E		
P	A	N	I	C		T				T		T
U				T		E		E	A	R	N	S
F	L	Y	H	A	L	F		A		I		E
F		A		G		U	P	S	W	E	P	T
E		L		O		L		E		V		S
D	Y	E	I	N	G		S	L	E	E	V	E

116.

D	O	G	E		U	P	S	T	R	E	A	M
I		R		Q		O		R		M		A
S	E	A	G	U	L	L		A	X	I	N	G
H		N		I		I		N		G		N
O	P	T		N		T		S	E	R	G	E
N				T	H	E	R	M		E		T
O		C		E				I		S		I
U		A		S	E	C	T	S				C
R	O	S	E	S		H		S		M	A	N
A		T		E		I		I		E		O
B	L	O	W	N		S	H	O	R	T	E	R
L		F		C		E		N		R		T
E	N	F	E	E	B	L	E		M	E	S	H

117.

C	L	E	R	I	C	A	L		A	L	P	S
A		R		N		B		D		A		I
S	H	O	O	T		B		O	O	Z	E	D
T		S		E		E		U		I		E
			C	R	O	S	S	B	O	N	E	S
C		D		M		S		L		E		T
O	R	I	G	I	N		L	E	S	S	E	E
N		S		T		H		D		S		P
S	P	L	U	T	T	E	R	E	D			
I		O		E		N		C		O		S
S	U	D	A	N		R		K	E	M	P	T
T		G		T		Y		E		A		E
S	L	E	W		O	V	E	R	D	R	A	W

118.

C	O	P	P	E	R		H	U	D	D	L	E
	P		E		I		I		O		A	
D	E	A	R		S	I	D	E	W	A	Y	S
	R		S		K		E		E			
R	A	Y	O	N		B	A	L	L	O	O	N
	T		N		A		W				S	
D	I	S	A	P	P	E	A	R	A	N	C	E
	V				P		Y		N		I	
M	E	M	B	E	R	S		B	O	I	L	S
			I		O		D		T		L	
R	O	L	L	O	V	E	R		H	O	A	R
	L		G		E		E		E		T	
A	D	D	E	R	S		W	O	R	S	E	N

119.

	C	L	A	I	R	V	O	Y	A	N	T	
S		A		S		I		E		A		N
T		M		O	M	E	G	A		D	R	E
R	E	P	E	L		W		R		I		T
O		O		A		E		N	O	R	T	H
N	O	O	N	T	I	D	E					E
G		N		E				C		A		R
P					A	B	N	O	R	M	A	L
O	V	O	I	D		O		R		A		A
I		A		E		T		O	G	D	E	N
N	U	T		L	U	T	O	N		E		D
T		H		H		O		E		U		S
	A	S	T	I	G	M	A	T	I	S	M	

120.

D		R		W		A		A		V		B
U	N	H	E	A	R	D	O	F		E	K	E
M		Y		L		J		F		T		A
M	O	T	E	L		U	N	I	F	O	R	M
Y		H		E		R		X				I
	O	M	I	T	T	E	D		F	A	W	N
C		I		S				F		T		G
R	I	C	K		A	N	D	A	N	T	E	
O				S		O		S		E		P
O	P	E	N	A	I	R		H	U	N	C	H
N		R		S		M		I		D		I
E	G	G		S	O	A	P	O	P	E	R	A
R		O		Y		L		N		E		L

121.

```
BETA#DESSERTS
R#H#F#N#P#E#O
ABREAST#RAVEL
N#U#I#I#E#A#E
DEMONSTRABLE#
I###T#Y#D#U#B
SWATHE#REPEAL
H#L#E#A#A###U
#CLEARSIGHTED
I#O#R#P#L#A#G
COVET#ITEMISE
E#E#E#R#D#N#O
SHREDDED#ETON
```

122.

```
SHADES#SAFEST
#A#E#L#T#A#A#
SNUB#AQUEDUCT
#K#A#M#D#E###
FEMUR#CINDERS
#R#C#S#O###E#
RIGHTEOUSNESS
#N###N#S#O#I#
AGILITY#RUDDY
###I#I#P#G#E#
CONCRETE#HAND
#A#K#N#R#T#C#
OFFSET#MISSED
```

123.

```
ALBINO#D#S#I#
V#U##GLUTTONY
EAR##R#S#R#S#
R#RESENT#ACES
T#O##S#P#T#R#
SEWED#MAJESTY
###N#D#N#G###
FAILURE#NYMPH
#N#A#I#E##E#U
DOOR#ZEALOT#M
#I#G#Z#S##ERA
UNDERLIE##O#N
#T#D#E#DECREE
```

124.

```
JUDICIAL#POEM
O#U#O#R#C#K#I
BLOOM#O#HALTS
S#S#P#U#O#A#S
###CENSORSHIP
A#S#T#E#E#O#E
MOHAIR#COMMON
B#A#T#E#G#A#D
REMAINDERS###
O#P#O#W#A#N#M
SCORN#I#PLACE
I#O#S#N#H#I#R
ALSO#NAVYBLUE
```

125.

```
#TWIGS#SHINE#
S#A#A#S#A#I#B
CRYPTIC#METAL
E#F#E#A#M###U
NEAP#ULTERIOR
T#R#S#P#R#N##
SWEEPS#CEASED
##R#L#F#D#U#E
CASTIRON#DROP
U###N#S#W#A#A
RIVET#SCANNER
B#A#E#E#R#C#T
#STORY#SEWER#
```

126.

```
MEAD#MASSEURS
A#W#C#F#H#T#E
LIFTOFF#ATOLL
I#U#V#I#R#P#F
COL#E#R#PRISE
I###NAMES#A#V
O#S#T###H#N#I
U#L#GUSTO###D
SAUNA#P#O#BEE
N#M#R#H#T#E#N
EMBED#EVEREST
S#E#E#R#R#C#L
SYRINGES#WHEY
```

127.

```
NEIGHS#BAMBOO
#L#R#L#A#A#N#
PESO#UNLOCKED
#P#W#M#L#R###
THINK#ACCOSTS
#A#U#P#O###H#
UNAPPRECIATED
#T###O#K#I#S#
ASCRIBE#PROPS
###O#L#A#S#I#
DAYBREAK#HOAX
#W#E#M#I#O#N#
LENSES#NEWEST
```

128.

```
TRANCE##G#DAM
#E##O#BRACE#O
SEMINAR#N#F#R
#N##T#A#GRAND
STEERAGE##C#A
#R##A#G#S#T#N
CYBORG#ACCOST
Y#U#Y#N#O##O#
C#R##BEAUTIFY
LUNCH#V#R##T#
I#O#O#ENGAGED
N#UPPER#E##S#
GET#E##ODDITY
```

129.

```
PRECEDES#BEAR
I#F#T#X###L#I
NIFTY#PADDING
S#I#M#I###X#I
##G#O#REBUILD
ROYALTY#U#R#I
E###O###T###T
N#A#G#SATISFY
DECRYPT#E#C##
E#C###A#R#A#S
REENACT#COMET
E#P###E#U#P#Y
DATE#ADAPTIVE
```

130.

```
#B#A#A#T#S#V#
ROTUND#OXTAIL
#A#T#A#N#E#R#
DRNO#PRIORITY
###M#T#C#E#U#
CHEAPEN#BORON
#E#T#D#S#T#S#
GRAIN#ACRYLIC
#O#C#C#H#P###
DICAPRIO#IBEX
#N#L#O#L#C#C#
FELLOW#APATHY
#S#Y#N#R#L#O#
```

131.

```
CUES#AGITATED
O#L#C#O#E#O#E
UNBLOCK#MINES
N#O#M#A#P#I#T
TOW#M#R#ELGAR
E###OUTER#H#U
R#E#N###A#T#C
A#M#WAIST###T
TEPEE#C#U#PHI
T#E#A#I#R#R#V
AURAL#CHEMISE
C#O#T#L#S#C#L
KERCHIEF#DENY
```

132.

```
I#C#P###F#B#L
COUSIN#SERENA
E#S#E#A#S#S#T
BATHTUB#TWEET
E#O#Y#I#I#T#E
REDO#CLOVE###
G#Y#I#I#E#R#G
###KNITS#DEMI
H#W#F#I#C#S#N
ELIZA#ECHOING
R#D#N#S#E#D#H
TRENCH#SCHEMA
Z#R#Y###K#S#M
```

Solutions

133.

	S	C	O	N	E		M	A	N	G	O	
U		O		I		W		D		I		F
N	A	M	I	B	I	A		D	U	N	C	E
T		F		S		V		I				R
R	O	O	K		J	E	T	T	I	S	O	N
U		R		T		S		I		T		
E	X	T	O	R	T		S	O	A	R	E	D
		E		A		G		N		A		I
F	A	R	R	I	E	R	S		S	W	A	G
A				N		U		G		P		E
C	O	P	S	E		N	E	R	V	O	U	S
T		E		R		T		I		L		T
	B	R	A	S	S		S	M	I	L	E	

134.

S	C	O	T	C	H		M	O	T	I	V	E
	O		R		I		I		A		A	
T	U	N	A		N	O	S	T	R	I	L	S
	N		F		T		S		N			
S	T	I	F	F		W	H	I	S	P	E	R
	R		I		I		A				N	
C	I	R	C	U	M	S	P	E	C	T	L	Y
	E				P		E		R		I	
A	S	U	N	D	E	R		B	U	L	G	E
			A		L		P		E		H	
W	R	E	S	T	L	E	R		L	O	T	S
	A		T		E		O		T		E	
S	W	A	Y	E	D		P	L	Y	I	N	G

135.

	F	L	E	E	T	S	T	R	E	E	T	
A		A		R		A		E		S		P
P		W		A	B	D	U	L		S	P	A
H	I	L	L	S		D		I		A		R
R		E		E		L		C	R	Y	P	T
O	B	S	E	R	V	E	R					I
D		S		S				A		S		C
I					C	O	N	F	E	T	T	I
S	C	A	R	F		P		F		U		P
I		D		I		E		L	E	M	M	A
A	L	I		F	U	N	G	I		B		T
C		E		T		E		C		L		E
	A	U	T	H	O	R	I	T	I	E	S	

136.

P	O	S	T	P	O	N	E		E	T	N	A
U		E		H		O				H		S
F	A	N	C	Y		T	A	M	P	E	R	S
F		O		S		I				S		E
		R		I		F	E	R	R	I	E	S
S	T	A	R	C	H	Y		E		S		S
A				I				M				E
P		G		A		P	L	A	S	M	A	S
P	I	R	A	N	H	A		I		A		
H		E				N		N		N		A
I	K	E	B	A	N	A		D	A	T	E	D
R		N				M		E		R		Z
E	A	S	T		L	A	U	R	E	A	T	E

137.

S	I	L	T		P	R	O	S	P	E	C	T
A		A		A		U		E		N		R
R	E	T	O	R	T	S		L	A	R	V	A
A		E		I		H		F		O		N
H	E	X		T		E		L	O	B	E	S
F				H	A	S	T	E		E		P
E		M		M				S		D		A
R		A		E	L	V	E	S				R
G	A	M	U	T		A		N		D	I	E
U		M		I		L		E		R		N
S	T	O	I	C		U	P	S	T	A	R	T
O		T		A		E		S		W		L
N	I	H	I	L	I	S	M		C	L	O	Y

138.

	I		U		A		W		H		B	
I	M	P	R	A	C	T	I	C	A	B	L	E
	A		S		H		P		W		A	
I	N	C	I	S	I	V	E		A	N	N	A
			N		E		S		I		C	
D	E	C	E	I	V	E		F	I	G	H	T
	T				E		S				E	
S	H	E	D	S		U	P	H	O	L	D	S
	O		I		C		E		B			
S	L	A	B		L	O	C	A	L	I	S	E
	O		B		I		T		A		O	
A	G	G	L	O	M	E	R	A	T	I	O	N
	Y		E		B		A		E		T	

139.

	S	W	A	N	S		G	U	L	F	S	
S		I		O		P		N		E		B
C	U	L	T	U	R	E		C	I	D	E	R
O		L		S		S		O				A
R	A	P	T		S	T	U	M	B	L	E	S
E		O		M		S		M		E		
S	A	W	Y	E	R		C	O	N	T	R	A
		E		C		G		N		H		N
L	U	R	C	H	E	R	S		M	A	I	N
I				A		O		T		R		O
R	O	M	A	N		S	C	R	A	G	G	Y
E		A		I		S		I		I		S
	S	T	A	C	K		S	P	A	C	E	

140.

W	R	A	P	P	I	N	G		S	A	S	H
O		T		A		A				F		O
N	A	T	T	Y		T	U	M	B	L	E	R
T		E		M		I				O		S
		S		A		V	I	L	L	A	G	E
A	R	T	I	S	T	E		I		T		M
R				T				Q				E
R		A		E		T	O	U	G	H	E	N
A	D	V	E	R	S	E		I		A		
N		E				A		D		Z		W
G	E	N	E	R	I	C		A	P	A	C	E
E		U				U		T		R		E
D	O	E	R		S	P	L	E	N	D	I	D

141.

	S		L		S		D		J		C	
S	T	R	E	T	C	H	Y		O	I	L	Y
	O		V		A		L		S		E	
F	L	O	E		L	O	A	T	H	I	N	G
	I		L		E		N				C	
A	D	D	L	I	N	G		W	I	G	H	T
			E		E		P		N			
D	O	W	D	Y		B	O	O	T	L	E	G
	W				S		W		E		N	
I	N	F	L	A	T	E	D		R	E	A	L
	E		A		O		E		V		B	
D	R	U	M		V	A	R	I	A	B	L	E
	S		P		E		S		L		E	

142.

R	E	E	S	E		E	V	A	S	I	O	N
E		T		L		M			C		U	
I		E		E		I		B	A	N	G	S
M	O	R	T	G	A	G	E		T		H	
B		N		I		R		C	H	A	T	S
U	N	A	W	A	R	E	S		E			A
R		L		C				P		C		C
S			S		C	A	T	H	O	L	I	C
E	L	O	P	E		B		Y		E		H
	E		L		M	O	U	S	S	A	K	A
I	V	I	E	S		A		I		N		R
	E		E			R		C		S		I
G	R	I	N	N	E	D		S	K	E	I	N

143.

T	A	K	E		P	H	Y	S	I	C	A	L
Y		A		I		O		T		O		A
P	A	R	S	N	I	P		R	U	M	E	R
E		A		V				A		P		D
C	O	N	S	E	R	V	A	T	I	O	N	
A				S		I		O		R		B
S	O	W		T	O	N	G	S		T	A	U
T		O		I		C		P				O
	T	R	I	G	G	E	R	H	A	P	P	Y
O		K		A				E		R		A
G	R	E	A	T		F	O	R	L	O	R	N
L		R		O		U		E		W		C
E	N	S	H	R	I	N	E		P	L	O	Y

144.

U	N	S	E	T	T	L	E		D	A	U	B
N		U		A		E				L		A
D	R	I	E	R		A	N	G	E	L	I	C
O		T		P		V				U		K
		E		A		E	M	P	I	R	E	S
M	U	S	E	U	M	S		A		E		E
I				L				R				A
L		S		I		L	O	O	K	O	U	T
E	N	T	E	N	T	E		C		P		
P		R				A		H		T		T
O	V	E	R	R	U	N		I	C	I	L	Y
S		W				T		A		M		P
T	I	N	A		S	O	U	L	M	A	T	E

145.

G	A	P	E		O	V	E	R	P	A	S	S
L		I		I		E		E		N		U
E	X	P	A	N	D	S		A	M	I	S	S
N		I		T		P		P		M		A
D	E	T	E	R		E	X	P	L	A	I	N
A				A		R		E		T		S
J	E	J	U	N	E		G	A	L	E	N	A
A		E		S		S		R				R
C	H	E	M	I	S	T		A	O	R	T	A
K		R		G		U		N		E		N
S	N	I	D	E		D	E	C	A	P	O	D
O		N		N		I		E		A		O
N	E	G	A	T	I	O	N		R	Y	A	N

146.

	H	A	T	C	H		C	O	M	F	Y	
A		E		O		M		P		U		B
M	A	S	C	A	R	A		P	U	R	E	E
I		T		X		J		O				N
D	A	H	L		C	O	N	S	U	M	E	D
S		E		C		R		I		A		
T	E	T	C	H	Y		S	T	O	N	E	S
		I		A		R		E		O		Y
D	E	C	O	R	O	U	S		D	E	A	N
A				I		S		D		U		O
L	A	N	E	S		T	H	R	I	V	E	D
E		A		M		Y		A		R		S
	S	P	R	A	T		T	W	E	E	D	

147.

H	Y	B	R	I	D		M		V		B	
O		A			R	E	C	E	I	V	E	D
O	I	L			U		E		R		A	
K		L	O	T	I	O	N		T	U	S	K
E		A			D		R		U		T	
D	O	D	G	Y		S	O	L	O	I	S	T
			L		M		E		S			
A	S	C	E	T	I	C		N	O	B	L	E
	C		A		L		L			O		D
T	R	A	M		K	L	A	X	O	N		B
	E		I		S		R			S	E	E
S	W	A	N	S	O	N	G			A		R
	S		G		P		E	A	T	I	N	G

148.

	D	I	Z	Z	Y		S	T	O	R	E	
S		N		I		S		O		U		T
I	N	D	E	P	T	H		R	O	G	E	R
E		E		S		O		T				O
G	A	M	E		C	R	O	U	C	H	E	D
E		N		C		E		O		I		
S	P	I	N	A	L		P	U	R	S	U	E
		T		T		S		S		T		N
H	A	Y	M	A	K	E	R		M	O	O	R
A				L		I		P		R		A
R	O	C	K	Y		Z	O	O	M	I	N	G
D		O		S		E		U		A		E
	S	W	E	E	P		P	R	A	N	K	

149.

	Z		U		I		I		I		S	
B	E	I	N	G	S		M	I	N	I	O	N
	R		D		O		P		T		C	
T	O	R	I		B	A	L	L	E	T	I	C
			S		A		Y		R		A	
C	O	N	C	U	R	S		D	E	R	B	Y
	U		I		S		G		S		L	
S	T	O	P	S		S	L	I	T	H	E	R
	M		L		Z		O		I			
S	O	N	I	N	L	A	W		N	E	E	D
	D		N		O		E		G		N	
R	E	V	E	R	T		R	E	L	I	V	E
	D		D		Y		S		Y		Y	

150.

R	E	N	O	I	R		H	O	B	B	L	E
E		A		D		C		S		E		R
P	O	R	T	I	C	O		T		L		A
O		R		O		U	N	R	O	L	L	S
R	E	A	L	M		R		I				E
T		T				T		C	O	D	E	R
		O		F	L	E	S	H		E		
C	I	R	C	A		O				N		J
O				I		U		L	O	O	S	E
I	N	S	E	R	T	S		O		U		T
L		A		I		L	I	G	A	N	D	S
E		P		E		Y		O		C		A
D	E	S	I	S	T		E	S	T	E	E	M

151.

H	I	K	E	R		H	U	R	T	L	E	S
O		I		E		A			R		D	
U		T		A		S		F	O	G	G	Y
R	U	T	H	L	E	S	S		P		E	
G		E		I		L		C	H	E	S	T
L	E	N	G	T	H	E	N		Y			U
A		S		Y				S		V		R
S			K		P	I	C	K	M	E	U	P
S	P	U	R	S		N		Y		R		I
	L		A		S	T	A	L	W	A	R	T
S	U	C	K	S		O		I		N		U
	M		E			N		N		D		D
A	S	I	N	I	N	E		E	V	A	D	E

152.

	K		P		D		K		O		S	
C	O	M	E	D	I	A	N		A	R	E	S
	R		C		V		A		K		R	
C	U	L	T		I	N	V	A	S	I	V	E
	N		O		D		E				E	
G	A	B	R	I	E	L		H	I	R	S	T
			A		S		T		M			
S	C	A	L	E		G	I	M	M	I	C	K
	A				G		T		U		A	
D	R	A	W	N	O	U	T		N	I	C	E
	P		A		O		E		I		K	
W	E	I	R		F	O	R	E	T	E	L	L
	L		Y		Y		S		Y		E	

153.

I	D	L	Y		O	N	E	S	I	D	E	D
N		E		H		A		L		I		I
D	E	A	D	E	N	S		E	A	V	E	S
E		S		A		S		D		U		C
F	I	E	L	D		A	N	G	U	L	A	R
A				M		U		E		G		E
T	R	A	G	I	C		T	H	R	E	A	T
I		S		S		A		A				I
G	R	E	E	T	E	D		M	O	T	T	O
A		P		R		R		M		I		N
B	E	T	T	E		I	N	E	R	T	I	A
L		I		S		E		R		H		R
E	X	C	U	S	I	N	G		R	E	L	Y

154.

M	O	S	T		M	A	R	S	H	A	L	L
U		W		B		C		C		X		I
S	T	A	L	E	S	T		A	V	O	I	D
I		R		L				T		L		S
C	O	M	P	L	I	C	A	T	I	O	N	
I				I		H		E		T		P
A	P	E		G	R	E	E	R		L	E	E
N		M		E		F		B				R
	C	I	R	R	O	S	T	R	A	T	U	S
C		T		E				A		R		I
L	A	T	I	N		P	R	I	S	O	N	S
I		E		C		U		N		P		T
P	O	R	T	E	N	T	S		G	E	L	S

155.

P	L	O	U	G	H			B		R	O	T
	E			A		G	L	I	D	E		U
L	O	Z	E	N	G	E		L		S		S
	P			G		N		L	O	O	P	S
D	A	M	A	S	C	U	S			L		L
	R			T		S		W		V		E
A	D	O	R	E	R		P	O	W	E	R	S
N		C		R		S		O			E	
G		C			H	A	R	D	C	O	P	Y
U	S	U	R	P		U		L			T	
I		L		O		C	H	A	S	S	I	S
S		T	E	S	T	Y		N			L	
H	A	S		E			E	D	I	T	E	D

156.

P	O	D	S		A	R	T	I	S	T	I	C
A		E		P		I		N		O		O
R	E	L	I	E	F	S		T	U	N	E	R
A		A		R		K		E		S		R
P	L	Y		A		E		R	O	U	S	E
H				M	O	D	E	M		R		S
E		R		B				E		E		P
R		A		U	N	D	I	D				O
N	A	V	E	L		A		I		B	A	N
A		A		A		H		A		R		D
L	I	G	H	T		L	A	T	T	I	C	E
I		E		O		I		E		N		N
A	L	D	E	R	M	A	N		R	E	N	T

Solutions

157.

```
BENT AGNOSTIC
R A A A B O O
ORDINAL LINEN
K A N L I G S
ELL O I TRUMP
N UNCLE E I
H C N R S C
E H CILIA U
ALICE O T TWO
R M M O I H U
THESE SHOWERS
E R N E N M L
DRAFTING DEWY
```

158.

```
G M A V A I
MIXEDBLESSING
S T S I S E
STURGEON URDU
I N S M I
CONCOCT HERBS
V E C L
BEEFY HOWEVER
R O F U L
PLUS INNUENDO
O S E C C A
MOTIONPICTURE
K L D L S N
```

159.

```
TALKER COMEDY
N I E O U O
GAIN INVOLVED
L G N E C
FOLDS ETCHING
G O A O U
COMMENSURABLE
U I S N L
ISONOMY STAIN
A A W I F
SPINSTER QUIT
A C E I U E
PLAYED TRENDS
```

160.

```
ANNALS H AXE
O Y SQUID A
OUTGREW T J R
V I A SPURN
TENACITY D E
A I S G G R
DURESS SLEEPS
E O T S O I
N A CHEROKEE
YEMEN E I R
I I U ENOUNCE
N NYLON U E
GIG L ESCUDO
```

161.

```
INCA ESPRESSO
N R C C E P V
TRAWLER PRIME
R I O I O N R
AEGIS BESIDES
N E E S L T
STEAMY GENERA
I L O L S T
GRANULE SNARE
E S T S I P M
NOTCH SCOURGE
C I E O N I N
ENCODING BLOT
```

162.

```
LAMBDA B F L
I A CLIMATIC
MUG T C L S
P NAMELY TOTS
E U D C E E
DUMPS BLARING
R R E E
OCTOBER EDGAR
R V A S O A
YETI DOLLOP T
E S M U HOT
APHORISM E L
Y S T PIERCE
```

163.

```
AIDED GRASSES
P O O A T L
A U W T RONDO
REGISTER L E
T H I A REARM
MUTINOUS N E
E Y G S C A
N A AMBUSHES
TRESS A C I U
A S ARMCHAIR
ADMIX B U N I
O G L M T N
ENSNARE BEING
```

164.

```
ALWAYS COSMIC
U E I R F I R
BELIEVE F D A
U L L ABILITY
RATED P C O
N O P ELLEN
D HURTS O
PHOTO A O S
L A I LUPIN
ENCORES E H E
A H S AWESOME
T E E L D L R
STRING ESTERS
```

165.

```
DEBT OBEDIENT
E I D E I M O
CONFESS SEEDS
I G C E C R S
PROPORTIONAL
H N S U L N
ENCAGE DRUDGE
R O E B A O
DRESSINGDOWN
A S T N I P A
CHINA DENTIST
T C N E G N E
STARTERS GEMS
```

166.

```
P G S E T V
RARITY BLOUSE
E A A F U N X
VINEGAR SCENE
I A S I I S S
EARS IGLOO
W Y U H N N S
AGATE MASH
A A L E M T A
SUSHI NOISIER
S I E S R O P
ELDEST ATONAL
T E T H S Y
```

167.

```
PALPABLE OMEN
O I S O E Y O
MIDST U LUTES
P O R V E H I
CORRECTION
A F N E T C E
BARMAN DREAMS
U I U Z O L S
NEGOTIABLE
D H I M Y P K
ATTIC B STOKE
N E S I I N Y
TEND SAUSAGES
```

168.

```
ARCH EMPHATIC
D O E I O E H
MAMMALS PASTA
I I V U E T R
NICHE SULTANA
I S E E T C
STRODE ASPECT
T E R A S E
REDWOOD NEWER
A R P J E O L
TRAMP OBSCURE
O F E I S N S
RETIRING ADDS
```

169.

	L		S		A		G		S		P	
F	A	S	T	E	N	E	R		H	E	A	R
	P		A		G		A		O		R	
L	E	E	R		E	X	P	L	O	I	T	S
	L		S		L		H				E	
I	S	T	H	M	U	S		B	E	A	D	S
			I		S		T		M			
W	A	S	P	S		P	R	E	P	L	A	N
	M				M		E		L		L	
T	O	D	D	L	E	R	S		O	I	L	S
	E		A		R		T		Y		O	
A	B	L	Y		C	O	L	L	E	C	T	S
	A		S		Y		E		D		S	

170.

S		D		L		B		D		F		O
P	R	I	M	I	T	I	V	E		L	I	V
I		S		C		A		B		O		E
C	A	C	H	E		S	T	I	N	G	E	R
E		I		N		E		T				A
	E	P	I	S	O	D	E		S	M	U	G
C		L		E				T		I		E
O	B	E	Y		D	U	C	H	E	S	S	
N				A		N		E		T		C
J	A	C	U	Z	Z	I		R	E	A	C	H
O		A		T		Q		A		K		U
I	C	E		E	Q	U	I	P	M	E	N	T
N		N		C		E		Y		N		E

171.

	F		F		E		M		P		T	
P	A	T	R	O	L		O	P	A	Q	U	E
	S		A		I		T		R		N	
C	O	R	N		S	H	O	R	T	A	G	E
			K		I		R		I		S	
T	R	E	A	S	O	N		A	C	U	T	E
	E		P		N		B		I		E	
A	L	L	O	W		D	A	M	P	E	N	S
	I		T		H		L		A			
D	E	M	E	R	A	R	A		T	A	I	L
	V		N		N		N		I		N	
N	E	S	T	E	D		C	R	O	W	N	S
	S		E		Y		E		N		S	

172.

B	R	O	A	D	W	A	Y		C	A	R	P
U		P		I		N		A		R		I
G	L	E	N	S		G		S	A	T	E	D
S		N		H		L		T		I		D
			R	E	C	I	P	R	O	C	A	L
P		E		A		A		O		L		I
R	E	T	O	R	T		U	N	S	E	E	N
O		E		T		E		O		S		G
B	U	R	D	E	N	S	O	M	E			
A		N		N		C		I		L		B
B	R	I	B	E		A		C	H	I	N	O
L		T		D		P		A		F		N
Y	O	Y	O		Z	E	A	L	O	T	R	Y

173.

F	I	S	T		C	H	R	I	S	T	E	N
E		E		P		A		N		E		O
A	S	P	I	R	E	S		D	E	M	O	N
T		I		I		T		I		P		A
H	E	A	R	D		E	A	S	I	E	S	T
E				E		N		T		S		T
R	E	C	K	O	N		T	I	P	T	O	E
W		H		F		D		N				N
E	X	A	M	P	L	E		C	A	G	E	D
I		R		L		T		T		I		A
G	A	M	M	A		E	N	L	I	V	E	N
H		E		C		C		Y		E		C
T	O	R	R	E	N	T	S		A	S	H	E

174.

	D	E	I	T	Y		H	A	P	P	Y	
D		D		W		H		T		A		F
E	R	U	D	I	T	E		H	E	W	E	R
S		C		N		L		E				O
P	E	A	L		S	P	O	R	T	I	N	G
O		T		F		S		T		N		
T	A	I	L	O	R		S	O	O	T	H	E
		O		R		L		N		E		M
W	O	N	D	E	R	E	D		C	R	A	B
I				W		M		F		V		O
P	A	R	K	A		O	P	E	R	A	N	D
E		I		R		N		E		L		Y
	S	P	E	N	D		C	L	A	S	P	

175.

S		M		C		H		D		E		L
K	O	A	L	A	B	E	A	R		Z	O	O
U		C		P		A		E		R		U
A	M	A	Z	E		D	I	S	T	A	N	T
S		R		R		O		S				I
	S	O	M	E	O	N	E		S	U	N	S
S		N		D				W		N		H
Q	U	I	Z		O	V	E	R	A	W	E	
U				P		A		I		O		S
E	P	S	I	L	O	N		T	H	R	E	W
L		O		U		D		I		T		A
C	A	N		S	T	A	U	N	C	H	L	Y
H		G		H		L		G		Y		S

176.

	D	E	H	Y	D	R	A	T	I	O	N	
W		R		I		U		I		P		I
I		R		E	L	E	C	T		T	I	N
T	R	A	I	L		F		A		I		T
C		T		D		U		N	I	C	E	R
H	O	U	S	E	F	L	Y					A
D		M		D				P		N		C
O					S	E	D	I	M	E	N	T
C	O	O	K	S		N		C		W		A
T		V		T		G		K	E	B	A	B
O	R	E		O	R	I	B	I		O		L
R		N		M		N		N		R		E
	E	S	T	A	T	E	A	G	E	N	T	

177.

L	O	D	E		M	I	N	I	S	T	E	R
A		E		M		M		N		E		U
U	N	C	L	A	S	P		V	A	N	E	S
N		O		N				E		A		T
C	I	R	C	U	M	S	C	R	I	B	E	
H				F		P		T		L		H
E	R	G		A	W	O	K	E		E	W	E
S		R		C		U		B				L
	D	I	C	T	A	T	O	R	S	H	I	P
C		S		U				A		I		M
A	L	T	E	R		R	O	T	U	N	D	A
L		L		E		I		E		G		T
F	I	E	F	D	O	M	S		C	E	D	E

178.

S	M	I	L	E	D		P	U	F	F	I	N
	O		O		R		A		E		O	
S	N	O	W		A	R	R	I	V	I	N	G
	S		L		G		A		E			
C	I	V	I	L		A	D	O	R	N	E	D
	G		F		B		I				C	
I	N	T	E	R	R	O	G	A	T	I	O	N
	O				U		M		R		N	
P	R	O	R	A	T	A		T	A	R	O	T
			O		A		P		F		M	
G	L	O	B	U	L	A	R		F	L	I	P
	A		I		L		A		I		S	
A	G	E	N	C	Y		Y	A	C	H	T	S

179.

I	N	D	I	G	O		E		F		R	
N		O			D	E	S	P	I	S	E	D
G	A	S			O		S		T		F	
O		A	T	T	U	N	E		T	R	E	K
T		G			R		N		I		R	
S	T	E	A	K		I	C	I	N	E	S	S
			C		B		E		G			
S	P	E	C	I	E	S		P	S	A	L	M
	R		I		L		E			T		U
F	O	O	D		I	N	T	E	N	T		T
	T		E		E		H			A	B	I
T	O	A	N	D	F	R	O			I		N
	N		T		S		S	K	I	N	N	Y

180.

S	U	C	H		P	A	C	I	F	I	S	M
E		A		I		V		N		G		I
N	O	M	I	N	E	E		C	O	N	E	S
T		E		C		R		O		O		U
I	L	L		O		S		H	E	R	O	N
M				N	I	E	C	E		E		D
E		T		V				R		D		E
N		R		E	T	U	D	E				R
T	R	A	I	N		P		N		B	U	S
A		V		I		H		T		E		T
L	E	A	V	E		O	R	L	A	N	D	O
L		I		N		L		Y		C		O
Y	U	L	E	T	I	D	E		T	H	U	D

Solutions

181.

S	L	A	P	U	P		S	C	Y	T	H	E
	A		R		L		H		A		E	
L	U	D	O		O	V	E	R	C	O	M	E
	D		V		P		P		H			
C	A	F	E	S		W	H	I	T	H	E	R
	T		R		F		E				M	
D	O	U	B	L	E	C	R	O	S	S	E	R
	R				A		D		L		R	
H	Y	D	R	A	T	E		D	I	R	G	E
			U		U		D		P		E	
W	A	Y	F	A	R	E	R		P	A	N	S
	L		F		E		U		E		C	
L	E	A	S	E	D		B	U	R	D	E	N

182.

I	N	K	S		M	A	R	K	D	O	W	N
N		A		A		N		A		B		E
A	F	F	E	C	T	S		L	E	V	E	L
P		K		Q		W		E		I		S
P	E	A		U		E		I	D	A	H	O
R				A	I	R	E	D		T		N
O		H		I				O		E		M
P		A		N	E	C	K	S				A
R	E	B	U	T		R		C		S	U	N
I		I		A		I		O		W		D
A	N	T	O	N		T	O	P	S	I	D	E
T		A		C		I		E		L		L
E	N	T	R	E	N	C	H		F	L	E	A

183.

M		A		J		G		R		A		T
I	N	S	T	I	T	U	T	E		P	R	O
S		T		T		L		V		E		R
S	L	E	E	T		P	R	E	S	S	U	P
Y		R		E		E		L				E
	C	O	M	R	A	D	E		S	K	I	D
O		I		S				V		A		O
D	A	D	S		S	T	R	E	A	M	S	
D				S		E		R		I		G
M	E	L	A	N	I	N		B	A	K	E	R
E		U		I		A		O		A		I
N	A	G		P	I	N	T	S	I	Z	E	D
T		E		E		T		E		E		S

184.

	A		J		B		S		O		P	
S	U	P	E	R	L	A	T	I	V	E	L	Y
	D		W		A		A		E		U	
D	I	R	E	C	T	O	R		R	A	G	E
			L		A		K		D		G	
R	E	A	S	O	N	S		I	O	N	I	C
	N				T		P				N	
A	F	O	O	T		V	E	S	T	I	G	E
	O		P		G		R		W			
G	R	I	T		U	N	F	A	I	R	L	Y
	C		I		T		O		S		A	
D	E	M	O	N	S	T	R	A	T	I	V	E
	R		N		Y		M		S		A	

185.

S	U	S	P	E	C	T	S		T	A	L	C
U		C		X		O				L		H
C	R	A	F	T		A	M	I	A	B	L	E
K		R		E		S				U		E
		C		N		T	O	K	A	M	A	K
P	L	E	A	S	E	S		I		S		I
R				I				N				L
E		U		O		E	C	S	T	A	S	Y
C	A	S	I	N	O	S		W		M		
E		A				C		O		O		H
D	O	G	F	I	S	H		M	A	R	G	E
E		E				E		A		A		L
D	I	S	C		T	W	I	N	K	L	E	D

186.

E		P		S				C		C		T
D	E	L	E	T	E		B	Y	P	L	A	Y
U		E		E		Q		C		I		S
C	H	A	T	E	A	U		L	I	N	G	O
A		T		P		A		O		G		N
T	H	E	N		A	D	O	P	T			
E		D		L		R		S		C		O
			R	E	R	U	N		L	A	I	R
E		W		A		P		E		P		I
Q	U	I	F	F		L	E	A	N	I	N	G
U		S		A		E		T		T		A
A	V	E	N	G	E		R	E	F	O	R	M
L		R		E				N		L		I

187.

E	N	S	I	G	N		B	U	R	E	A	U
A		R		A		S		P		L		N
S	T	I	M	U	L	I		D		L		U
T		L		N		L	O	A	F	E	R	S
E	X	A	C	T		V		T				E
R		N				E		E	A	R	E	D
		K		F	A	R	A	D		E		
G	U	A	N	O		B				V		F
A				L		I		S	W	E	A	R
M	E	R	R	I	E	R		T		R		I
B		H		A		C	R	E	A	S	E	S
O		E		T		H		E		E		K
L	E	A	V	E	N		C	R	I	S	P	Y

188.

D	E	B	A	R	K			I		P	U	B
	M			E		T	I	B	I	A		O
C	O	L	O	G	N	E		I		R		O
	T			A		A		S	E	V	E	R
L	I	M	E	R	I	C	K			E		I
	O			D		H		E		N		S
S	N	I	P	E	S		A	V	O	U	C	H
H		M		D		E		E			H	
A		P			A	G	E	N	C	I	E	S
L	O	U	S	Y		G		N			V	
L		G		A		E	Y	E	S	O	R	E
O		N	A	M	E	D		S			O	
W	A	S		S			A	S	S	E	N	T

189.

D		D		A		P		V		F		E
E	V	E	N	T	U	A	T	E		R	A	M
L		V		T		T		R		E		P
F	L	O	R	A		R	U	S	S	E	L	L
T		T		C		O		E				O
	W	I	S	H	I	N	G		S	W	A	Y
P		O		E				G		R		S
R	I	N	G		C	A	R	A	V	A	N	
O				F		I		L		N		G
V	E	R	N	I	E	R		L	A	G	E	R
I		A		S		B		O		L		E
S	A	Y		H	E	A	D	P	I	E	C	E
O		S		Y		G		S		R		K

190.

J	U	M	P		E	M	U	L	A	T	E	S
U		O		O		E		A		R		U
R	E	D	U	C	E	D		B	L	E	E	P
I		E		C		A		O		A		P
S	A	L	S	A		L	Y	R	I	C	A	L
P				S		S		A		L		E
R	U	S	S	I	A		S	T	R	E	A	M
U		C		O		I		O				E
D	R	A	I	N	E	D		R	I	S	E	N
E		R		A		E		I		W		T
N	A	V	A	L		A	M	E	R	I	C	A
C		E		L		L		S		N		R
E	S	S	A	Y	I	S	T		V	E	R	Y

191.

O	N	E	O	F	F		S	K	I	I	N	G
R		M		I		I		I		S		E
A	V	I	G	N	O	N		B		L		Y
T		N		D		T	A	B	L	E	T	S
E	V	E	N	S		E		U				E
S		N				M		T	R	I	E	R
		C		L	A	P	A	Z		N		
T	H	E	T	A		E				T		S
I				P		R		S	M	E	L	L
N	A	T	A	S	H	A		A		N		E
G		H		I		T	R	U	N	D	L	E
E		A		N		E		D		E		P
S	E	W	A	G	E		W	I	L	D	L	Y

192.

A		V		S				T		C		S
S	T	I	N	T	S		P	R	E	L	I	M
H		B		O		F		A		A		A
T	O	R	N	A	D	O		M	E	M	O	S
R		A		T		L		C		S		H
A	R	T	Y		B	L	E	A	T			
Y		E		S		O		R		W		O
			S	C	O	W	L		S	H	E	D
O		H		O		I		F		O		Y
B	U	Y	E	R		N	A	R	R	O	W	S
O		D		I		G		I		P		S
E	R	R	A	N	D		F	L	E	E	C	E
S		A		G				L		D		Y

Solutions

193.

	L		S		E		A		A		I	
M	I	S	M	A	N	A	G	E	M	E	N	T
	E		O		C		L		B		T	
B	U	C	K	A	R	O	O		L	O	R	E
			E		U		W		E		E	
C	O	N	S	I	S	T		A	D	E	P	T
	V				T		U				I	
P	E	R	I	L		A	N	Y	B	O	D	Y
	R		N		F		M		L			
F	L	E	D		A	D	O	R	A	B	L	E
	O		U		U		V		S		O	
P	R	E	C	O	N	C	E	P	T	I	O	N
	D		T		A		D		S		T	

194.

B	E	V	Y		I	N	I	M	I	C	A	L
O		E		I		I		E		E		A
O	R	G	A	N	I	C		Z	O	N	E	S
K		A		T		E		Z		T		S
C	O	N	V	E	N	T	I	O	N	A	L	
A				R		Y		S		U		S
S	E	S	A	M	E		F	O	U	R	T	H
E		T		E		O		P				E
	P	R	E	D	E	T	E	R	M	I	N	E
C		E		I		T		A		N		P
H	Y	E	N	A		A	N	N	E	L	I	D
I		T		R		W		O		A		O
P	U	S	S	Y	C	A	T		T	W	I	G

195.

H		M		R				P		P		M
E	D	I	S	O	N		K	I	M	O	N	O
L		R		T		H		N		L		I
P	E	R	G	O	L	A		C	R	A	M	S
E		O		R		T		E		R		T
R	A	R	E		O	C	H	R	E			
S		S		C		H		S		T		R
			M	O	U	L	T		T	O	F	U
A		F		M		I		B		O		N
F	O	R	U	M		N	E	E	D	L	E	D
I		E		U		G		T		K		O
R	E	S	I	N	S		R	E	V	I	E	W
E		H		E				L		T		N

196.

S	A	R	D	O	N	I	C		S	T	U	D
A		E		F		D				R		I
C	H	I	E	F		L	O	R	R	I	E	S
K		N		I		I				P		A
		E		C		N	E	T	T	L	E	S
B	I	D	D	I	N	G		R		E		T
A				A				I				E
C		G		T		A	M	M	E	T	E	R
K	E	R	N	E	L	S		E		A		
R		E				T		S		K		C
E	L	E	C	T	O	R		T	R	I	L	L
S		T				A		E		N		A
T	E	S	S		H	Y	D	R	O	G	E	N

197.

P	I	G	S		V	A	L	I	D	I	T	Y
R		R		K		I		M		N		O
E	G	O	T	I	S	M		M	A	K	E	R
S		O		L				U		W		E
S	I	M	P	L	E	M	I	N	D	E	D	
U				E		I		I		L		A
R	A	G		R	U	N	T	S		L	E	D
E		E		W		O		A				D
	U	N	C	H	A	R	I	T	A	B	L	E
S		D		A				I		U		N
K	N	E	L	L		W	R	O	N	G	E	D
U		R		E		H		N		L		U
A	S	S	E	S	S	O	R		S	E	E	M

198.

O	R	B	S		S	H	O	W	O	F	F	S
U		A		D		A		I		I		O
T	E	N	S	I	O	N		C	U	R	L	Y
S		A		S		G		K		E		A
M	U	L	T	I	L	A	T	E	R	A	L	
A				N		R		T		R		W
R	E	B	U	F	F		A	K	I	M	B	O
T		R		E		U		E				O
	D	I	S	C	O	N	T	E	N	T	E	D
S		O		T		I		P		R		W
L	U	C	C	A		T	R	E	M	O	L	O
O		H		N		E		R		U		R
G	R	E	A	T	E	S	T		S	T	E	M

199.

T	I	D	I	E	D		I	N	D	I	C	T
H		I		N		M		O		D		E
O	R	G	A	N	Z	A		N		L		A
R		E		I		L	I	S	T	E	N	S
N	E	S	T	S		E		T				E
S		T				D		O	C	C	U	R
		E		C	H	I	R	P		O		
L	E	D	G	E		C				W		P
I				R		T		B	L	O	K	E
F	E	R	R	A	R	I		A		R		A
T		E		M		O	I	L	S	K	I	N
E		A		I		N		L		E		U
D	E	D	U	C	E		E	S	P	R	I	T

200.

	C	H	A	R	D		J	E	E	P	S	
E		O		A		V		X		E		C
L	A	S	A	G	N	E		T	O	W	E	L
U		P		S		S		E				O
D	R	I	P		S	T	U	N	N	I	N	G
E		T		P		S		D		M		
S	T	A	V	E	S		P	E	E	P	E	D
		L		L		T		D		R		R
D	I	S	C	L	A	I	M		S	U	R	E
I				M		G		G		D		S
M	O	V	I	E		H	E	I	R	E	S	S
S		O		L		T		R		N		Y
	T	W	I	L	L		F	O	R	T	S	

201.

S	I	G	H		T	R	O	P	I	C	A	L
O		U		H		A		E		O		O
L	E	E	R	Y	A	N		R	I	N	G	S
I		S		P				S		Q		T
D	I	S	C	O	U	R	T	E	O	U	S	
I				C		A		V		E		P
T	A	P		H	E	D	G	E		R	E	A
Y		A		O		A		R				N
	D	I	N	N	E	R	J	A	C	K	E	T
S		N		D				N		N		H
C	A	T	E	R		R	E	C	L	I	N	E
A		E		I		E		E		F		O
M	E	R	M	A	I	D	S		N	E	O	N

202.

I	N	F	E	R		E	M	B	R	O	I	L
T		R		E		N			E		N	
E		O		L		S		F	I	R	T	H
R	U	N	N	E	R	U	P		G		R	
A		T		A		R		U	N	I	O	N
T	R	A	N	S	F	E	R		S			I
I		L		E				S		V		G
O			P		C	H	I	L	D	I	S	H
N	A	C	R	E		O		E		C		T
	V		O		T	O	N	E	D	E	A	F
H	A	R	M	S		V		P		R		A
	I		P			E		E		O		L
G	L	I	T	T	E	R		R	O	Y	A	L

203.

	S		A		R		S		E		A	
S	T	U	C	C	O		T	A	X	I	N	G
	A		C		U		A		P		A	
T	R	I	O		S	U	G	G	E	S	T	S
			M		I		E		R		H	
B	O	O	M	I	N	G		W	I	N	E	S
	C		O		G		V		M		M	
A	C	I	D	S		V	E	T	E	R	A	N
	U		A		K		R		N			
S	P	O	T	L	E	S	S		T	W	O	S
	I		I		E		I		I		I	
K	E	R	N	E	L		O	W	N	I	N	G
	R		G		S		N		G		K	

204.

C	O	W	S		F	R	E	N	E	T	I	C
A		H		B		A		E		A		R
R	E	A	D	E	R	S		V	I	D	E	O
B		R		L		H		E		P		S
O	F	F		L		E		R	O	O	F	S
N				B	U	R	S	T		L		C
I		C		O				H		E		U
F		H		T	E	N	S	E				L
E	X	U	L	T		O		L		H	I	T
R		C		O		T		E		A		U
O	A	K	U	M		I	N	S	U	L	A	R
U		L		E		O		S		V		A
S	P	E	N	D	I	N	G		K	E	E	L

Solutions

205.

```
BUSTA#BARRELS
R#P#C#O##A#A#
E#A#E#X#STASH
AIRCRAFT#H#T#
K#R#B#U#TERSE
FLOTILLA#R##X
A#W#C###I#S#I
S##P#TWINKLES
THREE#A#Q#E#T
#A#R#ALLUSIVE
GRAIL#N#E#G#N
#P#S##U#S#H#C
ASPHALT#TITLE
```

206.

```
#S#C#A#S#S#C#
HALLUCINATION
#G#I#O#O#Y#T#
COLESLAW#LETS
###N#Y#Y#E#A#
CANTATA#ADAGE
#R###E#H###E#
LARCH#OUTLAST
#C#A#C#L#E###
WHET#LAKESIDE
#N#C#I#I#S#E#
LIGHTFINGERED
#D#Y#F#G#N#P#
```

207.

```
ABSURD#WISDOM
#L#N#U#E#C#U#
LAID#FALCONRY
#C#E#F#L#F###
SKIRT#PREFECT
#H#G#A#E###O#
HONORBLACKMAN
#L###R#D#E#G#
NEEDFUL#STRUM
###E#P#F#T#L#
STILETTO#LEAN
#I#V#L#U#E#T#
SPEEDY#RESTED
```

208.

```
ATHENA#S#I#I#
R#A##SCOTLAND
MOW##S#M#L#H#
I#KARATE#USES
E#E##Y#D#S#R#
SADLY#HALOGEN
###E#U#Y#R###
CONTEND#XYLEM
#X#T#I#I##A#O
BYTE#COBWEB#T
#G#R#O#S##EGO
REHEARSE##L#R
#N#D#N#NURSES
```

209.

```
S#G#E###B#N#A
CARING#MUSING
H#A#T#P#T#C#E
INVERSE#TOKEN
S#E#Y#S#E#S#T
MULL#START###
S#Y#O#I#Y#T#H
###STALK#CAPE
C#A#T#E#S#K#A
RATIO#NUCLEAR
I#O#M#T#O#O#E
MENTAL#BUFFER
P#E#N###R#F#S
```

210.

```
#BEDEVILMENT#
U#E#A#S#E#O#E
N#R#RESIN#WED
IBIZA#U#U#I#U
N#E#C#E#SONIC
HUSHHUSH####A
I#T#E###H#G#T
B####CALAMARI
INSET#R#R#L#O
T#O#E#D#DEIGN
ELF#MOORE#L#A
D#I#P#U#S#E#L
#CALIBRATION#
```

211.

```
TAPS#CYNICISM
R#I#C#E#N#M#U
EXPLOIT#DUPES
S#E#M###O#U#H
PERSPICACITY#
A###L#A#T#E#M
SAP#AUGER#DUO
S#I#C#E#I###D
#UNSEASONABLE
M#B#N###A#A#L
APART#ANTHILL
M#L#L#W#E#Z#E
ALLAYING#MEND
```

212.

```
A#M#D###R#G#T
GOOGOL#GEMINI
E#N#U#R#V#L#L
LEGIBLE#EXTOL
E#R#T#S#A#S#S
SEEP#SPELL###
S#L#U#O#S#H#P
###INANE#DUPE
A#S#I#D#S#R#R
SHIRT#ESCORTS
H#G#I#D#O#Y#I
ETHANE#SPOUTS
S#S#G###E#P#T
```

213.

```
PICK#EMPERORS
E#H#S#E#C#V#I
DEADPAN#CREED
I#I#R#A#E#R#E
CONVINCINGLY#
U###N#E#T#A#O
RESIGN#DRAPED
E#T#O#F#I###O
#COUNTERCLAIM
E#I#I#E#I#M#E
MACHO#BETWIXT
U#A#N#L#Y#N#E
SPLASHED#ROAR
```

214.

```
WINDFALL#HIGH
O#E#A#O###C#Y
OCTET#DANGERS
D#T#T#G###B#T
##L#E#EPITOME
CLEANED#N#X#R
O###I###C###I
N#H#N#DIORAMA
CHARGER#R#L##
L#M###E#R#L#B
APPLAUD#EMERY
V#E###G#C#G#E
ECRU#SETTLERS
```

215.

```
SHOT#SETBACKS
T#U#W#X#O#O#O
ANTWERP#OLDER
R#D#L#O#G#I#E
FRONTISPIECE#
I###E#E#E#I#E
SCURRY#SWELLS
H#P#W#S#O###T
#AFFECTIONATE
G#R#I#R#G#B#E
AMONG#IRIDIUM
L#N#H#P#E#D#E
ENTITLES#REED
```

216.

```
KNAPSACK#LIZA
A#R#T#R#E#N#L
LATER#E#FEAST
E#S#O#E#F#H#I
###ENDPRODUCT
S#C#G#S#R#R#U
ARROWS#STARED
U#I#I#M#L#Y#E
COMPLAINED###
E#P#L#L#S#C#C
PRIDE#A#SKIRL
A#N#D#N#L#A#A
NAGS#ROLYPOLY
```

Solutions

217.

C		D		T		M		T		H		A
R	E	I	T	E	R	A	T	E		E	N	D
U		L		R		N		N		R		H
S	P	E	A	R		A	U	D	I	B	L	E
T		M		A		G		S				R
	S	M	A	C	K	E	D		W	I	L	E
P		A		E				S		N		S
R	O	S	Y		M	A	G	I	C	A	L	
E				M		M		R		C		C
S	I	T	U	A	T	E		L	A	T	C	H
A		A		I		L		O		I		E
G	A	P		L	O	L	L	I	P	O	P	S
E		E		S		E		N		N		S

218.

M	I	R	T	H	F	U	L		G	R	O	W
O		O		A		S				A		I
V	I	C	A	R		U	T	T	E	R	E	D
E		O		N		R				E		E
		C		E		E	C	H	E	L	O	N
T	R	O	U	S	E	R		O		Y		E
R				S				I				S
I		D		E		A	P	P	E	A	R	S
G	U	A	R	D	E	D		O		L		
G		M				V		L		K		S
E	X	A	M	I	N	E		L	E	A	R	N
R		G				R		O		L		U
S	E	E	N		S	T	A	I	N	I	N	G

219.

	V		U		I		B		C		L	
C	O	M	P	U	T	E	R		R	I	O	T
	L		G		C		E		A		C	
P	U	R	R		H	E	A	D	G	E	A	R
	M		A		I		D				L	
P	E	N	D	A	N	T		G	O	R	E	D
			E		G		V		V			
G	O	O	D	S		C	I	N	E	M	A	S
	X				R		C		R		C	
A	F	F	L	U	E	N	T		D	O	U	R
	O		A		E		I		O		M	
G	R	I	N		D	E	M	A	N	D	E	D
	D		A		S		S		E		N	

220.

A	S	H	O	R	E		F	E	A	S	T	S
D		A		I		C		N		A		I
A	M	N	E	S	T	Y		D		R		G
G		D		E		B	U	L	L	I	O	N
I	D	L	E	R		E		E				E
O		I				R		S	C	A	L	D
		N		R	E	N	T	S		B		
A	L	G	A	E		E				L		S
R				N		T		K	O	A	L	A
T	S	U	N	A	M	I		E		T		S
I		R		M		C	A	T	F	I	S	H
S		G		E		S		C		V		A
T	R	E	A	D	S		C	H	E	E	K	Y

221.

M		E		F		G		S		R		D
A	N	N	U	L	M	E	N	T		I	R	E
R		C		O		N		U		P		M
C	O	U	R	T		T	E	M	P	E	R	A
H		M		S		L		P				N
	A	B	R	A	D	E	S		W	A	R	D
C		E		M				C		U		S
H	U	R	T		I	S	L	A	N	D	S	
O				I		C		R		A		M
W	A	V	E	R	E	R		T	A	C	K	Y
D		O		I		A		O		I		R
E	E	L		S	U	P	P	O	R	T	E	R
R		E		H		E		N		Y		H

222.

B	I	G	A	P	P	L	E		B	R	E	W
A		O		R		A		O		E		O
B	O	N	G	O		U		L	O	V	E	R
Y		E		F		N		D		E		S
			H	E	N	C	E	F	O	R	T	H
H		T		S		H		A		T		I
E	G	O	I	S	M		A	S	L	E	E	P
R		R		I		D		H		D		S
A	S	T	R	O	N	O	M	I	C			
L		I		N		M		O		R		D
D	E	L	T	A		I		N	O	I	S	Y
R		L		L		N		E		T		E
Y	E	A	R		G	O	O	D	N	E	S	S

223.

S	I	S	T	E	R		O		E		A	
Q		U			A	B	R	A	S	I	V	E
U	R	N			I		D		O		O	
A		K	I	N	D	L	E		T	O	W	S
W		E			S		R		E		E	
K	E	N	Y	A		D	E	G	R	A	D	E
			E		O		D		I			
E	N	M	A	S	S	E		S	C	O	L	D
	Y		R		P		S			U		O
A	M	E	N		R	H	Y	M	E	S		I
	P		I		E		R			T	U	N
T	H	A	N	K	Y	O	U			E		G
	S		G		S		P	R	I	D	E	S

224.

	M		A		D		S		T		C	
J	U	M	B	L	E		T	R	E	M	O	R
	S		B		S		I		L		X	
V	E	E	R		C	O	N	D	E	N	S	E
			E		E		T		M		W	
S	O	L	V	I	N	G		S	A	R	A	H
	V		I		D		T		R		I	
M	E	D	A	L		S	U	C	K	I	N	G
	R		T		S		R		E			
C	H	A	I	R	M	A	N		T	O	P	S
	E		O		I		I		I		A	
B	A	N	N	E	R		P	A	N	I	C	S
	D		S		K		S		G		E	

225.

C	O	D	A		M	O	C	C	A	S	I	N
R		O		E		D		O		A		A
I	N	D	E	X	E	D		N	E	V	I	S
T		O		T				S		I		H
I	N	S	T	R	U	C	T	I	O	N	S	
C				A		O		D		G		I
A	U	K		V	E	N	U	E		S	O	T
L		N		A		G		R				E
	B	U	R	G	L	A	R	A	L	A	R	M
S		C		A				B		R		I
W	A	K	E	N		F	U	L	F	I	L	S
A		L		Z		O		E		S		E
P	R	E	P	A	R	E	S		F	E	N	S

Solutions

226.

```
# S M I T H # S H A D Y #
M # A # I # F # A # O # W
A R S E N A L # M E N S A
N # C # T # I # P # # # R
N O U N # H E R E U P O N
E # L # F # S # R # U # #
D R I V E S # V E R B A L
# # N # A # S # D # L # I
C R E A T I N G # K I L N
A # # # H # I # P # S # I
F I B R E # F R E S H E N
E # A # R # F # E # E # G
# D A I S Y # C R U D E #
```

227.

```
# R E C O M M E N D E D #
U # Q # V # A # O # L # S
N # U # E X P E L # A G O
C H E E R # L # I # N # V
O # R # L # E # N U D G E
M E R R I E S T # # # # R
P # Y # E # # # S # J # E
L # # # # K A L A H A R I
E N V O Y # N # L # W # G
T # I # U # N # U R B A N
E V E # C O U N T # O # T
D # W # C # A # E # N # Y
# E S T A B L I S H E D #
```

228.

```
D A P H N E # E # B # U #
E # O # # S A N G U I N E
C A T # # T # G # N # R #
A # A P P E A R # G L U T
M # T # # R # A # A # L #
P R O B E # E V I L E Y E
# # # R # F # E # O # # #
H O P E F U L # S W I S H
# D # A # C # E # # M # O
E D I T # H A N G U P # S
# S # H # S # D # # A P T
C O H E S I V E # # R # E
# N # S # A # D I S T I L
```

229.

```
# B # B # O # G # S # P #
C O R R O B O R A T I O N
# N # E # E # A # O # T #
F O R E N S I C # R O A M
# # # C # I # E # E # T #
M A C H E T E # A D I O S
# Q # # # Y # M # # # E #
M U D D Y # S U N R I S E
# A # R # L # S # O # # #
B R I E # E M I S S I O N
# I # A # W # C # T # V #
Q U A D R I L A T E R A L
# S # S # S # L # R # L #
```

230.

```
# A N N I V E R S A R Y #
E # O # M # S # I # I # H
L # W # P A T H S # V I A
E S H E R # A # Q # E # N
C # E # E # T # O W N E D
T H R A S H E D # # # # W
R # E # S # # # E # U # R
O # # # # H E L S I N K I
N O S E S # N # C # H # T
I # T # O # G # H E I D I
C O O # D O U S E # N # N
S # O # A # L # W # G # G
# C L O S E F I S T E D #
```

231.

```
# M I D G E # V E R B S #
E # N # L # T # N # I # P
I N T R U D E # V O T E R
G # E # M # N # E # # # O
H O R N # A T H L E T E S
T # D # D # S # O # O # #
H A I L E D # S P R O U T
# # C # C # M # E # T # A
B E T R A Y A L # C H U M
U # # # D # T # T # L # P
S P A R E # C H I N E S E
H # S # N # H # M # S # R
# S P A T E # S E U S S #
```

232.

```
S A G A # S T R I D E N T
O # R # D # O # N # R # R
U R A N I U M # V E R G E
L # S # S # T # U # A # A
S O P # P # O # L O T U S
E # # # L U M E N # I # U
A # E # A # # # E # C # R
R # M # C O V E R # # # E
C H I M E # U # A # L E T
H # R # M # L # B # A # R
I R A T E # C A L Y P S O
N # T # N # A # E # E # V
G R E E T I N G # A L O E
```

233.

```
# M # A # S # S # U # L #
W E A P O N # C E N S U S
# M # P # U # A # C # M #
P O L O # B O N H O M I E
# # # R # B # S # M # N #
T U R T L E S # S P O O F
# N # I # D # E # L # U #
T H R O B # E X P A N S E
# A # N # F # C # I # # #
T R O M B O N E # N I R O
# M # E # I # R # I # U #
V E R N A L # P U N D I T
# D # T # S # T # G # N #
```

234.

```
# R O A S T # S H I P S #
R # P # O # C # A # I # R
A T E L I E R # C O P R A
F # R # L # O # I # # # N
F U E L # T O W E R I N G
I # T # Q # N # N # M # #
A R T F U L # A D R I F T
# # A # A # W # A # T # W
R E S T R A I N # P A P A
A # # # R # N # H # T # N
C A B L E # C H A F I N G
K # A # L # H # Z # O # S
# C R U S H # T E E N S #
```

235.

C	A	R	D		D	O	U	B	L	I	N	G
O		E		A		R		A		N		A
I	N	S	I	P	I	D		T	U	F	T	S
N		E		P		A		T		E		H
C	A	T	E	R	P	I	L	L	A	R	S	
I				O		N		E		N		D
D	O	L	L	A	R		I	G	N	O	R	E
E		I		C		S		R				W
	A	N	T	H	R	O	P	O	L	O	G	Y
E		G		A		F		U		X		E
B	L	U	R	B		F	I	N	A	L	L	Y
B		A		L		I		D		I		E
S	O	L	V	E	N	T	S		S	P	E	D

236.

P	O	P	U	L	O	U	S		T	A	X	I
I		U		O		N				C		N
K	A	Z	O	O		L	E	N	I	E	N	T
E		Z		S		O				T		E
		L		E		A	M	U	S	I	N	G
P	R	E	E	N	E	D		N		C		E
R				E				E				R
E		G		S		T	A	T	T	E	R	S
C	R	U	I	S	E	R		H		X		
I		Z				U		I		P		S
N	O	Z	Z	L	E	S		C	L	O	S	E
C		L				T		A		R		E
T	I	E	S		I	S	O	L	A	T	E	D

237.

X	E	N	O	N		W	O	R	R	I	E	S
Y		O		E		H			E		A	
L		M		W		O		A	N	D	R	E
O	M	I	S	S	I	O	N		O		L	
P		N		M		S		S	W	A	S	H
H	E	A	D	A	C	H	E		N			Y
O		L		N				F		L		P
N			S		R	O	T	A	T	I	O	N
E	L	A	T	E		U		B		Q		O
	U		R		S	T	A	R	D	U	S	T
T	R	A	I	T		B		I		E		I
	K		D			I		C		U		S
U	S	H	E	R	E	D		S	C	R	U	M

238.

	N		A		S		P		S		D	
C	O	N	F	E	C	T	I	O	N	E	R	Y
	V		R		A		A		O		U	
T	A	L	I	S	M	A	N		O	H	M	S
			C		P		O		Z		B	
B	L	E	A	T	E	D		C	E	D	E	D
	U				R		B				A	
S	C	U	D	S		M	A	C	B	E	T	H
	I		I		S		H		E			
O	D	D	S		H	E	R	I	T	A	G	E
	I		M		R		A		R		U	
S	T	R	A	T	E	G	I	C	A	L	L	Y
	Y		L		D		N		Y		P	

239.

	E		B		F		D		R		A	
T	A	L	L	E	R		I	M	E	L	D	A
	C		A		E		G		I		H	
C	H	I	C		S	C	I	E	N	C	E	S
			K		H		T		C		S	
S	P	R	A	W	L	S		M	A	R	I	S
	A		N		Y		R		R		O	
B	R	I	D	E		R	A	I	N	I	N	G
	A		W		B		B		A			
O	N	T	H	E	J	O	B		T	H	U	S
	O		I		O		I		I		G	
B	I	T	T	E	R		T	R	O	L	L	S
	D		E		N		S		N		Y	

240.

	C	O	N	T	R	O	V	E	R	S	Y	
C		U		R		R		V		A		G
U		T		I	M	A	G	E		F	A	R
T	A	P	E	S		T		R		E		A
T		O		E		O		Y	A	R	D	S
I	N	S	E	C	U	R	E					S
N		T		T				M		H		H
G					P	A	L	O	M	I	N	O
E	T	H	I	C		B		N		D		P
D		E		Y		A		S	H	E	E	P
G	E	L		N	A	C	H	O		O		E
E		L		I		U		O		U		R
	C	O	N	C	I	S	E	N	E	S	S	

241.

P	S	E	U	D	O		A		S		M	
L		R			R	I	G	H	T	F	U	L
U	M	A			G		A		U		E	
C		S	A	L	A	M	I		B	E	S	T
K		E			N		N		B		L	
Y	O	D	E	L		O	S	M	O	S	I	S
			G		R		T		R			
L	A	N	G	U	I	D		G	N	A	S	H
	N		S		G		F			I		O
I	T	C	H		G	A	R	N	E	R		R
	H		E		I		A			M	R	S
B	E	D	L	I	N	E	N			A		E
	R		L		G		C	R	A	N	E	S

242.

	S		O		F		H		C		F	
S	P	O	N	T	A	N	E	O	U	S	L	Y
	U		W		N		A		D		O	
A	D	V	A	N	C	E	D		G	R	A	N
			R		I		S		E		T	
A	C	I	D	I	F	Y		P	L	A	I	D
	O				Y		H				N	
S	C	U	F	F		T	E	E	N	A	G	E
	K		L		I		C		O			
C	A	R	E		R	A	T	I	O	N	A	L
	T		D		O		A		S		L	
M	O	R	G	A	N	F	R	E	E	M	A	N
	O		E		S		E		S		S	

243.

	K	I	O	S	K		S	W	I	R	L	
V		N		L		H		I		I		N
I	M	A	G	I	N	E		Z	E	B	R	A
A		N		T		A		A				P
B	A	I	T		O	V	E	R	U	S	E	S
L		M		W		Y		D		I		
E	V	A	D	E	S		F	R	O	L	I	C
		T		D		S		Y		V		R
A	M	E	N	D	I	N	G		F	E	T	A
R				I		E		L		R		G
K	N	O	W	N		E	L	U	D	I	N	G
S		A		G		R		S		N		Y
	B	R	U	S	H		T	H	I	G	H	

Solutions

244.

T	A	B	S		P	R	O	B	A	B	L	E
R		E		S		A		I		U		X
I	N	S	E	C	T	S		B	E	F	I	T
A		O		H		C		L		F		R
L	I	M	B	O		A	R	I	Z	O	N	A
A				O		L		O		O		V
N	U	Z	Z	L	E		A	G	E	N	D	A
D		I		M		A		R				G
E	N	G	L	A	N	D		A	R	O	M	A
R		Z		S		V		P		X		N
R	E	A	C	T		I	N	H	I	B	I	T
O		G		E		C		Y		O		L
R	E	S	E	R	V	E	D		A	W	R	Y

245.

E	F	F	A	C	E		H	E	C	T	I	C
N		O		I		A		N		U		O
T	R	U	S	T	E	D		D		B		R
E		N		E		I	N	G	R	A	I	N
R	I	T	E	S		N		A				E
S		A				F		M	A	M	B	A
		I		E	L	I	T	E		U		
D	E	N	I	M		N				L		G
I				U		I		U	N	T	I	L
S	T	A	R	L	E	T		S		I		I
M		V		A		U	S	U	R	P	E	D
A		O		T		M		A		L		E
Y	O	N	D	E	R		P	L	A	Y	E	R

246.

M		P		B		S		L		S		L
E	V	I	D	E	N	T	L	Y		L	E	A
R		Z		N		R		R		U		D
G	A	Z	E	D		A	V	E	N	G	E	D
E		E		I		I		S				E
	G	R	A	N	I	T	E		A	M	I	R
B		I		G				D		E		S
L	O	A	M		S	Q	U	I	R	T	S	
A				F		U		C		R		P
B	E	S	I	E	G	E		T	R	I	A	L
B		E		N		A		I		C		O
E	Y	E		C	O	S	M	O	N	A	U	T
R		R		E		Y		N		L		S

247.

	T		D		M		D		D		D	
H	O	T	E	L	I	E	R		A	V	I	D
	M		E		S		O		W		A	
P	A	I	R		F	O	O	T	N	O	T	E
	T		S		I		P				O	
P	O	C	K	E	T	S		A	T	O	M	S
			I		S		I		R			
M	E	A	N	S		E	N	V	I	O	U	S
	V				S		T		C		N	
P	E	R	C	E	I	V	E		Y	O	L	K
	N		A		L		N		C		I	
J	E	A	N		L	A	D	Y	L	I	K	E
	D		S		Y		S		E		E	

248.

F	Y	E	S	I	C	H	T		A	T	O	M
R		X		N		O				O		A
A	B	O	U	T		L	I	B	E	R	A	L
S		T		R		L				P		A
		I		U		O	P	A	C	I	T	Y
J	A	C	K	D	A	W		B		D		S
A				I				D				I
U		U		N		G	E	O	R	G	I	A
N	O	S	E	G	A	Y		M		R		
T		E				P		I		O		M
I	N	F	A	N	T	S		N	O	O	S	E
L		U				U		A		V		T
Y	U	L	E		E	M	P	L	O	Y	E	E

249.

S		C		C		I		K		F		E
T	R	A	D	E	S	M	A	N		L	O	P
U		T		R		P		A		I		I
D	R	A	F	T		I	N	C	I	T	E	S
Y		R		A		S		K				T
	P	A	R	I	A	H	S		W	E	A	L
S		C		N				K		T		E
L	U	T	E		P	A	U	N	C	H	Y	
A				T		C		I		E		S
P	S	Y	C	H	I	C		G	I	R	T	H
P		O		E		R		H		E		R
E	L	K		F	L	U	C	T	U	A	T	E
D		E		T		E		S		L		W

250.

	L	A	I	T	Y		T	A	W	N	Y	
H		R		E		S		U		A		T
U	N	C	L	E	A	N		T	A	B	L	E
B		H		N		O		O				R
B	E	E	R		C	O	A	C	H	M	A	N
U		T		A		P		R		I		
B	A	Y	I	N	G		T	A	N	G	L	E
		P		A		S		T		R		N
S	E	E	D	L	I	N	G		G	A	L	A
E				Y		U		S		T		C
A	N	D	E	S		B	L	O	W	O	U	T
M		E		E		S		U		R		S
	S	W	I	S	S		G	R	E	Y	S	

251.

R	O	L	E		M	A	N	D	A	T	E	S
O		E		E		L		I		R		E
U	N	M	A	S	K	S		S	M	A	L	L
G		U		T		A		A		I		F
H	I	R	E	R		C	A	D	E	N	Z	A
A				A		E		V		E		W
N	A	M	I	N	G		C	A	M	E	R	A
D		E		G		G		N				R
R	E	L	I	E	V	E		T	I	T	R	E
E		O		M		R		A		E		N
A	D	D	L	E		M	A	G	N	A	T	E
D		I		N		A		E		R		S
Y	A	C	H	T	I	N	G		A	S	K	S

252.

B	R	U	T	A	L		A	V	O	W	A	L
I		N		M		O		I		I		A
C	A	R	I	B	O	U		S		C		T
E		A		I		T	W	I	N	K	L	E
P	I	V	O	T		O		T				S
S		E				F		O	N	S	E	T
		L		D	E	B	A	R		P		
L	A	S	S	O		O				E		A
O				L		U		L	U	C	I	D
I	N	S	U	L	I	N		I		I		O
T		E		A		D	R	E	A	M	E	R
E		L		R		S		G		E		N
R	E	L	I	S	H		T	E	N	N	I	S

253.

T	E	R	M	I	N	A	L		A	M	I	D
I		O		N		R		F		A		I
F	L	U	F	F		M		R	A	N	T	S
F		T		E		F		E		U		P
			A	C	C	U	M	U	L	A	T	E
C		U		T		L		D		L		N
L	E	N	T	I	L		V	I	O	L	A	S
E		S		O		E		A		Y		E
A	S	T	O	U	N	D	I	N	G			
N		E		S		G		S		A		S
C	R	A	W	L		I		L	A	U	G	H
U		D		Y		N		I		R		U
T	O	Y	S		E	G	G	P	L	A	N	T

254.

R	E	S	C	U	I	N	G		M	U	C	K
O		A		P		I				R		E
C	L	U	N	G		P	I	E	B	A	L	D
K		C		R		P				N		G
		E		A		E	S	P	O	U	S	E
R	E	S	I	D	E	D		R		S		R
E				I				O				E
A		F		N		O	B	V	E	R	S	E
S	P	O	N	G	E	S		I		U		
S		R				P		D		S		O
U	N	C	L	E	A	R		E	A	T	E	R
R		E				E		N		I		A
E	A	S	E		M	Y	S	T	I	C	A	L

255.

	C		C		A		S		P		M	
S	H	O	R	T	T	E	M	P	E	R	E	D
	A		A		L		O		N		M	
D	R	A	W	B	A	C	K		C	U	B	A
			L		N		Y		I		R	
C	L	O	S	E	T	S		P	L	E	A	T
	I				A		P				N	
A	C	R	I	D		P	L	A	N	N	E	D
	E		R		G		O		E			
I	N	F	O		L	A	U	N	C	H	E	R
	S		N		I		G		T		Y	
S	E	V	E	N	T	H	H	E	A	V	E	N
	S		D		Z		S		R		D	

256.

	S	N	I	C	K		S	T	E	W	S	
C		U		U		F		A		O		T
H	U	R	D	L	E	R		D	I	N	G	O
A		S		L		E		P				U
S	K	E	W		R	E	C	O	R	D	E	R
E		R		F		S		L		E		
R	A	I	S	I	N		D	E	V	O	I	D
		E		E		S		S		D		I
R	E	S	T	R	I	C	T		S	O	O	N
O				C		O		F		R		G
W	I	N	C	E		U	N	L	E	A	S	H
S		E		L		T		U		N		Y
	S	T	A	Y	S		B	E	L	T	S	

257.

A	W	A	I	T		R	E	C	I	T	E	S
G		P		R		E			M		N	
G		R		I		T		S	P	A	S	M
R	A	I	L	R	O	A	D		A		U	
E		C		E		I		S	L	E	E	K
G	R	O	O	M	I	N	G		A			N
A		T		E				S		B		O
T			B		E	L	E	C	T	R	I	C
E	L	V	I	S		O		H		I		K
	Y		K		I	N	G	E	S	T	E	D
C	I	V	I	C		E		M		N		O
	N		N			R		E		E		W
I	G	N	I	T	E	S		D	O	Y	E	N

258.

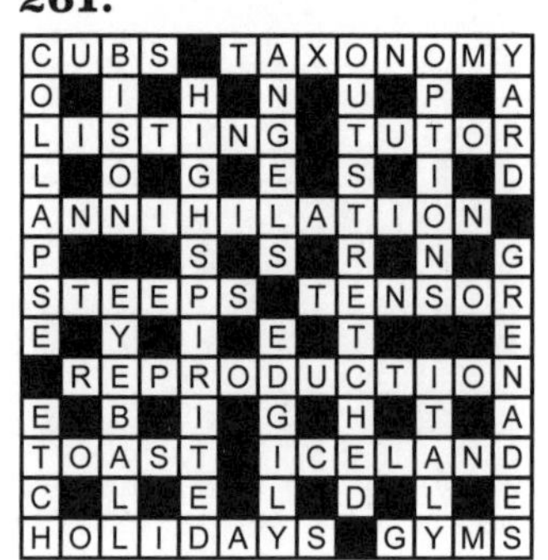

A		W		S				N		S		M
B	O	A	S	T	S		V	I	R	A	G	O
S		R		A		D		B		L		C
T	E	R	M	I	N	I		B	O	O	T	H
A		I		R		S		L		N		A
I	C	O	N		S	P	I	E	D			
N		R		P		A		S		T		C
			A	L	A	R	M		H	E	A	L
M		C		A		A		O		L		O
I	N	L	E	T		T	H	R	E	A	T	S
T		E		I		E		B		V		E
R	E	G	E	N	T		M	I	L	I	E	U
E		G		G				T		V		P

259.

O	C	T	A	N	E		A	C	T	I	N	G
D		W		A		I		H		O		A
O	X	O	N	I	A	N		I		T		L
U		F		L		V	O	L	C	A	N	O
R	E	A	M	S		E		L				S
S		C				S		E	A	R	T	H
		E		S	A	T	Y	R		E		
A	U	D	I	O		I				M		Z
B				L		G		P	I	E	C	E
J	A	M	A	I	C	A		A		D		U
U		A		C		T	U	G	G	I	N	G
R		D		I		E		E		E		M
E	V	E	N	T	S		O	D	E	S	S	A

260.

	S		R		I		A		H		A	
F	O	R	E	K	N	O	W	L	E	D	G	E
	F		C		S		A		A		R	
P	A	C	I	F	I	E	R		L	I	O	N
			T		S		D		T		N	
A	S	C	E	N	T	S		S	H	O	O	K
	K				S		B				M	
T	Y	P	E	S		M	O	N	K	E	Y	S
	L		X		P		R		I			
Z	I	N	C		R	E	S	I	S	T	O	R
	G		U		O		C		S		A	
T	H	E	S	I	X	T	H	S	E	N	S	E
	T		E		Y		T		D		T	

261.

C	U	B	S		T	A	X	O	N	O	M	Y
O		I		H		N		U		P		A
L	I	S	T	I	N	G		T	U	T	O	R
L		O		G		E		S		I		D
A	N	N	I	H	I	L	A	T	I	O	N	
P				S		S		R		N		G
S	T	E	E	P	S		T	E	N	S	O	R
E		Y		I		E		T				E
	R	E	P	R	O	D	U	C	T	I	O	N
E		B		I		G		H		T		A
T	O	A	S	T		I	C	E	L	A	N	D
C		L		E		L		D		L		E
H	O	L	I	D	A	Y	S		G	Y	M	S

Solutions

262.

M	A	N	I	C	U	R	E		A	R	E	A
A		A		O		E		H		I		C
G	I	V	E	N		C		A	U	G	U	R
E		Y		S		O		U		O		I
			S	T	R	U	C	T	U	R	E	D
P		S		I		P		E		O		I
R	E	P	U	T	E		A	C	Q	U	I	T
E		A		U		A		O		S		Y
S	U	C	C	E	S	S	F	U	L			
S		E		N		L		T		M		L
M	I	M	I	C		E		U	N	I	F	Y
E		A		Y		E		R		L		N
N	I	N	E		A	P	P	E	N	D	I	X

263.

V	O	T	E		E	D	U	C	A	T	E	D
E		O		D		U		A		A		I
N	E	T	T	I	N	G		R	O	L	E	S
T		E		S		O		D		L		A
R	E	M	I	T		U	N	I	F	I	E	D
I				I		T		O		E		V
L	I	T	A	N	Y		E	L	I	S	H	A
O		R		C		I		O				N
Q	U	I	E	T	E	N		G	H	O	S	T
U		B		N		D		I		R		A
I	N	U	R	E		O	U	S	T	I	N	G
S		T		S		O		T		O		E
T	R	E	A	S	U	R	Y		E	N	I	D

264.

	A		I		C		A		A		S	
P	L	I	N	T	H		V	A	N	I	T	Y
	T		S		A		I		A		A	
L	O	K	I		S	C	A	R	C	I	T	Y
			G		I		N		H		U	
P	A	N	N	I	N	G		B	R	A	T	S
	D		I		G		M		O		E	
D	E	I	F	Y		C	O	Y	N	E	S	S
	Q		I		L		N		I			
Z	U	C	C	H	I	N	I		S	O	A	K
	A		A		V		T		T		Q	
S	T	A	N	C	E		O	D	I	O	U	S
	E		T		R		R		C		A	

265.

	P	R	A	C	T	I	C	A	B	L	E	
M		A		U		T		V		O		P
A		V		D	R	A	K	E		C	A	R
G	R	I	N	D		L		R		A		E
I		O		L		I		S	A	L	A	D
S	O	L	V	E	N	C	Y					E
T		I		S				M		M		C
E					A	B	D	I	C	A	T	E
R	U	L	E	R		A		N		E		S
I		I		O		T		D	U	S	T	S
A	R	T		B	E	E	P	S		T		O
L		R		O		A		E		R		R
	D	E	S	T	R	U	C	T	I	O	N	

266.

S	H	A	B	B	Y			S		S	U	E
	E			U		I	N	P	U	T		V
T	A	N	T	R	U	M		U		U		A
	D			D		P		N	O	D	E	S
A	W	A	K	E	N	E	D			I		I
	A			N		L		A		E		V
E	Y	E	L	E	T		T	I	S	S	U	E
A		N		D		S		R			R	
R		T			I	C	E	B	E	R	G	S
L	A	I	R	S		A		R			E	
I		T		A		P	O	U	R	I	N	G
E		L	A	N	C	E		S			C	
R	Y	E		D			C	H	E	R	Y	L

267.

P	L	U	R	A	L		L	E	S	I	O	N
	O		E		I		I		I		D	
P	U	P	A		M	U	T	I	N	E	E	R
	S		L		B		E		E			
P	I	X	I	E		C	R	O	W	B	A	R
	N		S		F		A				B	
D	E	T	E	R	I	O	R	A	T	I	O	N
	S				V		Y		R		M	
E	S	C	A	P	E	S		V	I	V	I	D
			L		S		G		P		N	
E	M	U	L	A	T	O	R		L	E	A	F
	I		O		A		A		E		T	
C	R	A	T	E	R		B	A	T	T	E	R

268.

R	A	T	I	F	I	E	D		B	R	I	O
H		O		L		X		O		E		B
Y	U	M	M	Y		H		V	I	A	L	S
S		E		O		A		E		S		E
			I	N	G	L	O	R	I	O	U	S
S		M		T		E		E		N		S
Y	O	U	T	H	S		I	M	P	E	D	E
M		T		E		T		P		D		D
P	L	A	Y	W	R	I	G	H	T			
A		T		A		N		A		C		E
T	W	I	R	L		D		S	T	O	R	K
H		O		L		E		I		O		E
Y	A	N	K		B	R	I	S	T	L	E	S

269.

P		N		A		B		S		T		A
L	E	I	S	U	R	E	L	Y		O	U	T
O		G		T		L		L		R		T
Y	A	H	O	O		I	M	P	L	O	D	E
S		T		C		E		H				S
	S	C	R	U	F	F	Y		A	B	U	T
J		A		E				P		A		S
E	X	P	O		W	O	R	L	D	L	Y	
R				C		R		A		L		R
S	T	A	S	H	E	D		C	A	R	V	E
E		C		A		E		E		O		E
Y	E	N		R	O	A	D	B	L	O	C	K
S		E		M		L		O		M		S

270.

A	R	C	S		A	T	T	E	N	D	E	D
N		R		O		A		M		I		I
T	E	A	R	F	U	L		B	U	S	E	S
I		M		F		C		A		A		T
C	U	P		T		U		R	I	V	E	R
L				H	O	M	E	R		O		U
I		G		E				A		W		S
M		R		R	E	S	T	S				T
A	N	O	D	E		O		S		R	E	F
C		M		C		R		I		O		U
T	E	M	P	O		R	E	N	E	W	A	L
I		E		R		E		G		E		L
C	I	T	A	D	E	L	S		A	R	M	Y

271.

A		A		W				T		L		B
D	E	R	M	I	S		D	E	C	O	D	E
O		R		P		S		M		C		R
P	L	A	T	E	A	U		P	L	U	M	E
T		I		D		P		E		S		T
E	D	G	E		M	E	T	R	O			
D		N		T		R		S		E		N
			C	H	A	N	T		O	S	L	O
A		F		E		O		S		T		V
P	R	I	S	M		V	A	C	U	O	L	E
P		R		A		A		E		N		L
A	S	S	I	S	T		I	N	S	I	S	T
L		T		K				T		A		Y

272.

C	I	T	R	I	C		U		P		C	
O		A			A	P	P	E	A	S	E	R
Y	E	S			R		S		T		M	
O		K	U	N	G	F	U		E	W	E	S
T		E			O		R		N		N	
E	D	D	I	E		A	G	I	T	A	T	E
			N		D		E		E			
A	D	M	I	R	E	D		T	E	P	I	D
	E		T		S		M			O		R
S	E	M	I		E	M	I	N	E	M		O
	P		A		R		C			M	E	W
L	E	F	T	O	V	E	R			E		S
	N		E		E		O	R	A	L	L	Y

273.

S	T	A	F	F	S			I		S	I	P
	O			O		D	I	V	O	T		R
A	D	M	I	R	E	R		A		U		E
	D			E		A		N	I	N	E	S
C	L	E	A	N	I	N	G			N		U
	E			A		K		H		E		M
D	R	E	A	M	Y		M	I	D	D	L	E
E		L		E		J		T			O	
F		L			M	U	S	H	R	O	O	M
I	R	I	S	H		M		E			F	
C		P		O		P	E	R	U	S	A	L
I		S	T	U	D	S		T			H	
T	I	E		R			P	O	T	A	S	H

274.

M	I	S	S		S	C	I	M	I	T	A	R
A		W		S		A		E		A		O
R	E	A	C	H	E	S		A	U	N	T	S
K		M		O		U		S		K		E
S	U	P	E	R	N	A	T	U	R	A	L	
M				T		L		R		R		P
A	N	T	I	C	S		L	E	A	D	E	R
N		H		H		C		M				E
	C	R	E	A	T	I	V	E	N	E	S	S
S		E		N		C		N		D		I
C	L	A	N	G		A	S	T	O	U	N	D
A		D		E		D		S		C		E
R	E	S	I	D	U	A	L		P	E	N	S

275.

C	H	A	N	C	Y		M	A	R	R	O	W
H		N		L		B		L		E		A
I	N	C	L	U	D	E		L		E		T
E		E		E		W	H	E	E	L	I	E
F	U	S	E	S		I		G				R
S		T				L		R	U	M	M	Y
		O		R	A	D	I	O		O		
C	U	R	V	E		E				N		E
A				T		R		O	L	S	E	N
S	C	H	E	R	Z	I		W		T		Z
I		I		A		N	U	N	N	E	R	Y
N		N		C		G		E		R		M
O	O	D	L	E	S		W	R	A	S	S	E

276.

C		S		B		W		B		B		U
R	E	E	X	A	M	I	N	E		I	A	N
O		R		T		C		N		D		U
W	R	E	S	T		K	I	D	N	E	Y	S
E		N		I		E		S				U
	D	I	G	N	I	T	Y		M	O	Y	A
W		T		G				P		P		L
O	N	Y	X		U	S	U	R	P	E	R	
R				S		I		E		R		S
K	R	Y	P	T	O	N		C	R	E	P	T
M		A		U		F		E		T		A
A	I	R		B	L	U	E	P	E	T	E	R
N		N		S		L		T		A		R